1, 49

D1269735

THE SEARCH
BENEATH THE SEA

RARE FISH CAUGHT

TANANARIVE, Madagascar, Jan. 4. (AP)—Fishermen are reported to have caught and kept alive a coelacanth—a rare fish valued by scientists as a link in the chain of evolution.

The Madagascar institute of research said today it is sending scientists to the island where the fish was reportedly being kept alive by immersion in sea water.

The institute said it believed this was the first time a coelacanth has been kept alive for any length of time after being taken out of the sea. It said the rare fish was hooked last night off Grand Comore, a French-owned island lying between Madagascar and the African mainland.

The coelacanth lived millions of years ago. Scientists once knew of it only from fossils, and long believed it to be extinct. The first specimen was caught several years ago off Africa. Since then scientific fishing expeditions have taken several more.

The fish may grow to a length of three or four feet and has a distinctive armored head. It is from the coelacanth fish family from which the first land reptiles are believed to have evolved.

A few moments after the critical identification as a Coelacanth, on Hunt's vessel at Pamanzi, Comores, 29th December 1952.
On left, Capt. E. E. Hunt; *on right*, holding fin, Monsieur P. Coudert, Governor of the Comores; *on extreme right*, one of his staff. *Behind, left to right*, Lt. D. M. Raîston, Capt. P. Letley, Lt. W. J. Bergh, Comd. J. P. D. Blaauw, Cpl. F. Brink.

THE SEARCH
BENEATH THE SEA

The Story of
the Coelacanth

by

J. L. B. SMITH

Illustrated with Photographs

New York   •   Henry Holt and Company

This book is dedicated to
MISS M. COURTENAY-LATIMER
one of South Africa's
most able women

FOREWORD

THIS story has been dragged from my reluctant pen by the unflagging determination of my wife, consciously aided and abetted by numerous friends and unwittingly by publishers and literary agents from several countries.

In succumbing, for the sake of historical record, it has been my aim to present this extraordinary event as accurately as possible.

This has involved the mention of many different persons who played their part in the creation and course of this story. I have spared nobody, least of all myself, which is the extenuation I offer to those inclined to find my descriptive words harsh.

The general public is apt to regard people like leading scientists or cabinet ministers as almost superhuman and beyond or above ordinary human emotions. They are not, emphatically not, and to scale the heights a man must be prepared to wage an unending, bitter battle with those persistent fundamental weaknesses that constantly plague us all. One friend who kindly read the manuscript asked me if I realised how it revealed myself. I do not mind. No man is a god.

J. L. B. SMITH

Grahamstown
August 1955

ACKNOWLEDGEMENTS

I wish to acknowledge permission to reproduce matter, granted by:
Miss M. Courtenay-Latimer; Dr. E. I. Nielsen; Dr. J. Millot; Captain
E. E. Hunt; S.A. Broadcasting Co.; *Die Burger*, Cape Town; *Daily
News*, Durban; *The Times*, London; *Nature*, London; *Evening Post*,
Jersey; Jersey Electricity Co.

I am indebted to Dr. H. J. van Eck, Advocate Adrian A. Roberts
(formerly Law Adviser to the Union Government), and Professor
W. E. G. Louw for helpful criticism of the manuscript, also to Messrs.
A. S. Wheeldon and H. Rushmere for opinions on certain points.

To my wife I am indebted for her constant support, for valuable if
initially devastating criticism and for numerous illustrations.

This book stands as a tribute to the foresight of the South African
Council for Scientific and Industrial Research, whose continued generous
support enabled me to pursue this long quest.

AUTHOR'S NOTE

SINCE this book went to press, news has been received of the tragic death, arising from the shipwreck of his schooner, of Captain Eric Hunt, whose initiative and energy were so largely responsible for the discovery of the second Coelacanth at the French Comoro Islands.

According to reports Hunt lost his life while attempting to save others. The small boat in which he set out to seek help at the Comores, was later found empty and waterlogged, overwhelmed by weather or by sharks.

CONTENTS

Book I

THE PAST SURGES FROM THE SEA

Book II

TROUGH AND CREST

Contents

Book III

THE WAVE RECEDES

APPENDICES

PLATES

BOOK I

THE PAST SURGES FROM THE SEA

Chapter One

THE STAGE IS SET

THESE are wonderful times, and it is thrilling to be living now, though it would thrill me even more to know that I could still be here a hundred or a thousand years hence, for this immediate future promises to be of intense interest, even excitement, certainly to the scientist.

With a mind constantly reaching towards the potential marvels of the future, it has been my quite fantastic privilege to reveal to the world a living part of the utterly remote past, covering a span of time so great as to be almost beyond the grasp of the ordinary mind. In this process an obscure scientific name, Coelacanth (pronounced 'seelakanth'), jumped into prominence and into a permanent place in the common speech of mankind.

Such things do not happen easily. The appearance of the Coelacanth was like a gigantic tidal wave which washed me violently from my path, held me in its grip, carried me along, and set my feet on a quest that dominated some of the best years of my life. It caused me to lead an unusual life, of which many people came to acquire an attractive but distorted picture, seeing in me a scientist who dashed off on eventful expeditions to romantic tropical islands where wonderful fishes new to science were just waiting to jump into my net. They read of me as having almost casually telephoned a Prime Minister to ask for an aeroplane in which to make a sensational flight to fetch an incredible fish that attracted world-wide attention.

Whenever I return to civilisation, people want to know something about this apparently fascinating life, so I have been virtually compelled to give many lectures, over the radio and in person. I do not conceal the discomfort, hardship, danger, and unending hard labour that our work involves, but these do not obscure the glamour, and a constant stream of eager young folk, men and women, come to me with the same query. 'My present work is

dull. How can I become an ichthyologist?' So I tell them. First
you must get a University Master's degree in Biology, better still
a Doctorate, which means a minimum of five years of University
life. Then for ten years at least you must be prepared to do
laborious donkey-work, almost certainly poorly paid, as an
assistant to some expert in that line, much of it dull, monotonous
routine, like counting scales on hundreds and thousands of small
fish, probably more deadly than counting pennies in a bank, and
those at least don't smell. Even then you may not be good enough
to get anywhere, and there are few positions where you will be
paid. a good salary as an ichthyologist. Most turn sadly away,
but the few takers have made good!

This book is to tell the almost incredible story of the Coelacanth,
but as this is inextricably bound up with my own personality, it
would be as well to tell you something of how that was shaped.

My life has throughout been a series of contrasts and changes,
many due to the peculiar circumstances of South Africa. Of
English parents, I was born in 1897 at the inland Karoo town of
Graaff Reinet. In the midst of the stress and bitterness of the
Boer War my early years were spent in an atmosphere of deifica-
tion of all that was British, and hatred and scorn of the 'Boers', and
indeed of anything South African as distinct from British, including the country itself.

It has always been my uncomfortable instinct not to accept
uncritically the opinions of others, and while this has ultimately
been an asset in my scientific career, it did not always create the
most cordial relations at home or at school.

My early education was at several small Karoo village mixed
schools, and later at the abruptly different atmosphere of 'Bishops',
modelled on an English Public School. The next violent contrast
was the Victoria College at Stellenbosch, predominantly Afrikaans
and reputedly steeped in Nationalism and Politics, but I encountered a peaceful tolerance towards my firm political views. There
I gave my heart to Chemistry.

When the Great War came, in company with thousands of
others of like age, on the 7th August 1914, I was called up from
school and put into khaki and barracks at Wynberg, then into the
tender care of a Regular British regiment for training. The enforced close company of this strange unnatural substratum of

society was a bewildering experience. For example, venereal disease changed abruptly from the remote subject of schoolboy jokes to stark reality, for in the lives of these men it appeared to occupy the status of the common cold in mine, a curse but inevitable. After about a month some of us were returned to school as too young for campaign, and I went on to University life at Stellenbosch. As I was set on taking part in the war, I arranged at once to go to England to join the Royal Flying Corps after my 'Intermediate' Examination at the end of the year (1915). However, General Smuts, at that time almost a god to me, appealed to everyone to enlist for German East Africa first, so instead of learning to soar through the skies, I became an earth-bound, foot-slogging infantry-man instead. Thousands of half-trained men of all ages were jammed into a transport at Durban, and fed mainly on bread, tinned rabbit, and tea. While most others gambled I counted heads and life-boats and was appalled at the quotient, but we got safely to Mombasa, and thence to the badly mismanaged campaign that followed.

After sundry misadventures, including contracting malaria, dysentery, and the acute rheumatic enlargement of several major joints, I spent some months in military hospitals, first in Kenya, where I nearly died, then was shipped, helpless, back to the Union, and to hospital at Wynberg. Eventually I returned, virtually a physical wreck, to University life at Stellenbosch, where again even those students most strongly opposed to my convictions respected them, perhaps even more than before. Still racked with fever, and more often ill than well, I continued my studies until the end of 1918. Then came another abrupt change from Afrikaner Stellenbosch to Cambridge in England, where I carried out research work in chemistry. University life there was in many ways different from what I had known. Some of the students occasionally indulged in destructive riots, and the cost of the damage to public and University property, sometimes thousands of pounds, was covered by levies imposed by the University, which had to be paid equally by all students, the innocent majority as well.

In some of my vacations I travelled and tramped various countries on the Continent, learning to speak German and some Italian, and a good deal besides. I travelled widely and saw a good deal of the people and the country of my origin. Despite my undiluted English blood and early upbringing, I found myself resentful of criticism of South Africa, especially of comments on Smuts I heard in quite high circles. I became conscious for the first time of being a 'South African', and those from my own country I met over there were no longer 'English' or 'Afrikaans', but my own people. The childhood-fostered gap between 'Briton' and 'Boer' in my mind just closed up.

On my return to South Africa in 1923 I took an appointment at Rhodes University College, where I taught chemistry, a subject I loved as much as ever, and managed to find time for research, publishing a series of papers.

My father was fond of angling, and as a very small boy, with some of his cast-off gear, I vividly remember catching my first 'Dassie', a Bream-like fish, at Knysna. This wonderful shining thing I had pulled up from the unknown world below the water had a terrific effect on me, probably more than anything ever since. From then on angling has been a passion, a madness, sometimes even a reproach. In South Africa in my young days 'fishing', sea fishing, was rather frowned upon as a pastime for a member of a University staff. It is strange to look back on it now, when even the greatest are proud to display their catches. I had soon got to know all the common kinds of fishes, but as I attained manhood wanted to know more and found great difficulty in identifying strange types, and there were many. No one could help me, and the only books available were beyond easy use. The 'keys' were intelligible only to those already so expert as not to need them, so that it was a fearful job trying to identify unknown fishes.

I struggled on alone, baffled, but eventually worked out a numerical system for identifying fishes. It took all my spare time for more than a year, and its compilation involved the writing of more than a million figures, but it worked. It enabled me to track in a few minutes quite unknown fishes, and even to identify them from mere fragments. This was a tremendous step forward, and gave me power that normally comes only from much longer experience.

Having mastered the fishes that came from angling, I went on to collect others systematically on the Eastern Province coast, discovering to my astonishment that I was the first to do this.

Almost every tide there was something rare or new to South Africa, or even new to science. I made contact with the Albany Museum in Grahamstown, and was encouraged by John Hewitt, the Director, in my first timid entry into the scientific field of ichthyology. In 1931 I published my first short paper in the annals of that museum, with my own illustrations that seemed satisfactory. But an acquaintance of Cambridge days, a zoologist, wrote to say that he was surprised to see a chemist publishing a paper on fishes; the text was reasonable but the illustrations were terrible. That was my first step towards appreciation of the importance of good illustration in biology, which has become a feature of my work, in more recent times thanks largely to the skill of my wife.

My long and thorough training in the mathematical sciences, not generally part of the equipment of systematists, assisted me at every turn. My progress was indeed so rapid that it was not long before anglers and others came to me for information, and an increasing number of fishes were brought and sent for my opinion and identification. Correspondence on this matter steadily increased, and all phases of this work grew so rapidly that there were times when I was almost overwhelmed. Everywhere I turned there were new and fascinating things all round, my time was so fully occupied that one by one the ordinary pastimes of life fell away.

Chemistry covers a vast field, and is the basis of an enormous part of general life and of industry. The subject is continually changing, almost like a moving picture, and to keep abreast of developments is more than a full-time job.

With two such different and full fields to occupy my time, I was in a difficult situation. During working hours in term time I conscientiously did nothing else but chemistry, even when I was bursting to get on with a new fish. My free time and vacations were devoted to fish. I had papers on fishes and on chemistry published at the same time, and even managed to produce three text-books in chemistry.

In South Africa the character of the Universities has been influenced by the Scottish educational system, in which the emphasis is on a high standard of teaching. Their development has also been moulded by having to train young men and women for specific occupations essential to the welfare of a rapidly developing economy.

Research in Universities in South Africa has occupied a subordinate, and in some ways uneasy, position. University staffs are normally appointed and paid for teaching, and while research is officially encouraged, anyone who devotes more than normal time to such work runs the risk of being regarded as not giving proper attention to the teaching for which he is paid. It is certainly looked on as peculiar and possibly even as reprehensible to teach in one subject and to do research work in another. At the time of the first Coelacanth I was told that it is competent for the head of a University to order a member of the staff to desist from doing research work, even in his spare time, if in the opinion of the head it may be prejudicing the efficiency of his teaching work. All this is fundamentally sound. In general, no man can serve two masters; at least, not for long.

For many years the aftermath of the East African campaign led to continued ill-health, the precise origin of which baffled those I consulted. In succession they took away my teeth, my tonsils, and my appendix; but I have no harsh feelings towards those who assisted at my partial dismemberment, and am rather grateful that they did not focus their attention on any other organs as well. In desperation, my wife and I came to seek health in our food, and in a few years I achieved a new lease of life, which made possible the strenuous expeditions in tropical waters that ultimately led to the second Coelacanth.

The most important collection of South African fishes up to 1930 was in the South African Museum at Cape Town, collected and partly worked on by the late J. D. F. Gilchrist.* They had been the basis of a large monograph by K. H. Barnard,† Assistant Director of the South African Museum, at that time the leading authority on South African fishes. In the Eastern Cape there were provincial museums at Grahamstown, Port Elizabeth, East London, and Kingwilliamstown, each with a staff of only a

* Professor J. D. F. Gilchrist, a scientific pioneer, a small man of great heart and great mind, whose ability, energy, and endurance laid the foundations of South African ichthyology and of the great fisheries industry of today.

† One of the most able, versatile, and industrious biologists ever to settle in South Africa. His researches in several widely divergent fields are most valuable contributions to the advancement of scientific knowledge in South Africa.

Curator or Director, who was exhibition officer, scientist, as well as consultant on everything else. They were pleased to have my services as Honorary Curator of Fishes for their museums, which I visited regularly, and they kept or sent their fish rarities for my investigation.

I tried to get trawler crews to hunt and keep unusual specimens from their catches and especially from the 'rubbish', but found them indifferent, and came to realise that more direct contact was necessary. So I endured the miseries of small trawlers on South Africa's stormy seas, often so seasick as barely able to crawl along the slippery heaving decks to scratch among the slimy rubbish shoved aside.

To the crews I was no longer a remote scientist who expected them to do his dirty work while he stayed in a comfortable museum ashore, and they changed from indifference to interest and sometimes to enthusiasm.

I went out with small line-boats and lived with the coastal trek-netters. I walked to remote lighthouses, and to coastal farms and stores, always talking fish, fish, fish. All this took time and effort but paid handsome dividends, and a steady stream of treasures came rolling in.

The study of fishes is very much a full-time occupation even when not complicated by any other duty, but in my early days a few glimpses into a work on fossil fishes set me to find odd moments to explore this fascinating new, or rather ancient, world. I acquired a general knowledge of the types that had lived and died before our time, and found this perhaps the most absorbing of all scientific fields; but my life was already so desperately full that I dared not indulge that desire very far. Nevertheless, those weird creatures of bygone days were constantly flitting in and out of my consciousness, constantly filling me with almost an agony that they had gone for ever and could never be seen again. Fossil fishes are comparative rarities in most parts of South Africa. If it had been otherwise, I have often wondered if they would not have pulled me right away.

And so, by 1938, as all this shows, it was just as if the stage had been set for the Coelacanth. I was in close contact with the various museums, had by constant visits and voyages established cordial personal relations with trawler crews and with the firms that ran them, had widespread close contact with anglers, partly because I was one myself, and my brain held not only a rapidly increasing and almost comprehensive knowledge of the fishes living in our waters, but also a sketchy panorama of the long line of fascinating fishy creatures that from remote ages past had come and gone. After all, one of them was my own remote ancestor.

Chapter Two

THIRTY MILLION GENERATIONS

WHEN it was said that Coelacanths had been thought to be extinct for 50 million years, many people found it fantastic that scientists should even be prepared to make statements of that type. Such a period of time is of course enormous, but it is short compared with the time that covers the full history of our earth. Before we can show where the Coelacanth fits, it would be advantageous to make a rapid survey of what scientists now believe lies behind us.

Although fossils have been known for quite a long time, it is astonishing that their true significance has been realised only in comparatively recent times. One of the earliest fossils to be described was an almost perfect skeleton of a large salamander, found in rock strata in Germany, and it was regarded as the remains of 'a poor sinner overwhelmed by the [Biblical] flood'.

The science of 'Palaeontology' (knowledge of old life) is in one sense quite new, and in the last half-century it has developed in a manner that the first workers could scarcely have foreseen. In less than a century of intensive work some of the most remarkable intellects of all time have, from often only fragmentary remains, been able to unravel much of the history of life from the most remote past until today, and to present an almost complete picture of the main forms of life that have inhabited the earth. With this has come a rapidly increasing perception of the vast ages that lie behind us, and methods have been developed by which it has become possible to construct a scale to measure past time in a manner undreamt of not so long ago. The methods by which this is done are highly technical, and still newer and finer techniques are continually being developed.

Many people are curious about this. Here is one method by which the approximate age of a rock may be found. Uranium gives off radiations and small particles (of helium), thereby chang-ing into a special kind of lead. The time that uranium takes to do this is known—it is many millions of years. By measuring the amount of lead in the uranium, the time that has passed can be estimated. When this takes place right inside a rock, the amount of helium (a gas) also gives a confirmatory figure. There are several other methods as well, one involving 'isotopes'.*

It is interesting to note that while, with all advances in technique, readjustments of estimated past time occur, they are on the whole of a comparatively minor order, so that it appears likely that we really do know a good deal about the relatively enormous stretches of time that have passed in our making.

Almost everyone today accepts that our sun is a star, that in the universe there are countless billions of other similar stars, and that our sun started, somewhere and somehow, as an enormous mass of very hot gas. This, whirling and moving at an enormous speed through space, gradually cooled. Portions flew off at inter-vals, and these are now the planets, of which our earth is one. These smaller masses cooled more quickly than the sun itself. Originally, of course, our earth was so hot it was almost all gas. As it cooled liquid first formed at the centre; then the surface became

* A method that is proving of great value in dating remains of once-living organisms has been evolved in recent times. It is based on the fact that carbon in the structure of living organisms, both plants and animals, has been found (1946) to contain a constant small amount of a radioactive isotope of atomic weight 14. Compared with uranium this has a short life, the period of half change being only 5,600 years. Because of its presence the carbon in organic remains such as the bones of a skeleton, or of a tree trunk preserved by some means such as being buried in a swamp, will steadily show less and less radio-activity as time goes on. The amount is so very small that its measurement demands great skill and many precautions. It has been possible to test the method by the use of remains of accurately known age, and in the hands of an expert it yields remarkable results. A striking application of this method has recently caused a considerable scientific sensation. Early this century the biological world was aroused by the discovery in deposits at Piltdown in England of the bones of a skull claimed by many experts to be of an early type of man since named the 'Piltdown Man', dating back close on a million years. While some doubts were expressed about its validity, most British experts accepted this view, and the bones remained a treasured possession in the British Museum. The carbon-isotope method has led to the discovery that this skull is made up of bones of different ages, all comparatively recent, none really old. The whole thing was a deliberate fraud, there never was any 'Piltdown Man'. A book has recently (1955) been published giving the whole story.

solid, still entirely surrounded by a gigantic dense atmosphere of whirling vapours and gases.

All the enormous amount of water now liquid on the earth was then gas. There came a time when the whole mass had cooled so far that the cold of outer space caused 'rain' to form in the dense clouds that covered the whole earth. At first this rain never touched the earth, it was too hot, but eventually it did reach the solid crust, only to sizzle off at once again as gas. For a long time, probably thousands of years, all over the whole earth it never stopped 'raining', literally pouring, a process which caused quite rapid cooling. One can well imagine that there must have been continual 'storms' of violence undreamt of today. In passing, we may note that at present the main part of our earth is still liquid and very hot under its solid crust. There is, of course, abundant liquid water and the atmosphere of gas. The earth is cooling all the time, and it is steadily losing water and air to outer space. If the earth survives long enough there will come a time in the far-distant future when any water or 'air' that may be left will all be solid. One way and another, life as we know it now, free life on the surface of the earth that needs water and air, can only be a passing phenomenon in the infinite time span of the universe.

The sciences of Geology and Palaeontology go together and scientists in those fields have divided the time of existence of the earth into different eras, systems, and periods, which have for convenience been given names.

The table overleaf (p. 14) giving a Geological Time-scale is a summary of what is more or less generally accepted.

On the earth there is a sharp distinction between dead, or 'inorganic', matter and living things which nobody has yet been able to bridge. The earliest forms of life on the earth were doubtless preceded by the formation in some fashion of 'organic' matter; that is, non-living compounds containing carbon and other elements essential to living organisms of the type we know on the earth, that in some fashion came to be alive. Nobody has as yet succeeded in pushing any types of non-living 'organic' compounds over the borderline to 'life', but it is not impossible that suitable compounds are constantly being produced in nature, that the transition to living matter may still occur, so that even if

GEOLOGICAL TIME-SCALE

Eras	Systems	Periods	Years Ago	Types of Life
ORIGIN OF EARTH			3,000,000,000 at least	
PRE-CAMBRIAN	Eozoic Archaeozoic Proterozoic	. .	1,700,000,000	First lowly forms of life.
PALEOZOIC	Cambrian .	. .	500,000,000	Invertebrates
	Ordovician .	. .	400,000,000	Invertebrates
	Silurian .	. .	350,000,000	Vertebrate fishes
	Devonian .	. .	320,000,000	Rhipidistia Coelacanths Various fishes Amphibians
	Carboniferous	. .	280,000,000	Primitive plants on land Amphibians
	Permian .	. .	220,000,000	Amphibians
MESOZOIC	Triassic .	. .	190,000,000	Reptiles Mammal-like reptiles
	Jurassic .	.	150,000,000	Birds
	Cretaceous .	. .	120,000,000	Flowering plants Mammals
CAINOZOIC	Tertiary	Eocene .	70,000,000	Mammals
		Oligocene .	50,000,000	Mammals
		Miocene .	25,000,000	Mammals
	Quaternary	Pleistocene	1,000,000	Ape-man Stone-Age man
		Holocene. .	25,000	Modern man

all life on the earth were to be obliterated, there is at least a chance that it might start all over again.*

It is universally accepted that life started in the water, and the first living things are presumed to have been very lowly, something small and soft, like the simple, tiny protozoa that zoologists

* The constant presence and proportion of the radioactive C_{14} isotope in living matter inclines me to believe that the 'creation of life', or the 'animation' of matter, probably took place in suitable non-living matter under the influence of a special type and density of radioactivity. It may well eventually be possible to deduce what this was and to carry out the process in the laboratory, though the living matter so produced may not necessarily be the same as that which originally appeared on earth.

know so well, minute living blobs of jelly. 'Inspired guesses' based on faint signs in ancient rocks put the first appearance of living matter on the earth at about 1,700 million years ago. These first forms of life developed slowly and gave rise to other types, some more advanced, and by 450 million years ago there were numbers of 'invertebrates', backboneless creatures of many types, some quite large, in most of the waters all over the earth.

The first true vertebrates, or backboned animals, are estimated to have appeared by 400–350 million years ago. They must have developed from some ancestor without a true backbone, and they certainly were peculiar creatures, for they had no scales and no true jaws, just soft, sucking mouths. It is in one sense incorrect to speak of some at least as 'backboned', for they had no true bone but vertebral columns only of gristle. Some of them, however, had bodies covered with heavy bony armour, and these have left excellent fossil records.

There is evidence that at the close of the Silurian period and over the beginning of the Devonian some striking change was at work, for it was then that fishes something like the modern types we know first appeared. They had true bony jaws and overlapping scales, and a skeleton at least partly bony. Their fins were peculiar, rather like small paddles with a fringe of soft rays, so that they were named 'Crossopterygii' or 'fringe finned'.

These fishes represented a tremendous step forward in evolution in more ways than one. Not only did they at that very early stage show important features that have remained predominant in fish life to this day, but one group of them gave rise to forms that colonised the land and were indeed our own ancestors.

It would be as well to realise that up to the Devonian period the land was very different from that of today. There was abundant animal and plant life in the water, but apparently hardly any on land, which was bare, mainly rock. Indeed, only about this time did plants start to creep ashore, so that up to then there had been nothing to tempt creatures to leave the water. It is strange to think of static life like plants being able to move out and colonise a different medium, to come out of water and march across the land, but it was done. And as such things go, plants can move quite rapidly in that way. If you look at a pine forest you will see how trees can march across country, for there will be younger and younger trees stretching far out, developed from seeds carried by the wind.

Insects apparently went out on land about the same time as the plants, but before backboned creatures were living out of the water almost a hundred million years more passed, and that is a very long time.

In those early days there was apparently abundant life in most of the waters, but the vertebrate fishes such as the Crossopterygii appear to have lived mainly in fresh-water swamps. Now, fish need oxygen just as we do, but they get theirs from the water, which dissolves a little from the air. If water loses its oxygen, fish cannot live in it, and we have all seen what happens when dams and vleis start to dry up. Rotting vegetation in water uses up all the dissolved oxygen, and you find fish dying and dead all round the margins of such bodies of water. For the same reason one putrefying fish will kill many others.

There have apparently always been floods and droughts for long or short periods. In a short sudden drought there would be heavy mortality of swamp fish. In a slow drought fish would not be killed off so quickly, and it is apparent that sometimes in those early days, fishes gasping in putrefying pools, managed to live by absorbing a certain amount of oxygen directly through surface blood-vessels, probably in the mouth and gill cavity. Over long ages certain types probably learnt to gulp air and to breathe at least partly that way, first by necessity, then by choice. This would have tremendous consequences. First of all, when a drought came and pools began to dry up, such fishes could live long enough in air to flop out and perhaps reach other and better water, and so survive. Over long ages fishes doing this probably came to spend more and more time out of the water, possibly in getting from one pool to the other they found succulent food on the way. Gradually some fishes gave rise to creatures more suited than themselves to life on land, creatures that could live on land and in water, the so-called amphibians, of which the modern frog is an example. Fins began to modify and change to limbs, and so was taken this greatest step in the history of life as it affects us, the first real step that led to man.

This is where the Coelacanth comes into the picture. There were two main lines in the Crossopterygii, named Coelacanths and Rhipidistia. No one could fail to see, even from only fossil remains, how closely they are related. Because somewhat earlier fossils of the Rhipidistia than of Coelacanths are known, most scientists today hold the view that the Rhipidistia came first and that Coelacanths developed from them. Because this view was expressed by one or two leading workers, even without any really positive evidence, it is commonly held even today. If it were true, however, since all those forms lived under the same conditions, it is almost incredible that there should be no sign of transitional types. But in fact, there are the Rhipidistia, and there are the Coelacanths, and nothing in between. It is at least as likely

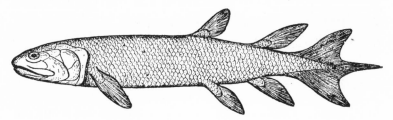

FIG. 1.—A Rhipidistian fish, *Eusthenopteron*, that is believed to be the ancestor of land animals. About 12 inches in length.

that both of these types came from some as yet unknown common ancestral form, and that form would be ancestral to man as well. I have a 'hunch' that one day the remains of something like this will be discovered in earlier strata.

Be that as it may, let us examine the history of these two important main lines of fishy evolution. Both lived in swamps. Their fins indicate that both were able to leave the water and flop about on land, either from necessity or desire. There is good evidence that the Rhipidistia gave rise to amphibia and hence to all other land vertebrates, including man, while the original stock, the Rhipidistian fishes themselves, all died out very long ago. The recent appearance of the Coelacanth has taught us a lesson, and we had better be careful and say rather that all the available evidence indicates that the Rhipidistia became extinct long ages ago. In other words, while they themselves were not strong enough to survive profound changes, by some accident they gave rise to creatures that found a new way of life on the land. It was in one sense their own weakness that led to the survival of and ultimate distinction for their descendants. The Coelacanths were quite different. They were tougher. It is not yet certain whether the first Coelacanths of 300 million years ago originated in fresh water or in the sea. It is often quite a problem to decide this particular point for any one fish. Fossils generally result when animals are buried in mud which later hardens to rock. This can happen, for example, at the mouth of a river which brings down quantities of mud and silt. In South Africa at least, when rivers come down in flood, fresh-water fishes are often carried out to sea and killed. If that happened in those far-off days, as it probably often did, near the mouth of such a river there could be laid down beds containing fish fossils, some at least fresh-water types, together with typical marine organisms such as shells. If no other fossils of these particular fishes happen to have been found elsewhere, they could easily be listed as marine. What has been established is that Coelacanths spread and lived over a great part of the earth, some definitely in swamps, some probably in rivers and estuaries and some in the sea. Some wonderful fossils have been found. For example, during quite recent excavations for a University Library at Princeton, U.S.A., some shales were encountered that were the remains of a swamp of about 190 million years ago. These contained an average of no less than twelve Coelacanth fossils per square foot. That swamp was certainly swarming with Coelacanths. I wish I could go back there and fish for Coelacanths in a Triassic swamp with a bent pin and worms as I have done for Kurpers. I wonder if there were suitable worms then. I am foolish enough to hope that somewhere there may still be such a swamp, and I wonder who will be the first to find it.

Looking back to the time before it was known that Coelacanths were still living, it is astounding to see that nobody seems to have realised the wonder of the Coelacanths, even as they were then known. There was so much that was remarkable about them even then. For one thing, the fossil series showed them to have had, from the very beginning so long ago, important characteristics, like jaws and overlapping scales, far in advance of their time, characters that are obviously good for survival, because even the most modern fishes have hardly improved on the Coelacanth pattern. As a distinct and characteristic line they survived longer than any other type of vertebrate, all unmistakable Coelacanths, living from beyond 300 million years ago to close on 50 million years ago, spanning the incredible time of 250 million years, and surviving terrific climatic changes and upheavals that wiped out countless other forms and types. What is equally as astonishing is that over those relatively vast ages of their existence they changed very little, less indeed than any other known vertebrate.

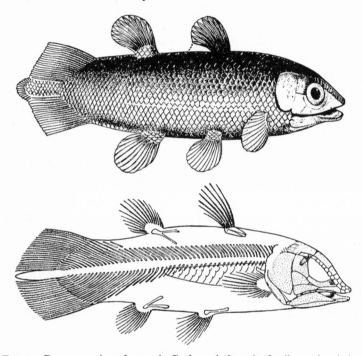

FIG. 2.—Reconstruction of an early Coelacanth from its fossil remains: below, much as seen from a fossil; above, as believed to have been in life. (After Smith Woodward.)

It is almost amusing that some scientists speak of Coelacanths as a 'degenerate side-line' because they have not given rise to other forms. This is a most peculiar view, since man then emphatic-ally falls into the same category, for man will certainly not give rise to any other form save those he moulds himself. The power to master changing conditions can never be degeneracy. Some Coelacanths probably left the water, but their innate strength kept the line going when the supposedly more virile Rhipidistians had been wiped out (at least the evidence we have says so), and now of course it turns out that, after all, the old Coelacanth was even more powerful than we knew. The ancient line still goes on, after probably at least 30 million generations. Thirty million generations, just think of it !

Another characteristic of Coelacanths is that although they spread all over the world, they differentiated very little, that is, even those widely separated remained much the same. For example, fossils show that at one period there were Coelacanths living at the same time on places as far apart as Greenland and Madagascar that were so much alike that it is doubtful whether they were not actually the same species. Over all those vast ages only about twenty-five different genera are known, no less than ten appearing in the Triassic, which was the time that Coelacanths reached a climax in types and numbers. After that they seem to have declined, but it is as well to remember that we do not know much about those that lived in the sea, for fossils of purely marine creatures are not easily formed or accessible.

Over those vast ages the known Coelacanths were all much alike in body form. The variations were few. Judging by their teeth, they tried all sorts of diets, most must have been plain predators, catching other fishes, but some obviously lived mainly on shell-fish, having powerful molars and dental plates for crushing rather than biting. Most of the extinct Coelacanths known from fossils were quite small, a matter of 5–20 inches in length. But as will readily be appreciated, the fossils are those of forms which lived where they were most likely to yield fossils, and that was chiefly in swamps. Water in swamps is not usually very deep, and life there is restricted, so that most fishes in swamps are on the small side. We almost certainly know more swamp Coelacanths than any others. It is therefore by no means certain that all Coelacanths of past times were small like that, and indeed in quite recent years the remains of one of near 5 feet long have been found in a rock stratum in Germany. It is plain that while we have a wonderful fossil record, it must be very far from complete.

So here we have the picture of the Coelacanths. This remarkable type appeared more than 300 million years ago, and has gone on, virtually unchanged as such things go, until the present time. In that long time countless other types of fishy creatures evolved, flourished, and vanished, many of them types that may have seemed more suited for survival than our old Coelacanth, but he has outlived them all. He goes plodding steadily on, his needs few and simple, and he will quite likely still be there when many of these 'active modern types', which are supposed to have driven him to the depths, will be gone and long forgotten. He reminds one of a solitary, tough old man, asking favours of none. Old man Coelacanth. Degenerate? Never!

Chapter Three

CINDERELLA

IN South Africa today science is very much a part of everyday life, and South Africans are playing an increasingly important role in the world of science, a number already having achieved international repute in their respective fields. It is not generally realised that this has taken place only comparatively recently, most indeed within the last generation.

It is not long since life in South Africa, especially in the south-eastern areas, was a grim battle for existence, not only with nature but also against raiding native hordes. It was the 'Mau Mau' on a much larger scale. At that time, and even long after conditions had become more settled, virtually all scientific. work in South Africa was done by visitors and later by trained persons imported from other countries. As many of them were scientifically isolated in South Africa, it is easy to understand that they maintained constant contact not only with their homeland but also with the overseas institutions from which they had come.

In those days, outside the largest centres, there were no real scientific institutions in South Africa, and the few small, local collections of historic relics and curios could scarcely be termed museums. Whenever anything unusual was discovered, and there were many such discoveries, it was generally necessary to send it overseas for expert opinion.

It is easily understood, therefore, that there came to be accepted a general belief that scientific institutions in this country, such as museums, and the work done in them, were inferior to what was old and established overseas. These younger 'Colonial' museums served the purpose of housing local material, but even in that case it was generally felt, and openly expressed, that any article of great value should not remain in any such small establishment, but be sent to some long-recognised overseas institution like the

British Museum. In some parts of South Africa this view still has its adherents, even today.

Sentiments of this kind were at least partly responsible for the late foundation and initially slow growth of the East London Museum. In December 1938 the East London Museum was little known, being one of the youngest in the country. It had indeed quite a struggle for existence, being supported by only a small grant from the Government, and distressingly small material support from its own community, which at that time did not regard it as of importance or value. The total annual income then was less than seven hundred pounds, which had to cover salaries and wages, material, stationery, everything. It is almost incredible that anything like a musuem could have existed under such circumstances, for it had started without endowment of any kind and was poorly equipped. Like most such institutions in South Africa it was supervised at first by a series of honorary part-time Curators, but eventually Miss M. Courtenay-Latimer was appointed as its first full-time Curator.

While there were some who found it strange that a relatively young woman should have been selected for this position, it is plain that those responsible had perception and sound judgment, for they could scarcely have made a better choice. Miss Latimer showed herself able, capable, and energetic, and was soon at grips with the many difficulties that beset her ideas and ambitions for the Museum. She had great difficulty, not only in managing all that she desired with such limited means, but also in convincing the Board and especially its Chairman of that time, that their Museum could be developed into one of the best known in South Africa, and even beyond, as indeed it is now.

From the start Miss Latimer wisely concentrated on building up exhibits representative of the life of the area served by the Museum, and this she carried out with characteristic energy and enthusiasm. As Miss Latimer realised that angling is the chief sport and hobby in that area, she got the commercial fishing firms to collaborate, and especially from Messrs. Irvin and Johnson's branch at East London received a constant stream of valuable marine specimens which were mounted and exhibited at the Museum. She wisely made personal contact with the officers and crews of the trawlers, and infected them with some of her own enthusiasm, so that they watched for unusual specimens of all kinds from the trawl, many of which were kept and brought to port. It became the custom to pile up the 'rubbish' so that she could scratch through it, and indeed she found many treasures that way.

It was therefore with no sense of anything unusual that Miss Latimer received a telephone message from the manager of Irvin and Johnson at East London in the late morning of the 22nd December 1938, to say that a trawler had brought in a pile of fish for her to examine. She called a taxi and with Enoch the native assistant of the Museum went down to the wharf some miles off. When she got there the captain had already left the ship, but one of the deck-hands took her to the pile of fish they had put aside, mostly sharks. Those she already knew and had got previously, but then, almost hidden, she noticed a large heavily scaled blue fish, and as a peculiar fin and the colour attracted her attention, she had the fish pulled out. It was a peculiar creature, like nothing she had ever seen before, and she stared at it in puzzlement for some time and examined its mouth and fins. She asked the old trawlerman if he had ever seen one before, but he replied that in his thirty years at sea in that work he had certainly never seen any fish of that type, and he pointed out that the fins were like arms, it looked almost like a big lizard. Miss Latimer thought it looked something like a Lung-fish, but in any case decided that it was obviously something rare which it would certainly be advisable to keep. The trawlerman said it was a lovely blue when taken from the water, but was a vicious brute, snapping its jaws fiercely. They had all been struck by its unusual appearance, for none of them had seen anything like it before, so they had called Captain Goosen to look at it, and when he touched the body, it heaved itself up suddenly, snapping its jaws viciously and had nearly caught his hand in its formidable fang-lined mouth. The captain ordered the crew to put it on one side so that Miss Latimer could see it, for by then he had decided to go straight in to port.

The fish was 5 feet long and heavy. As a matter of interest Miss Latimer got them to weigh it; 127 lb. It was a scorching hot day and the fish had a smell—all fish have on hot days—but the Coelacanth has one all its own, as we came to know only too well.

According to Miss Latimer, she had very considerable difficulty in persuading the taximan to consent to having the fish in his taxi at all, even though she had brought along old bags to put on the floor on which to rest any fish. The taximan was so reluctant that he stood aloof and distant while she and a native struggled and wrestled to get the creature into the vehicle.

One may sympathise with that taximan, while smiling at the incongruity, refusing to transport what was the most valuable zoological specimen in the world, though none of them knew it at that time. There are many fishes in South African seas that to anyone not an expert would appear much more strange than a Coelacanth, and, as has been explained, museum directors in South Africa have so many fields to cover that they just cannot be experts in every branch of science.

Getting this heavy fish to the Museum was one thing, what to do with it there was another. Miss Latimer had nothing in which to keep it, but first had a hunt through her pitifully few reference works to see if she could get some idea of what it was. But she found nothing; indeed, from its fantastic nature it would have been almost a miracle if she had. So, after making a rough sketch and taking measurements, she borrowed a hand truck, and with the native boy took it to a taxidermist who did that work for the Museum. (The 'Museum' did not even have a handcart of its own.) She also asked an expert amateur photographer to take some photographs, which he did, but for some reason the whole film was a failure.

According to Miss Latimer, the bony plates of the head, the scales, and the fins made her feel it was a Ganoid fish, probably a Lung-fish of some type, but she had no means of verifying this and relied on hearing from me. She told the taxidermist to keep all the parts he cut away in case they were important, and this he did; but by the 27th December 1938 they were in such an appalling state that not having heard from me by then Miss Latimer agreed to his urgings that they should be disposed of. Miss Latimer states that when she rather timidly ventured to tell the Chairman of the Board of Trustees of the Museum, the late Dr. Bruce-Bays, what she thought about this fish, he scoffed at her views, and crushed her by saying in rather harsh terms that 'all her geese were swans', and that if she wanted to keep the fish he would authorise it to be mounted. Surely that was enough, he asked?

There will be some who are not impressed by the mere record of these events. But they may be assured to start with that to handle and treat a large smelly fish on a hot day is no pleasant or light task. It is a formidable job, and much more so for any woman. By great good fortune Miss Latimer was no ordinary woman. I know from vast experience just how much she did at this time and under what great difficulties, with no encouragement from any source, rather the reverse, driven solely by that inner fire which makes her what she is. I shall always admire and respect her for it. She merits the admiration of every true scientist, and gets it. It was only Miss Latimer's instinct for what is valuable and her force of character and determination that saved that specimen; one less determined would have been overwhelmed.

The morning following the arrival of the fish, Miss Latimer wrote to me, enclosing the rough sketch and notes. Little did she know what she was touching off. Its effects were those of an atomic blast, of two atomic blasts, for twice the Coelacanth sent a wave that went all round the world, and the backwash of the second still goes on.

Chapter Four

STRANGER THAN FICTION

O N the side of the lagoon at Knysna, some miles from the sea, we have a house with a laboratory, where I do not only considerable general angling but carry out regular and periodic investigations on the extraordinarily rich and varied fish-life of this large estuary. It is an exceedingly interesting body of water, with many unique characters.

In December 1938 we had gone from Grahamstown to Knysna. I had been unwell, and was not fully recovered even in the New Year.

About midday on the 3rd January 1939 a friend brought us a large batch of mail matter from the town, very much of a Christmas–New Year accumulation, and this was sorted out between us, each settling down to his or her letters. Mine were the usual mixture of examination results and queries, and numbers about fishes. One was from the East London Museum, in Miss Latimer's well-known hand, the first page very much the usual form, as will be seen on p. 30, asking for assistance in classification. Then I turned the page and saw the sketch, at which I stared and stared, at first in puzzlement, for I did not know any fish of our own or indeed of any seas like that; it looked more like a lizard. And then a bomb seemed to burst in my brain, and beyond that sketch and the paper of the letter I was looking at a series of fishy creatures that flashed up as on a screen, fishes no longer here, fishes that had lived in dim past ages gone, and of which only often fragmentary remains in rocks are known. I told myself sternly not to be a fool, but there was something about that sketch that seized on my imagination and told me that this was something very far beyond the usual run of fishes in our seas. It was as if my common sense were waging a battle with my perception, and I kept on staring at that sketch, trying to read into it perhaps more than it held. In this surge of violent thoughts and reactions, the world about me had ceased to exist, until I heard my name called, it seemed from far away, then suddenly again, close by, and more urgently, and loudly. . . . There was my wife, staring at me from across the table with deep concern on her face, as was also her mother across at the corner; both were looking at me intently. I found to my surprise that I was standing. My wife tells that she was engrossed in a letter when suddenly she felt that something was wrong, and looking up saw me on my feet, staring at a letter in my hand. The light was behind me and she could see a fish-like drawing through the thin paper. 'What on earth is the matter?' she said, and I came back to the present. Looking again at the letter and sketch I said slowly, 'This is from Miss Latimer, and unless I am quite off the rails she has got something that is really startling. Don't think me mad, but I believe there is a good chance that it is a type of fish generally thought to have been extinct for many millions of years.' My wife says that she did wonder if I had got a touch of the sun, for she knew that I usually weighed every word, and this was quite the most extraordinary thing she had ever heard from my lips. I passed the letter over to her, and the two women read the first page and then examined the sketch, while, the rest of my mail pushed aside, I sat and stared into what this might mean if my first deductions were correct.

Yes, those fishes of bygone days had always intrigued me, and I went over in my mind what this could possibly resemble. As will be seen (Plate 1, facing p. 32), the sketch was in some ways impressionistic and not a very good representation of the animal. But that tail, and the clearly large scales, and those limb-like fins! One alone in a sketch might be passed; but all together! At the same time what I suspected was so utterly preposterous that my common sense kept up a steady fire of scorn for my idiocy in even thinking of it.

I was afraid of this thing, for I could see something of what it would mean if it were true, and I also realised only too well what it would mean if I said it was and it was not. On that sketch alone I could never decide anything; I must see the creature itself. That would almost certainly mean a journey to East London, most inconvenient at that particular time, for in the University of South Africa I was that year an examiner, and the centres had been notified to send the papers to Knysna. In that capacity

I was bound to complete my work within a specific period, and an absence at that time would almost certainly have prevented fulfilment of that obligation, for a reason I could scarcely present as justifiable. The other alternative was that the animal should come to me, but in my chaotic state of mind at that particular time, its great size, $4\frac{1}{2}$ feet long, had not registered, nor the date of its catching or indeed anything but its possible identity. Was this the fulfilment of the peculiar premonition I had always had?

One is hesitant about saying such things, but I have some peculiar sense outside the ordinary, sometimes spoken of as 'sixth sense', which warns me of impending events, usually danger or trouble, sometimes very long in advance. Again and again I have realised later that this subtle anticipation has caused me to act so as to avoid serious inconvenience and disaster, and those who live with me respect these 'hunches' of mine, even when they involve what seem utterly irrational prohibitions, and even though the others point out that when we have obeyed my apparently ridiculous directions, we often have no means of knowing that anything would have happened had we not done so. I don't always know either, but bitter experience inclines me at least to obey them. One of my most constant and peculiar obsessions had always been a conviction that I was destined to discover some quite outrageous creature, I had no idea what, but had come to suspect it might be a true sea-serpent or something like that. This was so firmly fixed in my mind that just as my peculiar set of circumstances and qualifications had set the stage ready for the appearance of the Coelacanth, so in one sense had this premonition prepared me to deal with such a fantastic possibility as had now arisen, and, indeed, even while my common sense rejected it, to seek for it in an obviously impressionistic sketch by someone not an ichthyologist.

My wife was speaking again—we had been married only nine months and, as I am older by a good many years, she was constantly finding unexpected pockets from the past, and here was one. 'I didn't know you had worked on fossil fishes,' she said; so I briefly told about my incursions into that field. 'What makes you think this may be one of them?' she asked. 'Well, mainly the tail. As far as I know there is no living fish with a tail like that. It is characteristic chiefly of the earlier members of a group known as the Crossopterygii; and the scales, the fins and the bony plates on the head all point the same way.' They studied the sketch closely, noting these points. Then my wife turned to the first page again, and she exclaimed sharply, 'Do you see when this was written?' and passed the letter to me again. Good heavens, 23rd December and this was the 3rd January, eleven days gone. Here is the letter, the sketch is on Plate 1.

EAST LONDON,
South Africa.
23rd December 1938

Dear Dr. Smith,

I had the most queer-looking specimen brought to notice yesterday. The Captain of the Trawler told me about it so I immediately set off to see the specimen, which I had removed to our Taxidermist as soon as I could. I however have drawn a very rough sketch, and am in hopes that you may be able to assist me in classing it.

It is coated in heavy scales, almost armour like, the fins resemble limbs, and are scaled right up to a fringe of filament. The spinous dorsal has tiny white spines down each filament. Note drawing inked in in red.

I would be so pleased if you could let me know what you think, though I know just how difficult it is from a description of this kind.

Wishing you all happiness for the season.

Yours sincerely,
M. Courtenay-Latimer

As I have already said, the East London Museum at that time had a very small income and hardly any equipment; it was a kind of Cinderella among the museums of South Africa, it even had only a young woman, also a Cinderella as it happens, as Curator. What had happened to this thing in the meantime? If this was something really wonderful, what had happened to it? It had been handed over to the taxidermist, and as they obviously had no idea of its being something sensational, it would be a miracle if they had bothered to preserve all the insides. It was summer, the flesh and intestines would certainly be putrid by now, but perhaps the gills and any skeleton could be found, as they had very likely buried all that. I must act, and quickly.

Knysna is 350 miles from East London. In 1938 the roads were shocking and the telephone service was not what it is today.

Long-distance trunk-calls were not to be undertaken lightly. They took an awful time, and you often could not hear clearly. Knysna has always been curiously isolated from the outside world. It will be noted later that letters to and from East London took never less than six days—350 miles. Even today they take as many as five.

There was a shop with a telephone near by. It was close on 1 p.m., and on my asking, the Knysna Post Office held out little hope of my being able to speak to East London that afternoon at all, it might just manage to get through before 5 p.m. when the Museum closed, but Miss Latimer had no telephone at her house. It is amusing to look back on the reaction of both Post Office and the staff of that shop. East London! That was a long way for a telephone call! After lunch I went into the village (Knysna), and as soon as the Post Office opened sent the following telegram:

'MOST IMPORTANT PRESERVE SKELETON AND GILLS FISH DESCRIBED,'

I also made provisional arrangements for a telephone call to the East London Museum for next morning, and back at the house wrote at once to Miss Latimer. I remember composing and destroying half a dozen scripts, each shorter and containing less than the one before, for I was afraid to say too much. Here is the final draft.

Written from KNYSNA.
3rd January 1939

Dear Miss Latimer,

Thanks for your letter of the 23rd last which has just reached me. Your news is most interesting indeed, and I am very sorry that I am not in Grahamstown or I should have come over to see your fish within a short time. I shall be away for some time, and I am hoping that you saved the gills and viscera of the specimen, since they are most important. If all that was buried, you may still be able to save the gills at least.

I cannot hazard even a guess at the fish at present, but at the very earliest opportunity I am coming to see it.

From your drawing and description the fish resembles forms which have been extinct for many a long year, but I am very anxious to see it before committing myself. It would be very remarkable should it prove to be some close connection with the prehistoric.

Meanwhile guard it very carefully, and don't risk sending it away. I feel it must be of great scientific value.

With kindest regards and best wishes for the new year,

Yours sincerely,

J. L. B. Smith

For the rest of that day I had enough worry for a lifetime. What was that fish? Had they saved anything of its insides? The night brought little rest.

As soon as the exchange opened next morning I was at the shop telephone, and spent an anxious three hours waiting for the call. Eventually it came. Yes, my worst fears were realised, all the insides had been thrown away and had gone off with the municipal rubbish cart. Miss Latimer could feel the agony in my voice; but I had no blame for her, for there were so many queer fish in our waters that no one but an expert could know if this one was what I suspected (and my brain said, 'Is it?'). So I asked her to find out at once where the municipal rubbish carts dumped their loads, because it could probably be worked out where those remains lay, and I had already decided in my mind that I might be able to get a plane to take me from George to go and scratch for them. I managed to telephone again next day. When I did so I learnt that all rubbish collected by the municipal service of East London was dumped out at sea. So that was that, and I could do no more about those insides. They were gone beyond recall. This was my first taste of the many frustrations Coelacanths were to bring.

I recollect that I asked the Post Office how much that call would be, and when I told the shopman and paid him, they were plainly astounded that anyone should be prepared to pay out so much for a telephone call about the insides of a fish. You may be sure they had heard everything.

My worries carried me along, my mind was in a chaotic state. Was this a prehistoric relic? If it was, the loss of the insides was a first-class tragedy. First of all, of course, I had to make certain what this thing was. It must not be forgotten that I was no expert on fossil fishes, just that in odd times my deep interest had led me to study what was known about them. My mind was busy all that time trying to assign that sketch to some clear type. It appeared to be something like a shark in its make-up, but so were those early Crossopterygians. I had to take into account

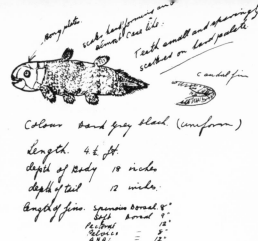

Miss M. Courtenay-Latimer

Miss Latimer's sketch and notes

A Coelacanth fossil, which dates back 170 million years, found by Dr. E. Nielsen in Greenland. Above is the nodule enclosing the fossil, 7 inches long. When tapped by an expert at the point marked X the nodule split into the two halves shown here, disclosing the fossil. Note the amazing resemblance to *Malania* in Plate 2.

Plate 1

The first three Coelacanths
Above, the East London Coelacanth, mounted, as first seen. *Middle*, the famous *Malania*, without first dorsal or extra tail. *Bottom*, the third Coelacanth, taken at Anjouan.

Plate 2

that it was only a sketch and clearly impressionistic, and so might be misleading. At the same time, it pointed directly to those Crossopterygian fishes of long ago. My peculiar photographic memory had recorded that the fossil Crossopterygii were described in Volume II of the *Catalogue of the Fossil Fishes* of the British Museum, published in 1891, but I had no such literature at Knysna, nor were any available there. Such works were at Grahamstown and Cape Town.

In the early days of my work on fishes, my collections were naturally incomplete, and as the largest were at the South African Museum at Cape Town, I had gone there several times to examine this material, and all too frequently this led me to question Barnard's* printed opinions. These tilts, whether refuted or established, he took with equal patience and good humour, and I had continual correspondence with him. I knew, therefore, at Knysna, that in time, as measured by the post, Cape Town was nearer than Grahamstown. On the 4th January I therefore telegraphed Barnard asking him to post me immediately that volume dealing with the Crossopterygii, which he did, as always, promptly, that being his way, and this arrived at Knysna on the 6th January 1939.

Miss Latimer's sketch and notes with that book left little doubt in my mind that if this fish of hers was not a Coelacanth, it was very like one. What a fantastic thing! Just imagine: a Coelacanth, still living, and all the greatest authorities of the world would be prepared to swear that all Coelacanth fishes had died out about 50 million years ago (it is estimated at 70 million today). Here was I in remote South Africa with the audacity to be convinced in my mind that this was a Coelacanthid fish. Even though I had done only spare-time work on fishes for less than ten years, I knew a good deal about them by then, and the careful and detailed papers I had published were known to scientists who worked on fishes all over the world; but I was still only on the way up.

Those were awful days, and the nights were even worse. I was tortured by doubts and fears. What was the use of that infernal premonition of mine if it was just going to lead me to make a scientific fool of myself? Fifty million years! It was preposterous that Coelacanths had been alive all that time, unknown to modern man. If that was a Coelacanth and it had been alive, then there

* Dr. K. H. Barnard (see p. 8).

must be others living somewhere, perhaps off East London. But was it reasonable to think that such big fishes as this could exist near a place like East London and not have been found before? In any case, the fossil Coelacanths had all been pretty small fishes, 8 or 10 inches or 1 foot long—this fish was 5 feet long, enormously greater than any known before. The trend of evolution was normally towards smaller size, the giants had mostly gone. Yes, everything was against its really being a Coelacanth. From almost every aspect it seemed impossible, the answer must be 'No'; and yet every time I took out that sketch, it said 'Yes', emphatically 'Yes'.

I have been asked why I did not rush off at once to East London when such a wonderful thing lay there waiting. Apart from my examination commitments, I could never quite bring my mind to accept that it could possibly be true. It was too fantastic. Then, as the insides had been lost beyond recall and the rest was safely mounted, or being mounted, there was no longer any great urgency. Thirdly, I didn't want to go until I had girded up my mind to the stage where I felt I could face the situation if it did prove to be true. I was afraid to go then, really afraid, and I am not at all ashamed to say so. I wanted to put off going to look at it until I had built up a reserve of inner strength to stand the terrific strain it would mean if it were true. If I found that I could call it a Coelacanth, or something like one, I expected to have to endure an initial storm of scorn and disbelief from the whole world of science until all the facts could be given to prove it was so; and that would not be easy to face. So I remained at Knysna, worry and lack of sleep stripping still more flesh from my skinny frame, my mind never away from that fish and East London.

On or about the 7th January I wrote a cautious letter to K. H. Barnard to tell him something of my belief, but requesting him to treat the matter as strictly confidential and not to mention it to anybody else.* Barnard's reply to that first letter of mine was as

* The disturbed state of my mind at that time is revealed by the recent discovery that I apparently did not keep copies of my letters to Barnard from Knysna about the Coelacanth. I have written to Dr. Barnard asking for those letters in order to reproduce them here, but he has replied that they are not in the Museum files and that it must be assumed that they were destroyed. The dates and contents of my letters to Barnard quoted here are therefore compiled partly from his letters in reply and partly from memory.

usual prompt, but it was couched in such incredulous and face-
tious terms that it served only to increase my fears of the reactions
from a wider field. I had to go and look at the sketch, the notes,
and the volume again, as I did a hundred times a day. They
acted as a soothing drug on a maniacal mind. I was not easy to
live with those days.

On the 9th January 1939, having heard no more from Miss
Latimer, I wrote again as follows:

KNYSNA.
9th January 1939

Dear Miss Latimer,
Your fish is occasioning me much worry and sleepless nights.
It is most aggravating being so far away. I cannot help but mourn
that the soft parts of the fish were not preserved even had they been
almost putrid. I am sorry to say that I think their loss represents one
of the greatest tragedies of zoology, since I am more than ever convinced on reflection that your fish is a more primitive form than has
yet been discovered. It is almost certainly a Crossopterygian allied
with forms that flourished in the early Mesozoic or earlier, but which
have been extinct for many millions of years. Comparatively little is
known of the internal structure of such fishes, naturally nothing of the
soft parts, since fossil remains are all that help us to know what they
were like. Your fish has the general external features of a Coelacanthid, fishes common in early times in northern Europe and America.
Whether or not it is a new genus or family I can determine only on
examination, but I feel sure that it will make a great sensation in the
Zoological world. I have been anxiously awaiting a letter from you,
because I hope you understand that the thing must on no account be
stuffed until it has been examined. It is very important that the
structure of the skull shall be determined and the relations of the
bones of the jaws. You do not happen to have noticed whether the
air-bladder was partly ossified or not? I asked you to see if you
can possibly send the skin, etc., to me by passenger train so that I
may examine them. Even if you have to have a special box made, it
will be cheaper to send that way than for me to come to East London
at present. If the skin is properly packed it will come to no harm,
and I have a large preserving tank here that has held larger specimens
than that. You should really have some such thing at the Museum.
It can be made very cheaply by a plumber out of stout galvanised
iron.
If you judge it quite impossible to arrange to send the skin I shall

have to come over. But I should like to avoid the trip for many reasons. (Examinations !)

I should like you to understand that any opinions about the fish I have expressed here are naturally provisional only, and can be confirmed only when I have seen the thing. But I think you will probably agree with me about the zoological affinities of the specimen. Well now I am anxiously awaiting your letter. I think it would be as well if you could telegraph me whether you can manage to rail the thing, only if you do don't forget to insure for, say, £100—I shall naturally be responsible for all expenses.

To honour you for having got this wonderful thing I have provisionally christened it (to myself at present) *Latimeria chalumnae*, and it may even be a new family.

Kindest regards,
Yours sincerely,
J. L. B. Smith

One curious feature of this whole affair was that at no time did I look upon it as anything but my own. There was no question in my mind that I had to take the full responsibility for the decision of the identity of this creature. Normally in a difficult situation of this type it is natural to consult others or to seek aid, but for some reason this never arose in my mind. It was perhaps due to that curious premonition that fate had prepared this occasion for me, and that, come what may, I must face it alone. It has since that time come to me from several outside sources that other zoologists were resentful that I took this on myself alone, and even more resentful that I carried out the subsequent investigation of the remains myself. Those criticisms left me and leave me quite unmoved. I was possessed or inspired, call it what you will.

Nevertheless, in those days at Knysna my soul was fearful and anxious, and away from that sketch and book I was sceptical of what my reason told me, but I knew I had to go on and take the decision alone. It was do or die. It was indeed characteristic of all my work on fishes that right from the very start I struggled alone, possibly because no help was available even had I wanted it, but certainly because I am what my wife calls a 'Lone Wolf' and work best on my own.

On the 10th January there came a further letter from Miss Latimer, dated the 4th.

EAST LONDON,
South Africa.
4th January 1939

Dear Dr. Smith,

I went straight off to see how the Fish Specimen was shaping, after you phoned.

It's terrible to think I only received your wire three days after it was sent,* on account of the holidays—but when the specimen came in and I found it to be something unique, I strove to do all I could to preserve it. As I found the work too much for me, I had it taken to Mr. Center and got him to do all the heavy work.

There was no skeleton. The backbone was a column of soft white gristle-like material, running from skull to tail—this was an inch across and filled with oil—which spouted out as cut through—the flesh was plastic, and could be worked like clay—the stomach was empty. The specimen weighed 127 lb. and was in good condition, only it was very hot and work had to proceed at once.

The gills had small rows of fine spines—but were unfortunately thrown away with the body.

Mr. Center has almost mounted the specimen now, and is not doing it badly at all—the oil is still pouring out from the skin, which seems to have oil cells beneath each scale.

The scales are armour like fitting into deep pockets. (By that I mean hard and heavy.)

The skull is in the skin and I have got Mr. Center to mount it with the mouth open. I have the tongue or hard mouth-plate here.

I have done every possible thing to preserve and not lose any points and feel worried to think in the end I allowed the body and gills to be discarded. They were kept for three days, and when I did not hear from you I gave the order for disposal.

Kind regards,
Sincerely yours,
M. Courtenay-Latimer

It is interesting to note that the final sentence in the letter indicates that when she did not hear from me within three days, Miss Latimer assumed I did not think the matter important. She knows me better now. We answer all queries and at once.

Miss Latimer received my letter of the 9th (see p. 35) on the 15th January 1939, and telephoned me the following day, giving

---

* In fairness to the post office it may be stated that Miss Latimer later realised that this was not correct, as will be seen from the date of her letter.

various details in answer to my queries. The more I heard the more certainly did it all point to a Coelacanth, but even so, my mind would not really accept this; it was too fantastic, it just could not be. Nevertheless, when it was all assembled, the factual evidence appeared overwhelming. On the 17th January 1939 I wrote again to Barnard, telling him briefly but frankly this time that I believed the animal to be a Coelacanth. His reply of the 19th January indicated that he was now really startled and no longer facetiously incredulous. I wrote again about the 24th January, giving more information, and this time, convinced, he was apparently so overcome by the almost unbelievable nature of the whole affair that he disclosed it in confidence to the Director of the Museum, Dr. E. L. Gill, who had at one time worked on fossil fishes and therefore naturally had an exceptional interest in this.

This was indeed all that transpired between myself and the authorities of the South African Museum. Not long after the discovery had been featured in the press, a report was published stating that I had been in consultation with the authorities of the South African Museum all along over the matter of the Coelacanth. As I had nowhere acknowledged any such assistance, this naturally implied a reprehensible omission on my part. This implication shocked me, for I have always been most punctilious about giving the fullest acknowledgment of any type of assistance received. In this case there had indeed been an almost exceptional degree of isolation. I had deliberately chosen to carry the terrible responsibility myself, making it indeed very much my own funeral. I could see no clear way of rectifying this in a public fashion in any satisfactory manner, so just let it go, but it remains in print and may one day rear its head.

All along I had been frantic to see a photograph of the fish, but none came. For some curious reason something always went wrong with the attempts. Below are quoted several relevant letters:

KNYSNA.
24th January 1939

Dear Miss Latimer,

I have been waiting to hear from you again about that specimen. I should very much like to see a photograph as soon as you can send one. I doubt whether I can get over till near the end of the month, now that the fish is stuffed it does not matter very much.

I am still convinced that the fish is a Coelacanthid, but hope you will not give any information to the press till I have had an opportunity of examining the specimen in detail. Will you kindly make a special point of finding out from the skipper of the trawler if the fish showed any signs of life when it was caught. I have an idea that it might perhaps have lain somewhere in the ocean bed in some preserving ooze or mud these millions of years. Chemically it is possible. It would be very interesting to know if it was definitely alive or not. If it was there is always the chance of another, and you can offer the trawler people £20 for another perfect specimen for me. If by any millionth chance one should be obtained, please have a large tank made, buy as many gallons of formalin as are necessary, and inject strong formalin all over into the body, and of course telegraph me immediately. It is most aggravating to be so far away, and I am very anxious to come as soon as possible. If you can detach one carefully, kindly send me one of the scales, as they are important in diagnosis.

Kindest regards,
Yours sincerely,
J. L. B. Smith

This shows clearly that my mind was perpetually reacting against the fantastic idea that any Coelacanth should still be alive. Could one not have been preserved in some antiseptic bottom ooze? But there was no doubt, it had been alive, for it had snapped at the captain's hand, and had lived for several hours after being caught.

EAST LONDON.
25th January 1939

Dear Dr. Smith,

Bad luck seems to have dogged this fish—I went down to ask Mr. Kirsten whom I got to take photographs of the fish in flesh today and he tells me the entire film was spoilt.

I wish you could come over to East London. I seem to have no one to get interested and feel very despondent about the photographs.

Yours sincerely,
M. Latimer

At last some scales arrived. They hammered flat most of my doubts. Coelacanth, yes a Coelacanth for certain. Phew! What lay ahead?

EAST LONDON.
1st February 1939

Dear Dr. Smith,

Thank you for your last letter. I have tried to get in touch with the Trawler but at present it is at sea. However, I have a promise that a message shall be delivered and I shall get all information again.

When I went down to fetch the specimen I was told it had been trawled 40 fathoms off Chalumna and it had been alive. I am enclosing three scales for you. You will notice each one fits into a socket twice its depth. They have not faded much.

Are you returning to Grahamstown—I shall most probably be able to take the specimen over to you then.

Yours sincerely,
M. Courtenay-Latimer

Written from KNYSNA.
7th February 1939

Dear Miss Latimer,

Many thanks for your letter and for the parcel of three scales. They leave little doubt about the nature of the fish, but even so my mind still refuses to grasp this tremendous impossibility. The discovery is going to be a real zoological sensation, and we shall have to see the trawler captain and crew in order to get their testimony, also the taxidermist. Your original letter to me will probably figure in my first report to the Royal Society. However, all this is confidential at the moment.

Thanks for your offer to bring the fish to Grahamstown, but the matter is so important that I must come over. My wife and I have decided to leave here a week earlier than we had intended, so as to be able to spend some days in East London. We hope to arrive about Wednesday the 15th next, and I shall probably telephone you immediately we arrive. It will save me time if you have or can have taken a full-plate size print of the photograph of the fish from which drawings can be made as basis. I only hope the taxidermist has not varnished the thing, as I must have details of the external structure of bones, etc.

No more now. It is curious that in spite of all this evidence, my intellect says that such things can't happen.

Kindest regards,
Yours sincerely,
J. L. B. Smith

I had perpetual nightmares all this while. Looking back, it is miraculous that my relatively frail health of that time did not crack under the terrible strain, but I was possessed and sustained by a curious belief that it was my lot to carry this through and that I should be able to do so. Most men find learning new things increasingly difficult after the age of thirty, and indeed I had experienced that myself in chemistry, trying to keep up with the progressive changes in theory. I started my study of fishes when already past thirty, and it was astonishing to discover that my brain soaked it up like a sponge, and even now it is still the same. I can only suppose it must be a kind of natural affinity. At any rate, before we left Knysna I had absorbed everything available that had been published about Coelacanths. I certainly knew a lot more than a few weeks before.

We left Knysna on the 8th February 1939, intending to go straight through to East London, but there was to be nothing easy about this, for we travelled in continuous heavy rain and were fortunate to reach Grahamstown, since by that time floods had rendered almost all roads impassable. Drifts and slippery mud made motoring in South Africa no light undertaking in those days. We had to wait a whole week before the roads to East London became usable, and after an awful journey reached there on the 16th February 1939.

We went straight to the Museum. Miss Latimer was out for the moment, the caretaker ushered us into the inner room and there was the—Coelacanth, yes, God! Although I had come prepared, that first sight hit me like a white-hot blast and made me feel shaky and queer, my body tingled. I stood as if stricken to stone. Yes, there was not a shadow of doubt, scale by scale, bone by bone, fin by fin, it was a true Coelacanth. It could have been one of those creatures of 200 million years ago come alive again. I forgot everything else and just looked and looked, and then almost fearfully went close up and touched and stroked, while my wife watched in silence. Miss Latimer came in and greeted us warmly. It was only then that speech came back, the exact words I have forgotten, but it was to tell them that it was true, it was really true, it was unquestionably a Coelacanth. Not even I could doubt any more.

And now, what lay ahead? I told Miss Latimer she could tell

her Board, but no one else, and they must for the moment please not make anything public. My plan was to make no kind of announcement until I could prepare a brief account and send it to some scientific journal—*Nature* of London was in my mind. I told Miss Latimer this; she agreed to inform the Board that evening, and we arranged to come to the Museum next day.

That night again I slept little, I was too excited. A real Coelacanth, and yet and yet, could such a thing be? Even though I had seen it and confirmed every single detail, one by one, I was like the old lady at the zoo, who, seeing a giraffe for the first time, said to her friend, 'I just don't believe it'. This was worse, far worse. My whole life seemed to hang on it. My wife has reminded me that I woke her that night at least half a dozen times, and each time I would say, 'Please forgive me, but is it really true about the Coelacanth? I haven't just dreamt it, have I?' And each time she solemnly assured me, sleepily, but with conviction, that it was true.

Despite all this preoccupation, early next morning I was out on the rocks hunting fishes in the pools, and when we went to the Museum I was still clad in field clothes: khaki shorts and shirt. Miss Latimer told me the Board were very excited and that the Chairman, Dr. Bruce-Bays, was coming in shortly to meet us. When he did arrive I was standing looking at the fish, listening to Miss Latimer, who was talking at the moment, and as her back was towards the door she was unaware that he had entered. He stopped dead and his gaze was all for me. I am slight and thin and had then hardly any grey hairs; in fact, despite all I have endured there are too few even now. His features did not change, but his eyes and that queer power of reading the thoughts in other men's minds told me exactly what was in his. What! Is this skinny little fellow your expert? In those clothes I must have appeared very young to that dignified and portly old man, far too young to be able to give so startling an opinion about this fish. He would have to weigh this matter very carefully indeed before permitting the Museum to be involved in any fiasco from youthful enthusiasm.

It is all very well to have a slender, youthful appearance and few grey hairs, but you pay for them. On Boards and Committees greybeards used to wonder who the devil this youngster was to open his mouth, and I had many battles and learnt a lot. You learn far more from those who resent or dislike you than you do from your friends.

After polite introductions and preliminary words, Bruce-Bays questioned me, quite sharply at first, but as I warmed to the subject, the tension eased and he was soon deeply interested in all I had to say. The many ramifications of the discovery soon convinced him that it was not just an old fish but something of very much greater importance. He forgot my apparent youth, my lack of flesh and my clothes, his doubts had clearly evaporated, and his parting words and handshake were warm, almost enthusiastic.

Miss Latimer had left no stone unturned to find out all she could about the circumstances covering the actual catching of the animal, and in response to my queries told me that the trawler had been working the usual grounds along the coast westwards of East London. On the 22nd December 1938, Captain Goosen decided to return, and on the way back thought it might be advisable to have a run on the bank off the Chalumna River mouth, an area that is normally poor but sometimes yields good catches. So here was another link in the story, one of the many fantastic chances. A trawler captain's impulse! If he had not acted on it? Captain Goosen sent me an account of that trawl. The net was shot about three miles off-shore, some twenty miles south-west of East London, the depth close on forty fathoms. The course was roughly elliptical, the axes about three and six miles respectively, the closest approach to the shore being about two miles. They ended the run about three miles off-shore where the depth was about forty fathoms, the average depth trawled. That particular area where they trawled was on the inshore part of a submarine shelf about ten miles wide, that slopes gradually to about sixty fathoms in depth at the edge, which is abrupt, and plunges to about two hundred fathoms. The bottom of this shoreward shelf is foul and trawling troublesome and difficult. In this case their catch proved to consist of about a ton and a half of edible fish, not the highest grade, about two tons of sharks, and—one Coelacanth!

Chapter Five

JEKYLL AND HYDE

DESPITE the world-wide sensation I knew this discovery would produce, had the matter rested with me nothing would have been given to the press. I was hoping that I might be able to publish the first reports about it in a scientific journal. All the scientists I had known in my formative years had been scornful of the press, and they decried those who appeared to seek or who welcomed publicity. I had come to acquire the rather quaint idea that it was scientifically 'improper' to give information about scientific discoveries to the press, an attitude which in its bareness is a type of scientific snobbery, and generally found in the immature or in those who are unlikely ever to feature greatly in that way. Most young scientists encounter this problem and are worried by it, and its solution lies in the realisation that it is fundamentally the man in the street who pays for scientific research, and he is therefore entitled to know the results. The majority of mankind have not the opportunity of doing scientific work, but there is no question that almost everyone is deeply interested in it and eager to know about it. Another type of intellectual snobbery is the dictum that science has now passed beyond the understanding of the ordinary man. That, however, is very largely a matter of presentation. With the possible exception of higher mathematics, there is not a single branch of science whose broad outlines the ordinary man cannot appreciate if it is properly explained.

The views I held about publicity at that time had to be pushed aside, for when the Board of Trustees of the East London Museum heard the full story from Miss Latimer, they were rightly eager to exploit the whole affair to the best advantage of the Museum. The publicity which this remarkable discovery would bring and the interest it would arouse would be of the greatest benefit to any institution, and I was in no position to refuse or to contest this view. At their request I agreed to receive a reporter and to give him information. He was obviously greatly impressed by the importance of the whole matter, and not only asked many questions but came back several times before he and I were satisfied that he had the whole story correctly presented.

He concluded by asking permission to have a photograph of the fish. This I emphatically refused, to his consternation, and he urged that the article would have much less value without a photograph, which I countered by pointing out that it would at least be world news from his pen. A good deal lay behind my refusal. Once you decide an organism is new to science—and that alone is a long story—it has to be named. A name alone is no use, you must give sufficient descriptive detail so that the species can always be recognised again, or else a good illustration, preferably both. If two people happen to describe the same organism as new, as often happens, the one whose name and account are published first has 'priority', i.e. the organism for ever thereafter bears the name he gave it followed by his name. Thus the Coelacanth is *Latimeria chalumnae* J. L. B. Smith. However, there is a type of scientific piracy, in that if you are foolish enough to publish a picture of some rarity that is unnamed, you take the risk of someone else getting in before you with a name. Thus an unnamed picture of the Coelacanth in a newspaper could have led to its being known for ever after something like *Neoundina moderna* J. O. L. Roger.

When my hand had been forced in the matter of immediate publicity, I had privately determined for the reason given above that as far as I was concerned, although the press could be given the fullest details, there was to be no photograph for publication. I wanted to do the thing properly, and intended that the first picture of the Coelacanth should appear with a brief description in some scientific journal—as it happened *Nature* of London. I had previously ascertained from Miss Latimer that she had definitely not permitted anyone to photograph the specimen, and as far as she could determine no one had had the opportunity of doing so without her knowledge. She pointed out it was unlikely that anyone would have been prepared to take any risks in securing photographs, since up to then no one had had any idea of the fantastic nature of the creature.

This reporter was certainly persistent, and after finding me unmoved carried his attack to Miss Latimer, whom he got to consider the matter, and she suggested we might make some compromise. It was only with very considerable reluctance that I agreed that he might take photographs, but on the express condition that they were to be published only in the *East London Daily Dispatch* and nowhere else. I insisted on this undertaking, and it was given by this man in the presence of Miss Latimer, my wife, and myself. On that, the specimen was carried outside and he was permitted to take several exposures. I asked him to show me all the negatives, but as it happened I never saw any, so did not know what good ones he had.

Two of the pictures, and they were excellent, duly appeared in the *Daily Dispatch* on the 20th February 1939, rightly labelled as the only ones in the world.

Some days after we had returned to Grahamstown I had a telephone call from a Durban newspaper, when it was mentioned that they had been offered a photograph of the Coelacanth by a person in East London. Considerably perturbed, I promptly wrote to inform Miss Latimer.

The next surprise was a telephone call from a friend in England to say that I was taking an awful risk in permitting any photographs of the animal to appear unnamed. I heard that they had been sent to various newspapers over there, most of whom had just ignored them, thinking it was a hoax. There came also a cable from London urging me to attach a name to the Coelacanth. As has been indicated I had long since intended to apply the name *Latimeria chalumnae*, which I now attached to the fish. Although greatly disturbed by all that had happened over the photographs, I was so desperately occupied at that time that I did not manage to find time to investigate how it had all come about.

Some years later I read in some paper that this particular journalist had been greatly admired for his clever 'scoop' in getting the pictures of the first Coelacanth so promptly, that he had made a good deal of money, and was indeed still drawing royalties from them. To improve things a bit, it went on to tell how he had had the foresight to photograph the Coelacanth when it was on the quay!

Owing to the peculiar circumstances of that time, there was no real urgency in the matter of the announcement of the discovery of the Coelacanth, and since odd points kept cropping up about which he wanted further information, as mentioned before this was delayed since not only did I give several interviews on the matter to this same reporter, but after he had completed his account I insisted on checking the final draft. The full statement therefore appeared in the press of South Africa only on the 20th February 1939. At East London there was in addition an announcement that the animal would be on view to the public on that and on the following day. We were early at the Museum, and all morning long lines of curious sightseers thronged the grounds and filed past this curious fish, so roped off that it could not be touched, and at my special request under constant guard.

I had told Miss Latimer and Bruce-Bays that scientists everywhere would be clamouring for details of its structure, and that despite the loss of the soft parts and skeleton, it was desirable that it should be examined as soon as possible. At my request they recommended to the Board that it should be sent to me for study at Grahamstown, and it was agreed to do this.

On the 20th February 1939 we returned to Grahamstown. It was a chaotic return. A brief account of the discovery appeared in the Grahamstown local press on that Monday the 20th February. It was accorded far less prominence than the report of a sports day of a local school. It was said later that when the Press Association message arrived, the editor had consulted a local zoologist and had been advised to be cautious. The story sounded really rather too sensational.

Several friends plied us with questions, but most people eyed us strangely. I was quite irrationally still fearful, because although my intellect was completely satisfied with the irrefutable evidence my eyes had seen, completely satisfied that the fish was indeed a true Coelacanth, it seemed too impossible, too fantastic, that this could have happened. A Coelacanth. Alive! Every night I had a nightmare, dreaming that I had found a Coelacanth, and it was confused and troublesome because I realised it was impossible. Then I would wake and ponder on this curious dream until suddenly I would realise that it wasn't a dream, but true. I had that happen to me hundreds of nights in the years that followed.

Sometimes it got all mixed up, for I would dream I had dreamt it, and when I did wake up it took a long time to sort it all out. This sounds fantastic, and it was.

The East London Museum sent the fish with a police guard on the 22nd February 1939 by rail to Grahamstown, and it arrived on the 23rd. It was taken to my house and put in its special room. It had a curious, powerful, and penetrating odour, an odour that in the coming weeks was always to pervade our lives, awake or asleep. From the start the whole family was rigidly drilled and kept on the alert. The house was never left alone, night or day, and if a fire should occur, the fish must be the first thing to be got out, and at once. Every waking moment was full of worry for the safety of that specimen, and I dreamt of little else.

In sending the specimen to me the Board of the East London Museum had stipulated that it was not to be exhibited to the public in Grahamstown. This caused some ill-feeling, for several institutions wished to have the specimen for a period for their own special purposes. For about two weeks after our return, the back-wash from the impact on the world beyond had not yet reached Grahamstown, and there was little about the Coelacanth in the local press, only in papers outside. They got hold of some fantastic stories, among them one that this fish (which weighed 127 lb.) had dripped ten gallons of oil!

There were many curious incidents in these first few days. Several colleagues asked to see the fish, and came to my house. After I had shown it to them, one, an Englishman, said to me, 'But you are surely not expecting people to believe so astounding a thing on your word alone. You will surely be sending it to the British Museum for them to make sure.' He was astonished when I said that I doubted if anyone there knew so much more than myself to justify such a step, and that I was quite satisfied it was a Coelacanth. I added that within a week or two I expected to know a good deal more about the intimate details of a Coelacanth than any other person in the world.

A Government scientist I had known for many years called to see me at my office at College. He put his hands on my shoulders and said earnestly, 'Doc., what has made you do this thing? It is terrible to see you ruin all your scientific reputation in this way.' I asked him what thing. He replied, 'Calling this fish a Coelacanth.' I said it was a Coelacanth. He shook his head in sorrow. 'No, man,' he said; 'I have just been talking to X [a scientist], and he says you are crazy, that it is only a Rock Cod with a mutilated and regenerated tail.' I dealt gently with him and my lack of concern shook his doubts, but he was not convinced.

Cables, telegrams, and letters from near by had almost drowned us, and soon the overseas correspondence developed into a flood. All scientists were frantic for information. It was an incredible time.

There was among many others a trunk-call from the editor of a well-known daily paper about the fish! 'Dr. Smith, are you quite positive that what you say is true?' 'No!' 'No! Then how could you have said it?' 'I didn't. What I said and what I say is, that as far as my knowledge, experience, and observations go this is a true Coelacanth.' 'What is the difference?' My answer was, 'If you showed me a flower and said "Is that blue", even if it looked blue to me as a scientist my attitude would be "I should say it is blue" not "It is blue".' Somewhat bewildered words from his end concluded the interview.

Possibly because I had been so incredulous myself, it was staggering to receive no incredulity from overseas scientists. One prominent American scientist wrote to say that he had been called up late at night by the editor of an important paper who told him that they had got a report from South Africa that a live Coelacanth had been found. He supposed it was just hot air. This man asked who had said so. He replied a man named Smith. 'J. L. B. Smith?' 'Yes.' 'Well, then, I think you should be safe to go ahead and publish.'

I set to and from a general preliminary examination of the chief external features prepared an outline description of the creature. This with a photograph was sent to *Nature* in London, and appeared on the 18th March 1939. If anyone anywhere had any doubts, that article killed and buried them. There never were any more, not even here in my own country.

I had sent a scale of the Coelacanth to a scientist correspondent-friend in the U.S.A. In replying to express thanks he said that this had been received in a solemn scientific meeting. He showed it to a colleague, and the excitement that followed just about disrupted the whole affair.

The publicity surrounding the whole discovery led many people to write, telephone, or call about the oddest things. One woman wrote to say that she had seen in the papers that I was interested in old things. She had a violin that had been in the family for over a hundred years, if she sent it would I tell her if it was valuable? Others had sailors' fish-monstrosity fakes, rare and valuable shells and other ancient curios, while one man offered me a share in a project to hunt for treasure in the middle of Durban, to be based on an ancient supposed pirate's map of buried loot. Many rare and presumably prehistoric creatures were reported at that time, mainly fishes. In our most difficult period I was wakened near midnight by an excited call from Knysna to tell of a wonderful creature one of the deep-sea fishermen had got— it had a face like a monkey, short legs, and an eye in the top of its head. Would I come at once and see it; yes, right away. I asked a few questions and suggested it was a 'Jakob', a curious shark-like creature, but not exactly rare. I did not go and later when the fish came, it was what I had suspected.

It was in this period that odd reports came to attach the term 'Missing Link' to the Coelacanth, a label that especially later was to prove exceedingly troublesome. There were letters from apparently ultra-religious people who roundly reproved me for ignoring the Bible in my preposterous statements about millions of years, and did I not know that the theory of evolution was evil and an anti-religious invention of the devil put into some men's minds to enable them to divert others from the path of true thought? These came from a wide area of the globe.

Meanwhile, for the eager world of science I was faced with the task of preparing a detailed description of what remained of the animal, and, of course, ample and accurate illustration was essential. I bore a heavy teaching and administrative burden in the Chemistry Department, which gave me hardly any free time during official hours. In view of the world-wide interest in my researches on this creature, I could well have done with some relief to expedite that work, but perhaps foolish pride kept me from asking, and as none was offered I somewhat grimly kept my teaching at normal intensity. Visiting scientists, and others by letter, expressed their astonishment at this situation. I gave no response, but it really was a trying ordeal. Each day I rose at 3 a.m. and worked at the animal until 6. Then I cleaned up and went for a four-mile walk over the hills. On my return I would write up my observations from the notes, and when I left for College at 8.30 a.m. my wife took these and typed them. On my return at lunch-time I would go over them again, and she would retype during my absence in the afternoon. On my return at 5–5.30 p.m. I would start in again and usually worked until about 10 p.m. I do not suppose I averaged four hours' sleep any night during the week, but slept late on Sundays. It was the same old mixture my life had always been, turbulence and trouble, only more intense. We had no social life, business and financial affairs took a back seat, and our food reached its destination over and between sheets of manuscript. We had no conversation, no thoughts, no ideas nor eyes, for anything except Coelacanth, all day and all night. We could never forget it, certainly not with that smell. It was an equally severe strain on my wife, especially as a child was due in about three months' time.

I had no compunction about doing the whole investigation my-self—I had earned it and I could do it, but I worked on that stuffed and mounted creature with very mixed feelings. It was a wonderful thrill to be the first to see the finer details of a skull of a living Coelacanth, and yet the loss of all the soft parts was a perpetual tragedy that clouded the investigation. I pushed this aside, for it was not irremediable and only made me determined to find more and whole specimens. There must be others some-where, and at the back of my mind 'a cloud no bigger than a man's hand' had formed, the forerunner of the project that came to over-shadow all else in my life—the hunt for the home of the Coelacanth.

The work progressed slowly. The structure of the skull was the most important part, and I decided to open the whole of the one side. It was done very, very slowly and carefully, every fragment of skin and bone kept in place. By that time I had received from all over the world all the latest publications on Coelacanths and related fishes, and it was wonderful to uncover a tiny bone and then after a hunt through all the pictures and drawings to find the same or its equivalent in some fossil of a fish that had lived several hundred million years before. In some cases the structures were exactly alike; it was indeed fantastic, this peculiar feature of Coelacanths, their unchanging nature.

The dissection showed the delicate nature of some of the bones just beneath the skin, which it is believed were developed to carry what are called 'sensory canals'. These are channels filled with a slimy substance, and served as sensory organs, probably able to detect small changes in pressure and to warn the fish it was approaching something solid, or that something was approaching it.

The structures on this head showed clearly that some of the bones were no more than modified scales, and that the teeth had developed from the tubercles on the scales.

The modern Lung-fishes have 'internal' nostrils, i.e. they open inside into the roof of the mouth, and some scientists asserted that the Rhipidistia had the same, and they even managed to convince themselves that the structures in the Coelacanth fossils proved that they had had them, too. All scientists who dealt with them certainly believed this. But I could find not a sign of them in this Coelacanth, and as its bone structure proved to be virtually identical with that of those older types, they probably had none either. It was not exactly a popular discovery in some quarters.

Highly technical detailed accounts of the relationships of the Coelacanth structures would be out of place here. Those who have any interest in these may read all such details in my monograph on *Latimeria*. Suffice it to say that I found several structures which had not been detected in fossils, including a mysterious central cavity in the cartilage of the front of the head, which led to openings that in a normal fish would be the nostrils, but which in the Coelacanth are not. We do not yet know what it is, how it originated, or what it is for. Nothing like it is known to occur in any other type of fish.

One special thrill in this slow and difficult work was to discover that the taxidermist in scraping the skin had missed removing a marvellous chain of fine sensory bones just behind the head. To hold these delicate and beautiful structures in my hand was a wonderful experience, just to realise that hundreds of millions of years ago these special bones had been in the heads of Coelacanths, and here they still were! Because so many leading scientists were deeply interested in what would be found in this fish, at intervals I sent round a circular giving a brief résumé of my progress and discoveries. These were greatly appreciated, but in their acknowledgments the exponents of different schools of thought would each urge me to use the particular nomenclature they favoured for the numerous bones of the head. I allied myself with none, and gave the bones numbers that meant more to me than possible significant names.

Various curious things happened. I received a letter from the Curator of a museum in Australia, who was shown some scales of the Coelacanth by an Australian. We attemped to discover how he got them, but that mystery was never solved. Some others got into the possession of a scientist in Johannesburg, but we did not solve that either, for as far as could be determined from the time Miss Latimer took possession of the specimen, no unauthorised person was permitted to touch it or even to approach it near enough to grab a few 'souvenirs'. I had given a special warning about that souvenir danger. One 'explanation' of possession of the scales was that they had been collected on the wharf at East London after Miss Latimer had gone off with the fish. This is scarcely plausible, for nobody then had any idea of the importance of the fish, and anyone picking up scales on the fish wharf at East London would indeed be a phenomenon.

Meanwhile the full backwash of the effect of the discovery overseas had come back to the Union. One was an enormous picture of the Coelacanth, together with an article by Dr. E. I. White of the British Museum, in the *London Illustrated News*. I did not find it flattering to remote scientists like myself, and it expressed the view that the Coelacanth had come from the deeper parts of the sea. (See Chapter Six, p. 59.) Coupled with this at the same time was a letter to me protesting against the proposed use of the name *Latimeria* for this historic find, and referring to Miss Latimer in terms that were scathing, to say the least.

I must confess to an angry reaction to this letter and replied expressing the strongest disapproval of such sentiments and remarks, and also published the following in regard to this criticism in *Nature* (6 May 1939):

> Few persons outside South Africa have any knowledge of our conditions. In the coastal belt only the South African Museum at Cape Town has a staff of scientific workers among whom is an ichthyologist. The other six small museums serving the coastal area are in extremely poor circumstances, and generally have only a

Director or Curator, who cannot possibly be an expert in all branches of natural history. There are not uncommon fishes in the sea which to any of the latter would appear as strange as, if not stranger than, a Coelacanth. It was the energy and determination of Miss Latimer which saved so much, and scientific workers have good cause to be grateful. The genus *Latimeria* stands as my tribute.

Meanwhile I was continuing my terrible struggle to do my ordinary full-time University work and the detailed examination of the Coelacanth. On the 19th April I wrote in answer to Miss Latimer:

The fish is a terrible job. I could work solidly on it for 6 months. There will be over 50 plates alone and I cannot finish before June at the earliest. . . . I am hoping that I can send you the fish by the end of May perhaps.

On the 24th April came a telegram from the East London Museum:

'BOARD WISH FISH RETURN IMMEDIATELY LETTER FOLLOWS.'

That was a shock. The work was far from complete and I was almost frantic. Miss Latimer's letter that followed explained that since the tremendous effect the discovery had produced overseas had been coming back to the Union, it had caused the public in her area to clamour to see the fish again. There had been a succession of people who had travelled long distances to East London, and at the Museum they had been overwhelmed by complaints at its absence, many from influential people. It did not pacify them to be told that scientific work was being done on the fish. They wanted to see it. What a primitive instinct it is to stare at the unusual, but it does satisfy something.

I telephoned Miss Latimer, and eventually we compromised. I should return it on the 2nd May 1939. Where I had worked intensely before, the time remaining was a frantic nightmare. In the end I managed most of what I hoped, but not all. At the end of this terrible strain it was mainly with a sense of relief that the animal was handed over to its police escort. It arrived safely, and apparently the Museum was thronged for days by eager sight-seers, who pressed in closely all the time. This widespread local resurgence of interest had several effects. The discovery of the Coelacanth had been prominently featured in South Africa, but it caused a far greater sensation overseas. As this continued to come back full blast to the Union, many of those connected with the Museum in East London came to feel that, in addition to its apparently exceptional scientific interest, the specimen might be worth a good deal as well. Since the Museum was in such poor circumstances,* rather than just keep such a valuable specimen would it not be better to sell it and use the money to develop the Museum? A few protagonists of the old 'Send it to the British Museum' policy also raised their voices, and all this induced Bruce-Bays to take action in the matter. Early in June he handed Miss Latimer the draft of a letter which he asked her to type (she was Curator, Secretary, Treasurer, and everything else). She read it with amazement and dismay, for it was to offer the Coelacanth to the British Museum of Natural History. She read it again and again, but then and there decided that she would never type it, that if it was sent she would resign, and promptly told several members of the Board about it and her resolve. A few days later Bruce-Bays came in and asked her if she had done that letter. She said she had not typed it, would never type it, and in what she considers one of the longest and warmest speeches she has ever made, told him in no uncertain terms what she thought of the whole thing. Miss Latimer expected opposition and even violence, but instead this mature, influential man was so overwhelmed by her personality and arguments that at the conclusion of this speech he quite meekly said it would be in order to leave the letter and the whole matter. It was so surprising a victory that Miss Latimer said it just took her breath away.

This did not end the matter, it came up again, and early in July 1939 I was asked to come to East London to advise the Board of Trustees of the Museum about it. This I did, pointing out to them how much the actual specimen would mean to their Museum, far more than any sum of money even greater than its value. It would constantly attract world-wide attention. That has been amply borne out by the course of subsequent events, and the Coelacanth was the first real step to fame for that Museum.

* Despite this, the Board of Trustees of the Museum had voted a suitable gratuity to Captain Goosen for what he had done.

After the fish had left Grahamstown we still had little leisure, for there was an enormous amount of work to be done in completing the manuscript of the monograph, virtually a book, with numerous plates and detailed accurate drawings, whose preparation took much time. The whole was finally dispatched late in June 1939, and it was only then that my wife was able to give any time to the purely mundane occupation of providing clothes for the infant that appeared five days later. He had a narrow shave from not only coming naked into the world, but of remaining so longer than usual.

Thus the course of the first Coelacanth—turbulence, trouble, and strain, the inevitable accompaniments of accomplishment. Any great event of this kind tends to become submerged by the little things, and it was only when I was able to detach myself and see the whole in its true perspective that the wonder of it all stood out like a shining beacon. It was a tremendous privilege to have been the first man to work on a Coelacanth. But I had to turn my back on that and look ahead, for now before me was the problem of finding more specimens, of finding where these incredible animals lived. The remote past had risen dramatically from the sea, at our very door; but did it really live there? From the first I doubted this, but had to make sure. Photographs and offers of a reward were sent to all fishing craft on South African shores, and daily I hoped to hear more. I spoke to the College authorities about the possibility of organising an expedition, but found no response at that time. In any case, the gathering clouds of war and the climax in September 1939, meant the end of all those dreams. Who cared about Coelacanths when bombs were going to fall? It was far more important to kill Germans than to find Coelacanths.

BOOK II

TROUGH AND CREST

Chapter Six

NO DEEP-SEA REFUGEE

AFTER the initial shock of the discovery had passed, one of the first problems to present itself was that of where these Coelacanths lived. They had, of course, been in existence incredibly long before any type of ape or man appeared, and all through the many thousands of years it had taken modern man to evolve and develop they must have been living as well. Yet right up to 1938 no scientist had ever seen or even suspected the existence of a living Coelacanth. As has been explained, it had been comfortably settled that all Coelacanths must have died out at least 50 million years ago, and they occupied merely a remote niche in the consciousness of most scientists, except for a very few most highly specialised workers. Now, in the shock of the discovery, scientists all over the world were busy considering the problem of how such a large and curious-looking creature had managed to escape notice all this time.

One obvious way out was the theory advanced by Dr. E. I. White of the British Museum, who not long after the discovery was announced, published an article, mentioned earlier, in an illustrated periodical, in which he stated:

> Our living Coelacanth, although trawled in only 40 fathoms, almost certainly was a wanderer from deeper parts of the sea to which its kind have retreated in the face of fierce competition with the more active modern types of fishes. This opens up the interesting possibility that other remarkable relic-forms may also inhabit the more inaccessible depths of the oceans.

I could never understand how this view could find acceptance. To me one glance at the Coelacanth disposed of any idea that it lived in the 'inaccessible depths of the ocean'; yet a number of scientists all over the world apparently accepted this with a sigh of uncritical relief. It explained the whole thing! It is astonishing to see how far this (at least to me) extraordinary theory penetrated. It even made scientists ignore facts. For example, it had been reported in the press all over the world that the first Coelacanth was taken by a trawler near East London at a depth of 40 fathoms (80 yards). This was clearly stated both in my monograph and in many other publications. In addition, it is well known that in South African waters trawlers have long operated at depths up to and even exceeding 300 fathoms. Yet a leading overseas scientific treatise published not long after the discovery, in discussing the Coelacanth, stated that the fish had been taken by 'A South African trawler dredging deeper than usual'. Then again, only a few years ago, a costly deep-sea expedition worked over the great ocean deeps of the world hoping to catch a Coelacanth there.

This idea that the Coelacanth might live in the depths has always seemed inexplicable to me, for when I looked at that fish, even the first time, it said as plainly as if it could speak: 'Look at my hard, armoured scales. They overlap so that there is a three-fold thick layer of them over my whole body. Look at my bony head and stout spiny fins. I am so well protected that no rock can hurt me. Of course I live in rocky areas, among reefs, below the action of the waves and surf, and, believe me, I am a tough guy and not afraid of anything in the sea. No soft deep-sea ooze for me. My blue colour alone surely tells you that I cannot live in the depths. You don't find blue fishes there. I cannot swim at speed for more than a short distance; I don't need to, because by levering myself from convenient concealment among rocks or from a crevice, I can pounce so swiftly on any creature passing by that it hasn't a hope. When I spot any quarry that stays quiet, I don't need to give myself away by swimming. I can stalk it by crawling quietly along gullies and channels, pressing close against the rocks for added concealment. Look at these teeth and enormous jaw muscles. Once they clamp tight on anything, believe me it can't get away. Even big fishes have no hope. I just hang on until they die, and then feed at leisure, as my kind has done for millions of years.' All this and more the shape and form of the Coelacanth presented to my eye with its experience of living fishes.

Even though we have a far from complete knowledge of the life in the great depths of the ocean, a good many fishes from there have been caught, and they have given scientists a pretty fair idea of the life in the utter darkness of those cold depths. They do not give me the impression that life is especially easy down there, and almost all the fishes are black, while crustacea and others are red. Blue is no colour of the moving life of the abyss.

In any case, however, the Coelacanth just did not fit. Its scales alone ruled it out, for truly deep-sea fishes have no need of scales, certainly not scales like those of the Coelacanth. It is by no means certain and not even likely that the fishes that live in the depths, or their ancestors, went there to escape competition with other fishes. My work has repeatedly shown the enormous stretches that even small feeble fishes have colonised, and all the evidence indicates that fishes tend to move and seek new places to live, just like any other creatures. All the types we know from the deeps are derived from ancestors who lived in waters of ordinary depth, and though most deep-sea fishes are of course greatly modified to suit the special conditions, all are clearly related to surface forms, none of which are any markedly better equipped to withstand 'competition' than the ancestors of the deep-sea forms. In the depths bodies are soft, bones are light, eyes are enormous or have become obsolete, and huge jaws are filled with long fangs, often barbed. There is no valid evidence to support the idea that any of them retired to the depths to escape competition.

When the Coelacanth was caught, that haul of the trawl brought up several tons of sharks. As is well known, the bag (Cod-end) full of fish is hauled aboard by a winch hung up over the deck, and the lower end opened by jerking a rope, when the fishes cascade into a heap on the deck. All but the most hardy are squeezed to death in the net, certainly all at the bottom, and the fall and the pressure of the heap above finish off the rest. Not many fishes, perhaps occasionally an odd shark, are ever alive. It is further characteristic that when deep-sea fish come up to the surface, even without being squeezed in a net, most die long before they even reach the top of the water. It so happened that the Coelacanth was at the bottom of the pile with which he was caught, and it was some time before that great weight above, mainly sharks, was hauled away. At the end of all this the Coelacanth was still so much alive that it snapped viciously at the hand of the captain, who had been called to examine this strange creature that had been caught. The crew all remarked on the fact that the Coelacanth still showed signs of life for several hours afterwards. No deep-sea creature could have endured all that and lived. So much, then, for any notion that this was a degenerate or feeble fish.

With all this clear evidence it was utterly impossible for me to accept the view that this fish lived in the depths. It seemed unlikely that it, or its ancestors like it, would ever have had to 'retreat' from 'competition' with other fishes. I know of no past or modern fishes that this Coelacanth, as a reef-haunting type, need fear, very much the reverse. To most reef fishes the Coelacanth would unquestionably be a terror, something like the larger and rightly dreaded Rock Cods. In any conflict between even the most vicious free-swimming types and the Coelacanth in his own environment of the reefs, I would back the old Coelacanth every time, and as a human diver among reefs I would unquestionably not like to meet a Coelacanth down below. Looking back, I find it as incredible as ever that the majority of scientists interested in the matter apparently accepted the idea that Coelacanths lived in the depths.

My complete disbelief in this 'inaccessible depths' idea did not, of course, solve the problem. The first question was whether this particular fish really belonged to the area where it was caught. Was it perhaps just very rare or had others been seen and not reported? Many people are diffident about taking or even reporting to museums what looks queer to them, for fear that it may be common and that they may be exposed as ignorant, and many rarities are lost that way. It takes some event to shake this, and every time a 'find' is reported in the press it brings a diminishing trail of other reports in its wake. When the first Coelacanth was exhibited at East London, several people said they had seen others. One man reported finding a fish just like it cast up on the shore north of East London many years before. He had been unable to do anything about it, as it was large and partly decomposed. A trawlerman said that in Natal waters, many years before, the net had brought up six large fishes that he felt sure had been Coelacanths, but the skipper had ordered them to be thrown overboard, as he doubted if anyone would eat such strange creatures. There were other stories, all rather vague, and in the absence of some characteristic parts, such as scales, or of photographs, it is impossible to estimate the accuracy of any such reports.

Despite careful inquiry all along the coast about East London, no evidence of any certainty was obtained. No line-fisherman in those parts could recollect ever having caught or seen any fish that could have been a Coelacanth. Nor had any trawler apparently ever certainly caught one before, anywhere about East London or indeed anywhere in South African waters, certainly not in any human memory. And many trawlers constantly sweep the ocean floor over great areas all along our shores, day and night, at all sorts of depths. While a trawler catches pretty well everything of any size in the parts it covers, line-fishing does not do the same. Repeatedly in much-fished areas I have caught by poison and other means fish, large fish, that never bite on hooks. Was there not still a chance that this Coelacanth might fall in that category?

All along the South African coast there are strong currents in the sea. The main stream is the Mozambique current that flows south and westwards, swinging close in to shore or farther out according to the wind. Though it does not change in direction, by its variation of position in relation to the shore it creates at times other almost equally powerful reverse currents. In such conditions line-fishing is extremely difficult and commercially impossible in any but fairly shallow water, so that if the Coelacanth happened to live among reefs at the 100-fathoms mark or deeper, it might possibly have escaped notice. On the other hand, there would almost certainly be regular strays to shallower water, or sick or dead fishes washing up, that would most likely have been noticed had they been about, as they would almost certainly be large. Most fortunately for me, shortly after the discovery, the South African Government Fisheries vessel came to East London, and working for some time over the whole area where the Coelacanth had been found, tried by every possible means to catch another or to find further traces, but failed to do so. The whole weight of the evidence therefore seemed to be unquestionably against the possibility that the Coelacanth could be living in the sea anywhere near East London, even at fair depths among reefs.

It is curious that most of the very primitive types of fish that still live on today are found in fresh water. This possibility had to be considered for the Coelacanth, too. As far as South Africa itself was concerned, certainly anywhere near East London, that could be ruled out, as everyone who knows this area will agree. Most fresh-water rivers in South Africa have no constant flow. Their courses are often so steep that in floods they run strongly, but for most of the year they are reduced to a series of disconnected and usually not very extensive pools. In floods a representative part of their fishes, sometimes great numbers, are carried into the sea and die, and in turn wash up on the shore. You can get a good idea of the fishes in the rivers that way.

In dry periods the pools hold a fish fauna extensive neither in numbers nor in kind, and they are constantly subjected to intensive fishing, not always legal or conservatory in nature. Taking all the evidence into account, while a few minute types may still remain unknown, that a large fish like the Coelacanth could be living unsuspected in our South African fresh-water rivers seemed just about impossible.

As is described elsewhere, my life in the months following the discovery was troubled and difficult, and there was little time for reflection. The problem of the origin or habitat of the Coelacanth was rather like a hovering storm, ever present, nagging at my mind. It seemed obvious that the chief hope of finding others lay in an expedition with a vessel well equipped to explore the life about the reefs, where ordinary line-fishing would not serve. Having no funds of my own and no sources appearing likely in South Africa, I made tentative approaches to several large overseas institutions; but the results were indefinite. There were rumours that this or that institution or body was preparing an expedition to come to South Africa, but nothing further. Meanwhile a picture of the Coelacanth and the offer of a reward for any further specimens had been sent to all trawlers and fishing vessels. On all these the Coelacanth came to be known as 'Old Fourlegs', and indeed bears that name to this day.

Although we remained hoping almost daily for further news, the Coelacanth storm slowly subsided, and eventually the gathering clouds of international tension and war finally disposed of my hopes for any expedition of our own or from elsewhere for that time.

All through the war years we constantly sought news and

evidence of Coelacanths all along our coasts. My wife and I walked many hundreds, probably thousands, of miles in all, showing the picture and telling the story to people of all classes, callings, race, and colour. But we got nothing of any value. Before the war ended it came to look as if the Coelacanth could not possibly live normally anywhere near where this one had been caught, and that it must have been a stray. There must surely be others. The problem of finding out where they lived became even greater.

If my deduction that the Coelacanth lived about reefs was correct, it was clearly such a predator that it ought to take a baited hook, or would at any rate be likely to be seen by fishermen sometimes somewhere. If that was the case, why had its existence not been reported before? That could be the result of many different causes. Coelacanths might, for example, live only about reefs where nobody fished. That might be because nobody lived on the shores where such reefs were, or the reefs might be far out at sea, as margins to banks where there was not enough dry land for anyone to live. It might even be that those reefs were constantly lashed by rough seas or powerful currents, or both, so that nobody could ever fish there at all. This would, of course, mean that if the Coelacanths lived in such a place they would never have been caught by any human agency, and would not easily be tracked by any means except that of going and finding the exact spot. It would certainly be a formidable task to cover all such places. On the other hand, it was equally possible that they had been and were being caught regularly in some area, but by primitive peoples to whom they would just be fish and who would not realise their significance. And in what part of the shorelines of the world were any or all of such conditions more likely to be found than in East Africa? Nowhere in all the temperate and tropical oceans was there at that time so great an area whose marine fauna had been so little investigated and which was so little known as East Africa. The whole area is full of reefs, rocky and coral reefs, some enormous, many hardly known. Add to this that the set of the current from north of Madagascar is always southwards. I could see no reason why the Coelacanth should not live normally in some remote and probably uncivilised part of that vast area. As I surveyed all the facts and evidence, it seemed very likely. This one, caught near East London, could easily have come rambling down the coast in the warm Mozambique current, as quite a number of tropical fishes constantly do.

The peoples of East Africa have from the earliest known times been ardent fishermen; but save for an Arab, Forskal, who lived in the Red Sea area in the eighteenth century, none have been ichthyologists or had any pretensions to scientific knowledge. The vast majority, especially those of Bantu origin, are even to-day of a low order of intelligence, and restrained from a more brutish existence only by the threat of force. As I wrote in 1946 in a report to the South African Council for Scientific and Industrial Research: 'There may well be places in East Africa where Coelacanths are commonly caught and used as food, and nobody would be any the wiser.' What applied to East Africa applied with equal force to the 3,000-mile-long coast-line of Madagascar. Numerous Coelacanth fossils had been found on Madagascar. There must be stretches of coast there that no enlightened scientific eye has ever seen, and the tantalising vision of savages feasting unsuspected on succulent Coelacanth steaks on a Madagascan shore did not seem too fantastic.

And so my eyes were turned to East Africa, but not with any joy. To search every reef in that vast area would take many years of effort. It would need time and money, plenty of money. I was no longer young, and as for money, I was a scientist, not a wool farmer, not even a millionaire.

Chapter Seven

OBSESSION

My illustrated monograph on the first Coelacanth appeared in February 1940.* As I thumbed through the pages of the first advance copy, my feelings were mixed. Pride in its achievement strove against the grim recollection of all it had cost. The book certainly gave plenty of information. One scientific friend, not an ichthyologist, remarked of it: 'Great Scott, if you could write so much about only parts of a fish, what would you have done with a whole one?' Truly, all that work still lay ahead.

War, war, war! Scientific work, other than for war, declined steadily. Who cared about fishes except as food for the forces? My double life went steadily on, we had to train scientists so they could make explosives to blast other men, but the proportion of women in the University classes steadily rose. All this time my Coelacanth monograph lay on my table, and my brain was constantly obsessed by the problem. In 1944 the men began to return and life became more difficult than ever, with shortages of staff, extra lessons, and vacation classes for returned servicemen.

It became increasingly difficult to be enthusiastic about hammering science into the heads of men who from all they had endured in conflict could not but regard the academic life with some scorn. After all, if you had been accustomed to soaring through the skies in your own plane, to killing wherever you could, and to daily narrow escapes from death, things like valency and equivalent weight just couldn't mean a thing.

Even in those dark days of war the fascination of fishes went on biting more and more deeply into my soul, and by 1945 I came to realise it could not be long before I cut loose from chemistry somehow. I had not sufficient means to live without assistance and could see no clear way. I had heard that the Prime Minister had intervened to make life easier for a few prominent scientists,

* In the *Transactions of the Royal Society of South Africa, 1939.*

but Grahamstown is very far away from the centre of things. Then came a letter from a complete stranger, the late Bransby A. Key, of Johannesburg, inviting me to write a popular book about fishes, saying that a thousand pounds had been made available for this purpose.

By a curious coincidence this letter was dated 26th September (1945), which is the joint birthday of my wife and myself (our young son grew up with the quaint idea that all married couples had birthdays on the same day). Partly as a result of my own early struggles in the study of fishes it had come to be my ambition to produce a book of this kind, and several years before, without any hope of funds to publish, I had set out to produce one. It soon became clear that its cost would far exceed any funds I might hope to raise, so that the whole thing, text and illustrations, was packed away.

After receiving this letter, I got out and examined that earlier manuscript. It was interesting to observe how much I had progressed in the meantime, for I could see clearly that what I had composed then was not good enough. My ideas had enlarged and crystallised since that time, and what I had in mind was much more ambitious and comprehensive.

In reply to Key it was possible to give him an almost complete outline of the book I envisaged, and to say that a thousand pounds was not enough. He replied at once that a satisfactory plan and a competent author were far more difficult to find than the money; that could be raised, and so a Board of Trustees was got together. Before the end of the year (1945), the project was in full swing.

If chemistry and fishes had been equally balanced before, fate was now loading the ichthyological pan. Here were not only my beloved fishes, but a work I had longed to do, something big, with a definite aim and end.

About this time we heard the first rumours of the foundation of the Council for Scientific and Industrial Research, which would co-ordinate all scientific research and administer funds in its aid. Would it be able to help me in the move I was now more than dreaming about? Would it help me to fishes, to change from sulphuretted hydrogen to formalin? Meanwhile, work on the book went on apace. Our house became more of a laboratory and a studio than a home. I sought out a number of young artists and trained them to draw fishes as we wanted them, which is, accurately and as they really are. Many failed and left, but those who came through the trial period did good work.

The year 1946 was one of the most difficult of my life. We had huge classes to handle, some had to be duplicated. My wife, also a chemist, just could not escape the appeals for help, and had to teach as well. It was almost as bad as the time of the Coelacanth. We became just machines. We had people all along the South African coast, trawlers and fishermen, sending a constant stream of fish for illustrations. In June-July 1946, for purposes of the book, we took five artists and a photographer and spent a month in and about Lourenço Marques. There was a Dr. Jekyll and Mr. Hyde flavour even about this. We lived in an extremely ancient derelict house, the furniture mainly boxes, but in a select locality, not far from the Governor-General's palace. Lourenço Marques was startled by the succession of notables who visited the ancient structure, and the photographer's antics below the coconut palm in front provided free entertainment for all the urchins of the neighbourhood. I spent most of my time collecting specimens, on the bay, about the islands, and along the coast, while my wife culled the market, made friends with the Portuguese deep-sea fishermen, ran the house with servants directed by gestures, tried in vain to keep her young son clean, controlled the artists, and showed our work to impeccably dressed and often uniformed visitors. It was fish, night and day, and we could not speak a word of Portuguese. This was so maddening that we decided we must learn that language, which we eventually did, but only after a grim battle lasting five years.

When we returned to the Union in July 1946, I learnt that there would be at least a possibility of a Research Fellowship from the Council for Scientific and Industrial Research, which by then had been established. I consulted the various authorities concerned, and eventually, in September 1946, gave notice of resignation from the Chemistry Department as from the end of that year. It was a most difficult thing to do, as I have always been greatly attached to chemistry and enjoyed teaching, and it meant severance of close contact with students, whom it has constantly been a very real pleasure to handle, teach, and advise.

The Research Fellowship from the Council for Scientific and

Industrial Research did materialise, and in 1947 my new life started. At first I had only one room, then more space was made available, and eventually the University agreed to have a separate Department of Ichthyology. This is now housed in one of the original military buildings, whose present contents would certainly startle those who lived there first. This is a curious and probably unique department, whose chief support comes from the South African Council for Scientific and Industrial Research.

At the time now described (1946), we had little in our heads but the growing 'book', but although this was more than enough to occupy our full time, the Coelacanth was never out of our minds. With the passing of the active phase of the war, from all parts of the world odd letters had begun to come in—Coelacanth! Eventually, in October 1946, I wrote to the President of the C.S.I.R., and said that as interest in the Coelacanth was reviving, it was inevitable that a search for more would be started, and it was naturally expected that South Africa should take the initiative.

He replied by return, expressing approval and suggesting immediate steps to further the project. I submitted a more detailed memorandum, and eventually a small committee was nominated by the C.S.I.R. to go into the matter.

In March 1947 the following notice was issued to the press:

LATIMERIA CHALUMNAE

The discovery of a living Coelacanthid Fish in South African waters, off East London, at the end of 1938, is an event still in the forefront of the minds of biologists. The published account of the mounted animal is as exhaustive as the material permitted, but all zoologists desire information about the soft parts of the creature which in this case were lost before they could be examined. The outbreak of war put a stop to preparations for expeditions to seek further specimens of this remarkable fish.

Now that the war is over, general interest in this project has been shown in various countries and in South Africa in particular. The South African Council for Scientific and Industrial Research has appointed a committee to consider how best to organise a marine expedition on a considerable scale. This expedition would aim not only at securing more Coelacanths, but would also explore and accumulate data in various fields of science in the relatively poorly known region of the Mozambique Channel.

The Committee is under the Chairmanship of Dr. S. H. Haughton, Director of the South African Geological Survey, and a member of the Council for Scientific and Industrial Research. The Honorary Secretary of the Committee is Professor J. L. B. Smith, of Rhodes University College, Grahamstown, and the committee requests that all Societies, Institutions, and private persons interested in the project should communicate with him.

Some bright soul sent a statement to the press in England about the proposed expedition, and said that volunteers were wanted, quoting my name in reference. Letters almost drowned me. I gained the impression that the British Isles were just bursting with young people wanting more adventures, and had to have a contradiction published. There ensued considerable correspondence with interested bodies and institutions all over the world, and two meetings of the Committee were held. The projected expedition was named the 'African Coelacanth Marine Expedition', or 'A.C.M.E.' for short.

I wanted to hunt and find Coelacanths, and knew exactly how I proposed to set about it; but some of the others had ideas of their own, and soon it became clear that a large-scale oceanographical investigation was to be hung on to the Coelacanth. I did not greatly mind as long as this led the way to the Coelacanth, and the area to which I had pointed, Madagascar and the Mozambique channel, certainly needed investigation. Just about nothing had been done there. When the details of the vessels and equipment necessary for all this came up, finance pushed up its ugly head. I intended to use explosives, and this raised further difficulties, for fishery interests might be antagonised. It was a long surging battle, in which I saw danger to my desire to find Coelacanths. The vessels were the chief problem, and there was at least a possibility of one being loaned by a group like the British 'Discovery' Committee. But when this suggestion was put to the Prime Minister, it was rejected by him. Despite my astonishment, it became clear that nobody else expected a Prime Minister to give reasons.

Before the end of 1947 it had become quite plain that the large-scale project that the Committee had visualised earlier was financially impossible, and I submitted my original plan, one much less ambitious and far less costly but at least as effective from the purely Coelacanth point of view. One essential part of my plan was a descriptive leaflet (Plate 3), showing a picture of the Coelacanth, giving a brief description, and offering a reward, in English, Portuguese, and French; and I proposed that this should be distributed everywhere along the coasts of East Africa, Madagascar, and all islands in those waters.

After a period of indefinite suspense, we drifted to the end of the A.C.M.E. project, it just fizzled out. Early in 1948 it was dead, and I have never really discovered whether it was international tension, finance, or the effects of the views of overseas scientists in higher quarters that finished it off. At any rate I was left up in the air with a sense of frustration. As a scientist I can never view with any pleasure the apparent ease with which some politicians appear to contemplate war, and the spending of countless millions on destruction and death, while they will in peace-time hedge and jib at a few thousand pounds for a scientific project. However, even if the Government would not help I was determined to go on, by myself if necessary. There was one way in which I could reach out and cover vast and remote areas without going myself and without great expenditure, and that was by means of the leaflet. So I told the C.S.I.R. I wished to proceed with that idea, which they approved, and both they and Rhodes University College agreed to guarantee £100 each as a reward for the first two Coelacanths obtained.

These leaflets were printed in Lourenço Marques, and distributed by every possible means. The Portuguese authorities sent numbers to every part of their shores, with instructions to officials not only to distribute them among all classes, but to explain them where necessary. This was done with characteristic promptitude and thoroughness. Our port authorities in the Union and those of Lourenço Marques agreed to hand leaflets to the captains of ships going north, and to ask them to leave some at every port where they touched. Batches were sent to every major port along the East African coast, with requests that they should be distributed among the fisher-folk. With a Portuguese official, my friend Carlos Torres, who speaks English, French, and Portuguese with equal facility, I visited the Consul for France in Lourenço Marques, and gave him an account of the whole matter, explained the leaflets and the object I hoped they would attain. I told him that in my opinion the Coelacanth was most likely to live somewhere about Madagascar or in its area, and asked if he would be kind enough to send a batch of the leaflets to the authorities there, as well as to write in explanation and to request them to distribute the leaflets as widely as possible in their territories. He became most interested and promised every possible assistance. A day or two later he informed me that the leaflets had been sent by air to Madagascar, together with a letter giving a full explanation of the whole project.

I felt that even if I could not go and look everywhere myself, money talks, and the leaflet would have thousands of eyes constantly looking on my behalf. Again and again we got evidence that the leaflets had gone far and wide, though we heard nothing of those sent to Madagascar, except later that officials had seen them. There is no evidence that the leaflets were distributed widely there, possibly because it was felt that it was too crazy an idea that Coelacanths should live round those shores. After all, had not competent scientists in Europe satisfactorily settled that Coelacanths had fled to the depths of the ocean? It seems fairly certain that none were sent to the Comores or, if they got there, they remained unused.

Even though I had high hopes for the leaflet, I was preparing for many years of laborious searching myself. Especially in the course of my later work on South African fishes, it had become clear that for a full understanding of them and of their peculiar faunal components, it would be necessary to study the fishes of East Africa as well. The more I investigated, the clearer did it become how very little work of any real value had been done in that vast area. I felt there could scarcely be any more fortunate combination of effort than to go hunting Coelacanths as well as other fishes in all that huge virtually unknown region, full of wonderful reefs and channels, just the parts where I judged that Coelacanths should live, and, big as they were, still remain unknown. The South African Council for Scientific and Industrial Research lent a ready ear to my proposals, and provided, and has since gone on providing, funds for this exploratory work. In addition, the Portuguese authorities were most co-operative and furnished invaluable aid on a considerable scale.

In 1947 and 1948 we carried out expeditions over the whole of the southern regions of Mozambique. The fishes of the southernmost part of that area were included in my South African fishes volume, printing of which had started in March 1948, and we completed our work early in 1949, the book itself eventually appearing in July that year.

By that time the public of South Africa had become interested in our work, and our basic support from the C.S.I.R. was supplemented by gifts of supplies and money from private persons and firms.

From then on we carried out a series of expeditions, going steadily farther afield each year. Always we carried and distributed the leaflets, spoke of the Coelacanth, and asked questions. In 1948 I met a native in the Bazaruto area of Mozambique who picked on the fish at once. Yes, he had once caught exactly such a queer fish, he got it one evening in the deep channel south of Bazaruto Island, but had never seen or heard of another before or since. In the water it was like a big Garrupa (Rock Cod), but when he got it out the big scales and the peculiar fins stamped it on his memory as unique. He spoke of its oiliness, the soft flesh, and the absence of bone, things about which he could never have known except from an actual specimen. He could not say if the tail was the same, but it was near enough. This was the only reasonably hopeful sign we got in all that long search up the east coast of Africa. It remained the only one.

Before the book on South African fishes appeared, the publishers told me they expected it to sell well, and that it would probably be necessary to have a second edition within a year. The volume was issued in July 1949, six weeks before we were due to go on an expedition to East Africa. The whole edition sold out in three weeks! It was a situation! We were in the throes of our final arrangements for departure when we received a frantic call from the publishers to prepare for another edition. I do not yet know how it was done, but it was. The proofs followed us in batches over a long stretch of Mozambique, and were corrected under what one may term somewhat unusual conditions and in places where such work had certainly never been done before. A book of that type takes almost a year to print, and that second edition came out the following year.

Meanwhile we went steadily on, gradually extending our knowledge of East Africa, its reefs, conditions, and fishes, and continually exposing undreamt-of scientific wealth. There was so much that I almost got to wishing there was no Coelacanth urge to divert me from what had now become a most fascinating pursuit, unravelling the marvellous fish-life of East Africa.

In 1950 the 'Discovery' organisation wrote to say that the research vessel *William Scoresby* would be going on a voyage, and would call at and look for Coelacanths in South Africa. She was the vessel which from letters from overseas I had hoped we might get from this organisation for our A.C.M.E. expedition, but Smuts had refused to permit us even to ask.

The *William Scoresby* had bad luck. She arrived in April 1950. The engineer had to be shipped back from Cape Town, the vessel had to be dry docked. Her chief scientific officer, Robert Clark, came by land from Cape Town to Grahamstown to tell me their plans. They hoped to find Coelacanths at East London, and had come well equipped with lines, nets, and special traps, and requested my co-operation and advice.

I warned him of the difficulties he would encounter, currents and foul bottom, and advised consultation with trawlermen. I cancelled a trip to Lourenço Marques so as to be able to visit East London and go out with them for part of this time, and arrived there after they had worked for a few days. Very few things upset Robert Clark, but even he was a bit depressed. They had no Coelacanths. There was no point in my going out to sea with them, for they had no traps, no lines, or whole nets either. The patchy bottom and swift apparently opposing currents at variable depths had beaten them. The traps were lost, the lines ripped away, and the nets all torn. Instead of taking me out to sea, they took me down to the saloon and opened a bottle of champagne, of which my share was by choice only the smell.

Later in 1950 we worked in the area about the island of Mozambique, most of the time at and about Pinda, truly the most wonderful haunt of varied fish-life. It is a jungle-covered peninsula, wild and remote, with a lighthouse at its northern tip. The reef is enormous, at least five miles by eight in extent, and there is every variety of bottom, from sand to coral, sheltering fishes of all kinds. It was a hard life, supplies were difficult, water is very scarce, it is hot and we were plagued by packs of man-eating lions that terrorised the whole area. Almost every night they tore open the natives' flimsy huts and savagely choked their last frenzied screams. It was horrible to hear the triumphant roar that accompanied a kill; we even had one of the brutes come and cough at us early one morning from the top of a thicket-clad cliff as we worked on the reef below. In the morning we would find their pug marks near our bedroom window. It was not pleasant.

The Portuguese had done their work well. Even in remote lighthouses such as this the leaflet was posted for all to see. Again and again some headman would show it, stuck on the pole of his hut. As a treasured possession, it would sometimes be produced from the inside of a fisherman's garment. There could have been few even in those remote parts that had not heard about the Coelacanth; they all knew that ten thousand Escudos were offered for this fish. To the natives all along the coast the Coelacanth is now known as 'Dez Contos Peixe', i.e. 'Hundred Pound Fish'. In our travels we came to realise that most of them doubted whether there really was anyone so crazy as to pay that vast sum for just one fish, and we tried to convince them. Added to that, experience taught me that while the average native could recognise a picture of a fish he already knew well, it was the exception for one to be able to recognise an unknown fish from a picture.

In 1951 we worked over one of the wildest and least-known parts of East Africa, the northern territory of Mozambique, between Port Amelia and the Rovuma. This was one of the most arduous of all our undertakings. Along the coast are a number of islands, densely bushed but waterless and uninhabited. There are no communications and no supplies; from the point of view of our work the normal conditions were difficult, as there is constant high wind with occasional storms, currents are fierce, and there is a rise and fall of 14 feet at spring tides. We lived and voyaged all along those terrible shores in a small vessel provided by the Portuguese; indeed, we could never have done this work but for their aid. Taking advantage of the few occasions when the wind abated a trifle, we would rush from one island shelter to another, often only precarious. Fishes, well, they were there in millions, wonderful fishes so unsophisticated that they almost climbed aboard themselves, and we got marvellous collections; but never saw a trace of anything like a Coelacanth, nor had any of the few humans we encountered, white or black.

In all this time I was still the only scientist in the world to believe that the Coelacanth came from somewhere about tropical East Africa. My views were looked on as obsession rather than as logical deduction. I was plainly crazy even though this was leading to the discovery of marvellous scientific wealth in modern fishes. Constantly very conscious of all this incredulity, at the time now described I became increasingly puzzled and worried, because just north of Mozambique the great westerly current of the Indian Ocean divides, part going north and part south, the latter our powerful Mozambique current. If the true home of the Coelacanth lay anywhere south of that division of the current, it was easy to understand how one at least had wandered down to our waters, as many other tropical fishes constantly do; but despite all our searching we had so far failed to find that home.

The fact that the Coelacanth did get to East London made it far less likely that its home lay anywhere north of the level of Cape Delgado, opposite which the current divides. As we had so far failed to find that home in the area of the southern branch along East Africa itself, while it increased my uneasiness it also focused my attention on Madagascar, which was also washed by that same branch.

All along that part of the East African coast, and exactly opposite, lay the thousand-mile long stretch of Madagascar, not so far away. Even if my mind had not constantly been drawn across that channel by the Coelacanth, there were always vivid reminders of our nearness to Madagascar. In that wild part we found ruins that puzzled us at first, extensive ruins of forts that faced the best landing-points on the shore. Eventually we came to learn that they were the sole remains of an extensive colonisation of this northern area of Mozambique by the Portuguese of earlier times. Those hardy pioneers had scarcely become established when fleets of sailing canoes drifting silently ashore in the dead of night discharged hordes of raiding natives, who killed, ravaged, and pillaged, then sailed away as silently as they had come. They were the Saccalaves, hardy seafaring natives from Madagascar. So near was Madagascar, where the seas and reefs could not be very different from those of Mozambique, and I was comforted by the feeling that even though Madagascar lay beyond my present reach, my leaflet had gone there, and I hoped, that as in Portuguese territory, many natives would have seen it and be aware of the rich reward this fantastic fish would fetch.

Under all the increasing weight of scientific treasure we got in these seas, even in my obsessed state, the shadow of the Coelacanth slowly receded, though we never ceased to talk and to show its picture on the leaflet. My wife was even more persistent than myself, she always had that quest in the forefront of her mind, and never let anyone forget it. We ended that series of expeditions with little hope that Coelacanths lived normally anywhere in Mozambique waters, for we had covered virtually every possible and likely spot. Even if that native had got a true Coelacanth at Bazaruto it could well have been a stray, as I believed the first at East London must have been.

Northern Mozambique was far enough from East London, where the first Coelacanth was caught, but now it began to look as if it must have come from somewhere even more distant. That was far enough for a 'degenerate' fish to travel in all conscience, without my now supposing it to have travelled still farther. From a place as remote as northern Mozambique a fish of the Coelacanth type meandering along the coast, even with the aid of the current, would probably take several years to reach as far as East London, every minute of the way beset with dangers. While there were those who regarded the old Coelacanth as degenerate or 'wooden', I did not, and I had no doubt that if he wanted he could travel half the globe.

We went on; we never ceased to hope, relying on the leaflet to do our work in Madagascar, and unaware that it had not reached the Comores. Whenever I planned any expedition and studied charts, always my eyes and mind would stray to the Comores, those mysterious blobs in the blankness of the seas, like drops left behind from a dripping Madagascar torn from the body of Africa.

In that wild part of northern Mozambique I have described, those Comores were a constant obsession. Again and again I stood looking across that blue water. They lay south of that critical current divide, in the southward arm. Yes, they obsessed me, and they were so tantalisingly near, much nearer than Madagascar; Grand Comoro was barely 200 miles away, scarcely more than a day in our small vessel. We had no compass, for coastline navigation in our boat did not demand one. I knew how the currents ran and their speed, and could have used my watch, the sun, and the stars to find the way to the Comores. Those islands are all high and can be seen a long way off, but my wife showed an unusual lack of enthusiasm whenever I raised the project. Nevertheless, I was sorely tempted just to go and look, but there were too many obstacles. It had been difficult to reach this virgin part at all, and it was proving so rich it would have been almost a crime to have gone somewhere else on a mere chance when every moment where we were was yielding rich results. We had very little water and, in any case, I could not take their vessel to foreign territory without the prior consent of the Portuguese authorities, who were nearly as far off from us as the moon. In that wind-lashed sea, among those remote islands, we were quite cut off from civilisation. Its isolation was emphasised by the way in which the only occasional native fishermen we saw, whether ashore or afloat, fled at our approach. This amused our crew, who always laughed with delight at their flight, and they explained that those men were almost certainly fugitive canoe-tax defaulters.

Chapter Eight

DUNNOTTAR DILEMMA

ERIC HUNT first came into this story in 1952 in Zanzibar, where we were working at that time as part of an extensive expedition covering Zanzibar, Pemba, part of Tanganyika, and Kenya. We had been greatly assisted in all phases of our work by the authorities of each country, and at the close of our time in Zanzibar, at the request of the authorities, we held an exhibition of our discoveries for the public, and this was crowded out all day. Hunt came late in the afternoon with a friend who knew my wife, and so was introduced. He wanted certain information about fish, as he did a good deal of commercial fishing.

We had a pile of the Coelacanth leaflets there for people to take, and Hunt spotted these and was soon immersed in one. My wife noticed his absorption and asked if he was interested. His reply left no doubt that he was, and he asked if he might have some of the leaflets to take to the Comores. Comores! My wife jumped at this, as may well be imagined; we might indeed have been working at those very islands at that moment had not the Kenya authorities been so anxious for us to come there. What did Hunt know about the Comores? Well, he had a schooner and lived by trading between Africa and the Comores, and knew them well. Her quick reaction led him to ask my wife at once if she thought there was any possibility that the Coelacanth might be at the Comores?

More than a possibility she told him, and that I had long believed that Coelacanths would likely be found somewhere about Madagascar—for one thing, fossils were well known there, and as for the Comores, well, they had long been something of an obsession with me. She told him how I wanted to go there, and how I had tried to find out about their natural history, but there just didn't seem to be any. She told him, too, something of our experiences the year before when we had been working at the Querimba

Islands in the northern part of Mozambique, and how I had very nearly set out to reach the Comores in the tiny vessel we had then. As far as the leaflets were concerned, they should already have gone to the Comores, because a big batch had been sent to the French authorities in Madagascar some years before, and they had been asked officially to distribute them. However, she was pleased to give Hunt a batch of the leaflets, and he remarked that if it should happen that they caused a fuzzy-headed Comoran to get the £100 reward for catching a Coelacanth, the Governor would indeed be 'Tickled to death'. He himself would certainly be thrilled to have a part in anything like that. After studying the leaflet, Hunt asked many questions, and in addition my wife gave him a good deal of extra information that might help him. She was impressed by his quick grasp of essentials, and finally showed him the account and pictures of the Coelacanth in a copy of my book on South African fishes, which we had there and which he studied closely for some time. Finally, he said that he was confident he would recognise any Coelacanth he might come across, and my wife told me she thought he would, too. She considered Hunt to be 'all there'. In addition to this, he had undertaken to try to get specimens of a certain peculiar small fish he had seen in the Comores, but which we did not recognise from his description. It was arranged with people in Zanzibar that he was to be supplied with formalin for that purpose. My wife emphasised the importance of this, but as things turned out it was never sent to Hunt, a not unusual type of failing in those climes.

This was September 1952 and shortly afterwards Hunt took the leaflets to the Comores, showed them to the authorities and spoke about the Coelacanth. One visiting official had apparently seen and heard about the leaflets before, but appeared to have the impression that they represented an insane idea and a useless search, for fish of that type lived in the deep sea, and it was certain that they had never been seen anywhere round there. Hunt, however, had little difficulty in interesting the Governor, who had them sent round to all the islands of the Comores and distributed by native runners, who also as far as possible explained their import to the natives. When you know natives of the type found there, you wonder how anything like that could be explained to them, except that money talks everywhere, especially big money of that order, it would speak in a loud voice even in their simple lives. Hunt came and went. He sometimes carried local produce, and dealt also in dried fish and sharks. There is an enormous trade in salted sharks in the tropical western Indian Ocean, for they are greatly relished by all races and command an astonishing price. This was one of our problems at Zanzibar, for when we found a rare shark on the market, its price was so ruinous we could not afford to buy it as a specimen. I soon hit on the idea of hiring sharks and other big fish for the special purpose of photographing them, of making notes and taking measurements, and then bargaining with the owner for parts like the teeth and sometimes the head and skin. There was not much they did not eat. The sharks are salted but not sun dried; this is a special process not used in South Africa. The smell from the big concrete underground shark salting-pits of Zanzibar is pretty grim. When the wind shifts to the north you have it all day and all night. The food of those near by tastes of it.

At the close of our work in Zanzibar we went to Pemba; then to Kenya, where we spent several months working over a wide area of the coast. This expedition was most absorbing, but exacting and exhausting. The whole area proved so rich that we almost killed ourselves in that hot and humid climate trying to squeeze the utmost from the time. We had got together an enormous collection, certainly more than ten thousand selected specimens, with numbers of great rarities and many fascinating forms new to science. The last few weeks that took us into December 1952 had been especially trying, with little wind, the nights close and still, and since malaria was rampant, we lay naked and sweating under nets, vainly trying to sleep. All you got was a kind of vague and patchy, formless, clammy doze.

Throughout this expedition we had continually carried on the Coelacanth hunt, talking and giving out leaflets. It had been my good fortune to solve the mystery of the identity of a strange fish, a man-size Parrot-fish which was only occasionally seen. It was a curious creature with a big hump on its head, but at that time its scientific identity was unknown. I hunted for this creature continually and offered a reward for one, but in vain, until the day before we were due to leave Shimoni finally for Mombasa, when by the greatest good fortune I spotted over two hundred of these peculiar large fishes in a deep channel off Pungutiachi Island (South Kenya), and by means of considerable exertions managed to capture no less than eight of them, the largest weighing over 130 lb. We preserved a complete head, and the skull of another, and took these with us. Near mid-December we embarked in the Union-Castle* liner *Dunnottar Castle* at Mombasa. All our collections, including the Parrot-fish head preserved in the cold store, went with us.

The day before we left Mombasa, a reporter from the *Mombasa Times* came aboard with one of our Coelacanth leaflets, and was full of questions. We gave him the main story, which he clearly found fascinating. One of his last queries was whether we believed that the leaflet would really find the fish we sought, and we said we hoped it would. The issue next day prominently featured the Coelacanth story, quite a scoop for that paper with what lay only a little time ahead.

On the way south we called as usual at Zanzibar, and there my wife went ashore to visit the market, and to renew acquaintance with various people of the most diverse social strata she has a way of gathering to her net, all of them very useful in our work. As she neared the wharf, there was Hunt on his schooner, and she waved to him. He came round to meet her launch, and told her then that he had only recently returned from the Comores. She went aboard his schooner, he was awaiting a friend to go out on a trial run, the engines had just been refitted, wouldn't Mrs. Smith like to come as well? With little time and much to do, she was unable to accept this invitation, but inevitably she asked Hunt if he had found any clues to Coelacanths. No, he had none, but was as keen as ever and had a whole lot more questions to ask about the creature, keen, searching questions which showed that he had done a good deal of thinking about the matter in the meantime, and which made my wife even more confident of his ability to recognise a Coelacanth for certain if he ever saw it. The leaflets had been distributed in all the islands, and the Governor was both interested and co-operative, because, of course, a thing like that

---

* The Union-Castle Mail Steamship Co. Ltd. may well be termed a National Institution as far as South Africa is concerned. From this Company and from all its officials, ashore and afloat, we have received constant consideration as well as assistance on a considerable scale, representing in all a substantial contribution to our work and to science.

would certainly put his territory 'on the map'. Had he got the
formalin? Not yet, but it was promised and he expected it any
time. She wished him luck, and started to leave when he said,
'If I do get a Coelacanth and haven't any formalin, what do I do?'
She said he should not even think of such an awful possibility,
but he said (doubtless knowing East Africa better than she did),
'Yes, but just suppose there isn't any, tell me what I could do?
There is no refrigeration at the Comores.' So she replied, 'Well,
heaven forbid it should happen, but the only way would be to use
salt. Like those smelly sharks.' And he replied, 'O.K., thanks.
Anyway, when I get a Coelacanth, I'll send you a cable.' And they
both laughed with amusement. So did some imp of fate also
laugh, for only ten days later all those things happened: a Coelacanth, no formalin, salt, and the cable.

My wife's encounter with Hunt brought him and the Comores
to the forefront of our minds, and they were like a hovering
cloud in our consciousness, receding only slowly as we left them
far behind. We often spoke of both Hunt and the Comores, but
during the short voyages from port to port, we were hard at
work all the time describing and figuring our rarities. Not only
this, but that whole voyage south was as usual strenuous, for every
port brought interviews and visitors, both officials, friends, and
press. Captain Patrick Smythe gave us every assistance and consideration, excusing even our reluctance to sit at his table on the
ground that we were too exhausted to be polite to strangers, and
it was on that account arranged for us to have a table to ourselves.

Before dawn on the 24th December 1952, my wife and I
were up on the bridge to gaze on the lights of Durban that lay
shimmering in the haze that hid the land. It was a real thrill to
see our own country again. Most of the pilots up the east coast
are old friends, but it was especially nice now to meet one of our
own. We were leaning over the rail beside the searchlight on the
bridge as we slid through the harbour mouth, scanning the anglers
who as usual lined the piers. I drew a deep breath of contentment
and said, 'It's wonderful to be back again. It will be a long time
before anything gets me back to the tropics again.' That same
imp of fate must have laughed again, and even more loudly,
for within six hours I was frantic to be able to do just that, and
quickly.

We docked at 7 a.m., and no sooner was the gangway down than we were beset by friends and the press, some of the latter new to us.

In mid-morning we were in the lounge with Stanley Dagger, our good 'Elastoplast' friend, who keeps us supplied with the most essential field dressings. One of the junior officers came up and said, 'Telegram for you, sir', and I took it absentmindedly—it had rained telegrams that morning. This bore the red 'Urgent' tab, one of a number. I had noted a young man who came with the officer and he now introduced himself as a reporter new to me. It had rained reporters, too, but I asked him to sit down for a moment while we continued our conversation. In a lull I slit open this telegram and read it casually. At first the words had no meaning, then I found myself on my feet staring at it, for two words stood out: 'Coelacanth' and 'Hunt'. 'What's the matter?' asked my wife in alarm. 'Hunt's got a Coelacanth,' I said. She jumped up, took the telegram and read it. It had been redirected from Grahamstown to Durban. It read:

'REPEAT CABLE JUST RECEIVED HAVE FIVE FOOT SPECIMEN COELACANTH INJECTED FORMALIN HERE KILLED 20TH ADVISE REPLY HUNT DZAOUDZI.'

Dzaoudzi, where on earth was Dzaoudzi? It sounded like Somali-land or some such place, we had never heard of any place of that name before, not in the Comores, anyway. One of the younger officers came up at that moment with some message from the Chief Officer, and I asked him if he knew where Dzaoudzi was. No, never heard of it, but he could soon find out for me, and he went off, while my mind groped in chaos asking if this could be true. 'Five-foot Coelacanth, Hunt.' Yes, Hunt would know a Coelacanth. A five-foot Coelacanth. Could it be true? The young reporter had his ears cocked, and he asked some questions that remained unanswered. The young officer came shooting back. 'Dzaoudzi is on a small island called Pamanzi in the Comores, sir.' So by Heaven, Hunt had got one in the Comores. It was those Comores, after all. Good for Hunt.

Comores, hot as hell, was how he had described them, and had said there was no refrigeration plant there. Formalin! How much? If it was the amount that had been planned for Hunt, it wasn't nearly enough for a five-foot Coelacanth. What a predicament.

What was the date? Killed on the 20th! Already four days since it was caught. Dzaoudzi was almost certainly not the kind of place where you could just go and buy formalin.

I was too distracted to speak very much, for with all these perplexities my mind was slipping about like a rubber-clad foot on a muddy street, and would not get settled firmly in one place.

It is rather remarkable that neither in my mind nor in my wife's was there in those early tense moments of realisation any

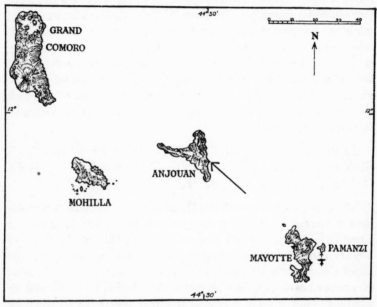

FIG. 3.—The islands of the Comoro group. The arrow shows where *Malania* was caught.

vestige of pleasure or rejoicing. We had endured so much over the first Coelacanth that we just had a feeling that Coelacanths meant trouble, at least to us. And now this had come in a fashion and at a time that looked as if it was going to be no better, probably worse. There were so many difficulties sticking out clearly ahead, we could hardly see anything else.

Dagger soon after took his leave, to be replaced almost at once by Guy Drummond Sutton, Frank Evans, and then Dr. George Campbell, all Durban men and old friends. I took the reporter aside and told him that he had come upon one of the most astounding events and that it would certainly be world news. If he used it properly he could have the scoop of a lifetime. I gave him quite an amount of information, warning him to use nothing but that, and none of what he had heard earlier except what I repeated now. As I went to join our party he went away, but he was so much younger than I that his thoughts were easy to read and they did not flatter me. The scepticism I had felt in him was possibly responsible for the manner in which that interview was reported and headed of all things 'Sea Missing Link'. As it happened, I did not see this until much later, but early next morning that same young man came aboard seeking further news, and was met by my wife, who had just seen the report. She asked him at once why on earth that phrase 'Missing Link' had been used, and assured him that I would be most displeased, as a Coelacanth was emphatically not a missing link, and I had certainly not used such terms. He said that it was a catchy phrase and sounded good as a title. It was not until Natalie Roberts wrote it up next day that the whole affair was reported in what I regarded as its true perspective, but those unfortunate words 'Missing Link' went out in advance all over the world, giving the whole affair a false aspect that it did not need. It was interesting enough as it was.

After this reporter had left I went back to our party and told them what had happened, and this of course attracted their immediate and concentrated attention. They wanted to know what I was going to do. I said that at the moment I just did not know, the situation would have to be weighed carefully. Was I going to try to fetch it? I couldn't say at that moment, it was going to be very difficult to do that, anyway. I knew that part of East Africa and the route, and flying there is no easy matter. I doubted if any private plane could do it even if we had the funds to hire it, which we hadn't. It would almost certainly have to be done by a Government plane if at all. At that moment I was not prepared to say anything definite, not even if I was going to try to go and fetch it. It needed thinking out carefully.

'What a pity Smuts isn't alive,' said one of the men. 'He would have helped you.' 'Smuts!' burst simultaneously and explosively from my wife's lips and my own. 'Smuts!' Our reactions were so violent that they stared at us in amazement. 'No, sir,' I said. 'I once wanted to ask Smuts to help me in almost exactly such a case, and he wouldn't even see me. Smuts! No.' They collapsed like pricked balloons. Smuts was off.

My wife suggested that if it proved impossible for me to go in time to save the fish, it might be done by the French authorities in Madagascar. She reminded me that I had met the chief of their scientific organisation at a conference in Johannesburg not long before; what was his name? 'Millot,' I said, 'Dr. J. Millot'; and that I had had him in mind, but as far as I knew he was likely to be in Paris and not in Madagascar.* I knew that in our files we certainly had nothing but an address in Paris. Was there not any French scientist in or about Madagascar who could help, she asked? My knowledge of scientists was naturally chiefly in the ichthyological field, and although there had been a few publications about sea fishes from Madagascar, those were mostly odd papers produced by scientists in France. There had been no man of any prominence in my field resident at Madagascar for at least fifty years. There was no avenue of approach that way— as far as I knew, Madagascar was a complete blank for any purpose now.† In the case of the Comores hardly any marine biology had been done there. From my unique knowledge and experience I could predict probably 90 per cent. of the fishes that must live about the Comores, but an ichthyology of that part just did not exist. It was most unlikely that there would be any competent marine biologist there. If there had been, Hunt would surely have mentioned it.

It was clear that I had to seek for no ordinary help. This was a time for desperate measures, something at the highest level. The Prime Minister was the obvious mark, but the very idea of again trying to ask a Prime Minister for a plane to hunt dead fish, even a dead Coelacanth, made me shy away like a once-wounded animal from a gun. My natural reluctance springing from the Smuts episode was increased by the fact that Dr. Malan was almost certainly seeking brief rest from the many heavy respon-

* This proved to be the case.

† We learnt later that a French Fisheries Officer was actually in the area at that time, but the *Zoological Record* listing his publications did not appear until 1955. In any case, he was not at headquarters in this critical time (see p. 159).

sibilities he carried, and he was far from young. To all suggestions about Malan I said firmly, 'Not until we have exhausted all other possibilities.' My wife was the most persistent on that theme, and when I repeated, 'Only as a last resort', she prophesied that I would go to him in the end, which I did. Trust a woman to have the last word.

Frank Evans said there was a Sunderland flying-boat at Durban which would be just the thing if I could get it. He knew the local chief and would go off and have a word with him, and my wife went with him to send Hunt a cable which I had drafted, as follows:

'IF POSSIBLE GET TO NEAREST REFRIGERATION IN ANY CASE INJECT AS MUCH FORMALIN POSSIBLE CABLE CONFIRMATION THAT SPECIMEN SAFE. SMITH.'

There is little pleasant in the recollections of those particular hours of the 24th December 1952. Everything with Coelacanths so far had been troublesome, and here was quite the worst situation I had ever encountered. There were so many difficulties that there seemed no way out. This precious fish was so far away, in one of the worst places in the world for safe preservation with probably only a mere speck of formalin. I had probably been to more remote areas of the coastal regions along East Africa than any other man, and if only this fish had turned up in some part I knew, how much easier it would have been, even in foreign territory like Portuguese East Africa. But here it was in quite unknown foreign territory, so little known that it might almost be another planet, and I had no knowledge of conditions and no personal contacts in that part. The tense uncertainties of the situation in some aspects resembled those of the first Coelacanth, and yet how different it was this time. The doubts about its being a Coelacanth the first time were due to a battle between facts and my common sense, the fish itself was accessible enough. Now the doubt about identity came from the difficulty of getting to the fish, and although he was exceptional, the whole thing rested only on the word of a layman I hardly knew and on that opinion I must stake a great deal. I was not even at home, with the re-sources of my Department and organisation, but on a vessel in

Durban due to leave soon, all our enormous volume of baggage and valuable collections to be cared for, and Christmas holidays just on us. My mind rebelled. I was already unutterably weary, and the weakness that plagues us all urged me to throw the whole thing away and leave it alone. It welled up like a flood, and heaven knows there was enough excuse. This really threatened to overwhelm me, largely because I realised it would be necessary, absolutely necessary, to ask things of others, something that always makes you vulnerable, and I was deadly tired. What a situation! But I have faced many, and knew that I could not give up, I must go on. I had to remind myself that there was a lot more in this than my own personal feelings, it had long since passed beyond that. It was a matter of national prestige, for the whole Coelacanth affair was South African, everything in it was tied up with South Africa. It was our responsibility and our misfortune that my wife and I alone at that time realised the full implication, and that it was my obligation to go on with it. I had to go on even if it killed me in trying to do it, and when I said so to my wife, as my partner in this venture she calmly agreed with that view. I had to go on.

Our old friend Dr. George Campbell stayed to lunch, and it was a comfort to have him near. Captain Smythe had heard that something had happened and came over to our table for a time, when I gave him a brief outline of the situation and my predicament. He at once offered all possible help, and meant it. When he had gone I turned again to the meal, seeing and hearing nothing, my mind far away. The others realised my abstraction and went on quietly discussing the matter, leaving me to my thoughts, and I ate, absently, at least I believe I ate, for I sat on, isolated, my mind going round and round. Malan, the Prime Minister; H'm! Prime Minister; Smuts; H'm! I became quite oblivious to my surroundings, my mind went drifting off and back to that other time, and I went through it all again, as vivid as when it actually happened, yes. . . .

Chapter Nine

HIS OWN SHEEP

WHAT a curious sequence of events it had been ! Some years before while preparing certain parts of the manuscript of my large volume on our fishes, information was found to be lacking about certain types of fish and related matters of the waters of the South-west Cape, so I arranged to go out from Cape Town with one of the trawlers of Messrs. Irvin and Johnson, a commercial fishing company which had greatly assisted my work in many ways. Their vessels had added greatly to the knowledge of our fishes, constantly bringing rarities ashore; indeed, it must not be forgotten that it was a trawler of this firm which caught and saved the first Coelacanth.

This Cape trawler on which I was to go was the *Godetia*, one of the two new vessels that were more or less experimental, since they were very considerably larger than those previously used in South Africa. They certainly were very much more luxurious than anything of that type that I had ever seen before. I shared the skipper's cabin and had a real bed, away from noise and smell. After the other trawlers I had known, this one was almost incredible. I could not help thinking of the lumpy mattresses in narrow box-like bunks close under the iron deck. Just above one's head were steering chains that rattled and crashed on the iron plates every few seconds; indeed, unless the sea was smooth, without any intermission day and night. Those were the trawlers on which I had lived and suffered. To a landsman they spelled discomfort, smell, and nausea.

In this grand new vessel there was a real saloon and real lavatories, not just the heaving rail and the sea. It was an interesting experience, and different in many ways from the life on a trawler on our south coast, where the work goes on night and day, the crew often without proper sleep for days on end if catches are good, when they do not mind. In this cold Atlantic sea the trawling is mostly in rather deep water, several hundred fathoms. At night here the fish leave the bottom and rise in the water, some right to the surface, so that a trawl net which scrapes the bottom all the time catches hardly anything then. As a result, trawling is profitable only by day, and as there is no anchoring in such deep water, the vessel just drifts, and all night long she rolls and rolls in the long Atlantic swells. A landsman finds this agonising and his only hope of sleep is to wedge himself in.

On our way out, some miles from shore, the skipper told me we should soon be met by 'Blondie', a large seal well known to the trawlers, easily recognised by a lighter patch on the side of the head. Seals always turn up when the trawl net is being pulled in, but apparently one or two of the more intelligent come and meet the vessels on the way out, stay with them all the time they work, and accompany them part of the way back. 'Blondie' had been known for many years. Sure enough, there was a hail from the bows soon after, and I saw this quite large seal puffing a welcome as it easily kept up, appearing alongside at intervals.

Most of the fish caught in a trawl are swept into a long bag in the middle of the length of the net, the apex of which is known as the 'Cod-end'. When the net is hauled up from the bottom, the water pressure becomes less, the gas in the air-bladders of the fishes expands, and usually before the rest of the net is up, the 'Cod-end' comes shooting to the surface and floats there, buoyed by thousands of these distended bladders. Often they are so much enlarged as to stick out of the mouths of the fishes, and look like great swollen red tongues.

As the mass floats on the surface, protruding tails fruitlessly beat the water, and all kinds of the smaller fish are forced through the meshes of the net. These provide a wonderful feast for the snorting seals, which splash around, grabbing with gusto and gobbling the dainties, seizing them crosswise, shaking them, throwing them into the air, to make them easier to swallow. They have clear-cut likes and dislikes, small Stockfish apparently being their favourite, while the more abundant 'Rat Tails' (Coryphaenoidid fishes) are scorned. In this they are like humans, who will not eat those perfectly wholesome but less-attractive-looking and quite unfortunately named 'Rat Tails'. It is not only the seals that eat their fill, but sharks soon gather round. At first they cruise cautiously at a distance, snapping up the fishes that have drifted away, but they soon come closer, and once their appetite is roused, go raging round, and unless checked will even ravenously attack the net, tearing great holes and causing loss of fish as well. Sometimes they become so insensate that they throw themselves out of the water on top of the floating mass, tearing at the enmeshed fish below. Trawlers carry rifles for these brutes, and during each haul the skipper generally accounts for a number, some of them 10 to 12 feet or more in length. One shot in the head and you see the ugly beast sinking slowly into the green depths, rolling over as it goes.

We got all the specimens I wanted on that trip, and some unexpected rarities as well. We were due back on a Monday. On the Thursday night the wireless news mentioned fish mortality at 'Walvis Bay, maddeningly only a few words, but they were enough for me; indeed they were as effective as an electric shock.

On the South-west African coast, mostly in late summer, fishes are sometimes killed in millions, sometimes in such vast numbers as to be a serious menace to health when those thrown ashore begin to decay, and their disposal is a great problem. This wholesale slaughter is believed to be due partly to volcanic activity and mostly to quantities of sulphuretted hydrogen, released into the sea from bottom deposits. This stinking gas is poisonous to all animal life, but especially to fishes, for it removes dissolved oxygen from the water. 'One man's poison is another man's meat' is a transposition that applies here, for while this is hard on the fish and a great trouble to all who live on that coast, an event of that nature is an ichthyologist's dream, for every kind of fish in the sea is killed, and even though like most things in nature it is extravagant, it gives the scientist an opportunity he could otherwise hardly accomplish by any means himself. While interested people can pick out a few obvious oddities from among the piled masses of dead fish, it is essential that an expert should work through such an accumulation himself, for while the queerest-looking creatures may be merely common and scientifically well-known forms from deep water, an apparently ordinary-looking fish may well be a scientific treasure.

For many years I had been waiting for an opportunity like this, and here it was and I was much nearer than usual. Despite the hot sun, the sea at Walvis is cold and the fish do not decay seriously for several days. I slept less than usual that night and next morning sat at the wireless. More news came, it was one of the greatest killings for many years. This was Friday, the trawler was due back only on Monday, the catch was moderate, there was still plenty of room in the fish-holds. I naturally wanted to return at once, and so the battle started, a running naval battle, with all the odds normally on the skipper, but I kept on. Eventually he agreed to return early, but only by one day, and we were set to arrive at Cape Town by the mid-morning of Sunday. I was in a fever of anxiety and slept not at all, my mind was buzzing like a machine. Walvis Bay is less than a thousand miles from Cape Town, but it might in some ways be on the moon—at least, it was like that in those days. To go from Cape Town to Walvis by sea or road was ruled out on account of time, air was the only way. Nobody on the trawler knew anything of private planes, they doubted if there were any.

The moment we docked—Sunday—I went to the telephone. It took some time to find out, but it soon became pretty certain that no charter plane was available that could reach Walvis Bay. The Air Force was the only way. After incredible difficulty (Sunday!) I made contact with a responsible official in that force, but he was less than encouraging, saying that it would be impossible even to think of such a thing without the permission of the Commander-in-Chief who was in Pretoria, and even then the Government might not permit it. It was very clear that as time was the vital factor, to try to do anything via Pretoria was quite useless; it would have been even on a weekday, and this was midday, Sunday.

I was determined not to be beaten. Smuts! He was the key. He had the reputation of being interested in science. I had not met him, but was due to do so the very next day. The Trustees of my book of fishes (then in preparation) had decided to ask him to write a foreword. Our Albany member, T. B. Bowker, had arranged that I should meet Smuts, and an appointment had been made for the next afternoon, Monday. That would be too late. How could I see him that day?

I sat in that office at the docks going over in my mind whom I could get to give me the approach. It *would* be Sunday of course

—any other day would have been better. I decided to ask assistance from a man whom I had known for many years and who knew Smuts. I was soon putting the problem to him, to ask if he would telephone the Prime Minister to find out if he would see me. While he was enthusiastic about the whole idea his reply disturbed me, for he said that as he was only an Ordinary Member he dare not telephone the Prime Minister directly. I was astounded and said so. 'You don't know the Oubaas as I do,' he said. 'If I did that it would be as much as my seat is worth. He is a holy terror to the rank and file. But [he added] you are different. The Oubaas is very interested in science and I am sure if you get to him he will help you.' I asked whom I should telephone, but he advised me not to telephone at all as they might just put me off, being a Sunday. He said it would be best for me to go straight to Groote Schuur and ask to see the Prime Minister. I was more than dubious about the wisdom of this, as I knew what my own reactions would be in such a case, but despite my strongly expressed doubts he said that he really felt that it might succeed where a more formal approach might fail. It was only with considerable reluctance that I eventually agreed to do what he advised. It was then well past noon, and after clearing up affairs with the trawler and seeing to my fishes, I was taken to Groote Schuur by some friends. The Prime Minister was out. He had some overseas banker with him and they had gone to Muizenberg, but were expected back late in the afternoon. I put my case to two officials who received me. It is one of my assets and one of my troubles that I can read other men's minds. The younger of the two said little, but as many others had done, and many were still to do, he plainly thought me mad to go to such lengths for long-dead fish. The other was more cautious, though I could feel that he also thought it insane; still, you never knew which way the Oubaas was going to jump, he might rise to this and actually give this apparent lunatic the plane he wanted, so it would be better not to turn him away irrevocably now, but to wait and see. He told me that the Prime Minister did not like being troubled on Sundays, as I could well appreciate, but I emphasised that it was only the factor of time that drove me to this end, and that I had been advised against my judgment by one who should know to come in that way. I asked if I should go away and telephone later, but after consideration he said it might be as well to stay until Smuts returned. That was twice I had been advised to try the direct personal approach by those who should know, so I told my friends that I would wait and should telephone later, and they went off.

They put me in a room, but I could not sit still and found my way outside, pacing up and down beneath the magnificent trees that toned the sunlight almost to gloom. Every minute was an age. When would this man return?

It was an awful time. I can stand a good deal, but find suspense wearing, for while my imagination helps my work it clouds my life. I could see those precious piles of fishes starting to rot, being eaten by birds, washed away by the waves and buried by sanitary gangs. Some time later a kindly official came out to offer me tea, so I went inside, still steeped in anxiety, and ate and drank without any memory of what they served. This man questioned me again, astutely and with interest, and I got to speaking of my work. Quite suddenly I realised that he had become interested, even my ally, and would do all he could. Plainly concerned, he set out to alleviate my pressing tension and showed me round the lovely mansion, but the rarities and treasures meant nothing to me, I could see only those rarities and treasures rotting on that sun-drenched dazzling sand at Walvis Bay, and in the end he left me to start again my restless pacing beneath the trees. Would this man never come?

I had gone some way from the house, the sun was already so low that it was turning dark beneath the trees, when I heard the throb of a car which passed round the corner of the house out of sight. I had, from my reluctance to worry any man at this time, suggested that I should not be in the house when Smuts came, but that if he was willing to receive me I should come in. Slowly now I made my way towards the house, and went on pacing up and down the gravel path along the side. A good fifteen minutes passed. Suddenly my sixth sense told me I was being scrutinised, and from upstairs. Unobtrusively I scanned the windows, but they were screened and told me nothing. I waited tensed and anxious, and when the official came to seek me, he had no need to speak, for I could read his message in his walk and bearing. To his great regret he had to tell me that the Field-Marshal would not see me. He had told him the outlines of my story and had even ventured to press my case, but in vain. I thanked him, asked him to telephone, and my friends came soon after.

Tomorrow I should see Smuts, but it would be too late, my treasures would by then be rotten. Even so, I had no hard feelings for his refusal, only disappointment in his lack of vision. I reflected philosophically that I was probably once again paying the price for my youthful appearance, for my figure and looks belied my years. And yet Smuts must have known at least something of my work and reputation. With his scientific leanings he would certainly have been aware of the Coelacanth, more than aware indeed, for he had been kept fully informed about the A.C.M.E. project, when he had not wanted us to make any move to secure a vessel from overseas. It was a curious situation, for the C.S.I.R. fell directly under Smuts.

I went to the House next day and lunched with our member for Albany, Tom B. Bowker, who took me along and introduced me to the Prime Minister's Secretary. Yes, the appointment for 2.15 p.m. was arranged. The Prime Minister was entertaining some visiting American journalists to lunch and had not yet returned to his office, but it was a good time, for the House was quiet, and all should be well. Suddenly there was a stir, and the Secretary went off. He returned in a few moments and stood in the doorway, a curious expression on his face, looking at me before he spoke. His exact words I do not remember, but they were to the effect that he wished I had told him about my visit to Groote Schuur before letting him go in to the Prime Minister, and why on earth had I not tried to speak to him before going out there?

I gave him a brief outline of events and of the advice I had received and acted on. He was non-committal and diplomatic and asked me to wait for a short time, but he said that the situation was very complicated, and meanwhile the Prime Minister was receiving his American guests one by one. He vanished before I could get anything more, and I sat, amazed and bewildered, watching a series of thrilled Americans going and coming from heaven. Eventually I seized the Secretary and demanded to know what the position was, and after some parrying finally learnt that Smuts was annoyed that I had ventured to go to Groote Schuur, and that in consequence he now refused to see me. His Secretary plainly had some concern on my behalf, because he said that if only he could have a few words with the Prime Minister he might manage to right matters. He called a typist and asked me to write and express regret for having attempted to speak to Smuts at Groote Schuur, as that might help.

Eventually, getting on for 4 p.m. my patience was exhausted and I demanded to know the position. The Secretary said he was sorry, he could do nothing more, Smuts refused to see me at all. So I left, abruptly, this time not without deep annoyance in my heart, for I could not but feel that it was not my youthful appearance that was to blame, but my nationality, that if I had been a scientist from some other land I might well by now have been snatching treasures from the sands of Swakopmund. Thanks to him, they were gone. To be esteemed by foreigners was more important than the special plea of a scientist of his own country. I was not the only South African scientist who had been treated in this way, there was Broom. . . . It all brought to my mind again the fable of the shepherd and the sheep,* as true today as it was then so long ago. I was one of his own sheep.

Some time later I had a meeting with the Trustees of my book fund to finalise a number of issues. We had many reasons to be pleased, for the public had been responsive, the quality of the specimen work of the *Cape Times* was all that could be desired, and the estimates proved to be within our means. Towards the close of the meeting the Chairman raised the issue of the Foreword, saying that he supposed he could take it that we were all agreed that 'The General' should be approached to do us the great honour of writing the Foreword. 'If by that you mean Smuts,' I said, 'I regret to say that I will not have his name associated with my book in any way.'

This was clearly a bombshell, but I was adamant without many words. The only reason I gave was that in my view it would be more proper for the foreword to be prepared by a scientist, rather than by a politician who had no fundamental interest in the subject or the author. When this matter had come up for

---

* Some sheep caught by a storm sought shelter with a shepherd, who, scenting profit for himself, put them with his own flock, whom he deprived of the best food and the warmest beds to give to the strangers. The storm over, the strange sheep prepared to leave, when the shepherd entreated them to stay and asked, 'Did you not like the way you were treated?' 'Yes,' they said, 'but we saw how you treated your own sheep.'

discussion at a much earlier meeting, Smuts had been mentioned. I would rather have had some person prominent in science, I had in mind the President of the South African Council for Scientific and Industrial Research, at that time B. F. J. Schonland,* but at that stage this issue meant little to me personally and I had made no comment. Now, however, I proposed the President of the C.S.I.R. and this was accepted.

After that meeting, the Secretary of the Board of Trustees, the late Bransby Key, asked me to give him some moments, and as soon as we were alone raised the matter of Smuts, would I mind telling him what it was all about? After brief consideration I gave him the outlines of the story. To my astonishment his reaction was violent, and he called Smuts by names that had a Chicagoan stockyard flavour. He then told me how he had been treated by Smuts in much the same way, but with even less excuse. Another of his own sheep!

This decision had some repercussions. A subscriber, who had been led to expect that the book would bear the signature of Smuts, when he heard that it would not, came to tell me that the absence of that signature was bound to have an effect on sales. If it did, it was not what he expected. I was told that shortly after publication, in the larger centres those seeking to buy copies were at times compelled to form queues.

When the news came through that in the General Election Smuts's party had suffered defeat, it was a shock to many people. Even more startling to the world at large was the news that in his own long-standing constituency, virtually a stronghold, Smuts had himself been defeated, and by an opponent who outside political circles was till then not widely known. After the initial shock I was not really surprised. I knew why. His own sheep had turned against him . . .

* One of the most outstanding scientists produced by South Africa, born in Grahamstown, a leading physicist of our time, the first President of the South African C.S.I.R., virtually its creator, whose ability and unflagging energy put this organisation in the front rank within a short time of its inception.

Chapter Ten

STARTS AND STOPS

I CAME back suddenly, to the early afternoon of the 24th December 1952, to the table in the saloon on the *Dunnottar*, to George Campbell on his feet at my side, his hand on my shoulder, shaking me back to the problem of the Coelacanth, to the reality of the hard times ahead. He squeezed my shoulder, and looking at my troubled face, smiled and said, 'Cheer up, J. L. B., you'll win'. That is how patients are brought back to life.

There was no ordinary telephone for the use of passengers on that ship, the only one was on the bridge for official use, but Captain Smythe had told me that the bridge and telephone were at my service. I realised that I was almost certainly in for some record telephoning, so asked for the head of that Service in the Durban Post Office, gave him a brief outline of the situation, and asked if he would kindly make things as easy as possible. After that the Post Office was marvellous. The willing and efficient service all members of that organisation gave us there is one of our most pleasant recollections, for it certainly lightened our burdens all through that most difficult and exhausting time. In the matter of finding a wanted man I would back the South African Post Office any time against Scotland Yard or even the famous Canadian 'Mounties'.

Practically all the funds for my support, work, and expeditions come from the South African Council for Scientific and Industrial Research, which administers the funds allocated by the Government for scientific work. I was responsible to that Council, so they came first to my mind, and who better than their President, at that time Dr. P. J. du Toit, formerly head of the world-famous institution of Onderstepoort, and he had been one of the most outstanding of all its Directors. Yes, 'P. J.', as he is known, was the man to consult. Would the Post Office kindly find Dr. P. J. du Toit at Pretoria, and say I wished to speak urgently to him?

While I waited on the bridge, my mind was racing, trying to probe the future; would this call never come, half an hour already gone? I called up the Post Office and inquired as to its progress, impatient at the delay—they had not been able to find Dr. du Toit, but the Pretoria office was busy. It is amusing to look back on my early impatience, for I had still much to learn. My wife came up to the bridge and was talking to me when the telephone went. I jumped, but a Quartermaster standing by took the receiver and was apparently having his own conversation, a series of 'Yes, yes, yes', so my attention switched back to our talk, when we heard him say a final 'yes', and 'He's right here', followed by 'Professor, your Secretary wants to speak to you'; and there was Mrs. McMaster, to say that another cable had come from Hunt, addressed to the University authorities this time, wisely covering my possible absence, and it had been sent over to her. It read as follows:

'HAVE SPECIMEN COELACANTH FIVE FEET TREAT-ED FORMALIN STOP ABSENCE SMITH ADVISE OR SEND PLANE REPLY—HUNT DZAOUDZI COMORES.'

She told me she had intended going on a short holiday that afternoon. Would it be in order? I assured her it would, though later, selfishly, certainly wished I hadn't.

My wife left, so I returned to my restless pacing up and down the bridge, covertly watched by sailors polishing brass. The telephone again, I was there in a bound, but it was for the Chief Officer. Up and down, up and down, a cheery greeting from the Chief as he went, then the telephone again. Sorry, there was no trace of Dr. P. J. du Toit, he could not be found anywhere. I was left feeling quite bewildered. I knew that with all his interests he travelled often and widely, but I had just not expected him to be unavailable then.

Well, something had to be done quickly, for if P. J. wasn't there I'd have to get on myself. In my mind I went over the Cabinet Ministers one by one. Donges and Sauer stood out, they were old Stellenbosch University contemporaries, and were personally approachable on that account, but there was nothing to justify it beyond that, their interest could at best be only general. My choice for several reasons settled on Eric Louw,

Minister of Economic Affairs. The South African Council for Scientific and Industrial Research had not long before been placed under his direct charge; he knew of my work, and I knew him personally. In my dealings with him I had found him prompt, efficient, able, and of keen perception. Yes, he was the man. From the lines on his face his duodenum probably twisted the same way as mine, and I had a suspicion that he might look on Christmas time with the same jaundiced eye as myself. So began my long vigil on the bridge of the *Dunnottar Castle*. Would the Post Office please find Minister Eric Louw and get him on the telephone as soon as possible? Half an hour later the Post Office telephoned to say that Minister Louw was in the U.S.A. on an official visit, and it would take a long time to make contact with him there. In America he was no use in this matter, anyway, so I had to start all over again. Donges? Sauer? Yes. Donges. Would the Post Office kindly find Minister Donges, and tell him I wished to speak to him on an urgent matter.

After some time the telephone authorities told me that they had tracked Minister Donges, but as he was on a train running from Pretoria to Cape Town, I should have to wait until they could catch him on arrival there, some hours ahead. Another agonising wait, then another message, they had got hold of him on his arrival at Cape Town Station, and he said that he would be able to speak to me in half an hour's time from his home. Half an hour. That half-hour seemed like a year. So I spoke to Eben Donges, Minister of Internal Affairs, one of the most able men of our University days, a formidable antagonist in debate. He turned away from one of the most successful and lucrative legal careers for political life, and soon became a character notable in Parliament, where not even the keenest jibes or thrusts, not even those of Smuts himself, could shake his imperturbable calm, a wonderful asset in his position. I rapidly outlined the situation, which he grasped as quickly, for he knew the main essentials of the story of the first Coelacanth. He said that if he had been in Pretoria and in normal times he might have been able to do something, but where he was, in Cape Town, at such a time, the most difficult in all the year, communications almost impossible, he felt that what he could do then and there would probably not help a great deal when time was such a vital factor. Had I tried to approach the Prime

Minister? So I told him something of why I had not, and he agreed with my view. He suggested that Paul Sauer, Minister of Transport, might be able to do something. As far as he knew, he was still in Pretoria. Why not try him? Best of luck.

Back to the starting-post once more. Holidays! Christmas holidays! Would the Post Office please find me Minister Paul Sauer, believed to be in Pretoria. Again I paced up and down that confined space, my brain going over the matter for the thousandth time. It was a long-drawn-out agony. I could not leave that bridge and had no food and no desire for food, even the tea they had brought me remained untouched. The telephone! The Post Office to say that there was no reply from Minister Sauer's office or from his house in Pretoria. Should they go on trying there? Yes! Do anything, only find him. Up and down, my mind as hard at work as my feet. Sauer! My mind went back to our University days, and right back to the first Sauer, 'Red Blanket' Sauer, noted politician of pre-Union times. Paul Sauer the younger soon made his mark at the University as a facile speaker. Some years before the war I was travelling with a former senior member of our University staff, a versatile man whose knowledge covered a wide field, something of an expert on wines, and with an extensive if not undue practical experience of them. We met Paul Sauer in the dining-saloon and lunched together, and those two were soon off on a technical discussion of wines beyond my ken. I noted with some amusement that my colleague had met his match, in knowledge at least. He remarked later that it was surprising to find a South African who knew so much about wines.

The sun went down, the lights came on, and they brought me more tea on a tray. I must have walked many miles on that bridge. It was quite late when they finally succeeded in tracing Minister Sauer and got him on the telephone. So off I started and outlined the matter again to him, but Sauer was immediately emphatic that he could do nothing, he could not authorise any civil plane for such a purpose, he had none to spare, anyway. Why not try to use the French airlines, he believed that they might serve the Comores, they certainly had regular services to Madagascar, but I could rule his Department out. There might possibly be some hope with the French. Had I tried them? Well, see what you can do there and good luck.

Back to the start once more, and to telephone the French Consul in Durban just to see. From the Post Office a message, sorry no reply, and too late to do any more. So there I was, baffled, unhappy, in some ways bewildered, my mind not yet settled clearly on any definite course of action.

Lost in a maze of uncertainties I went to the cabin, to the first of a series of restless, virtually sleepless, nights. As I rolled and tossed I could see that fish in the humid heat of the Comores, Hunt trying to turn a responsive nose away from the mounting odour. Was it a Coelacanth, anyway? What a fool I should be troubling Cabinet Ministers if it wasn't. Hunt had been exceptionally interested and persistent, and my wife was quite confident he would know a Coelacanth if he saw one, but, all the same, people far more expert than he had made mistakes of that kind.

'Five-foot Coelacanth.' Size does make a difference, and it certainly was a comfort that this fish was about the same size as the one at East London. Now if Hunt had cabled that he had a Coelacanth 5 inches long, how much less certain it would be, but also how much less trouble, because he could have put it in a bottle and sent it by post, without saying anything to anybody, without my having to think of troubling anyone for a plane. And yet, it was queer how everything has its points, nothing is a hundred per cent. Size is important, very important. An elephant is far more exciting than even a rare *Peripatus*. If you asked the average man if he would like his son to be a hefty 6-footer, with perpetual difficulty in finding clothes to fit him, or a 5-foot skinny runt, you knew the answer. If the original Coelacanth had been only 5 inches long it would not have stirred public imagination a fraction as much. People would have looked at it and said, 'Oh that! Well now, fancy all that fuss about a little bit of a thing like that. H'm!' And they would have gone away with the unspoken thought, 'These scientists!' But a solid great thumping 5-foot fish; now that gives one a feeling of satisfaction. That is at any time something worth looking at, and when it is a living fossil and a phenomenon as well—well!

I woke with a start from an awful confused nightmare about a Coelacanth at the Comores and a dreadful fear that it would probably be putrid before I could get there to save it; and then I realised it was no dream, but real and true.

That long night my tortured and almost fevered brain worked through all the people who might help, and in the end crystallised on the Minister of Defence. Early next morning, Christmas Day, 1952, would the Post Office please try to find the Minister for Defence? And once more I paced the bridge. Late the night before my wife had discovered that the French Consul of Cape Town was on board and she had got from him the private number of the French Consul in Durban. So at a reasonable hour I asked the Post Office to try this and they soon had him on the telephone. I gave him some account of the matter and of the difficulties, but had to confess that at the moment I did not know what could be done, and nor did he; but we parted with the assurance that whatever he could do to assist would be done. It is indeed pleasing to record that every single representative of France in the Union with whom we had any dealings gave our requests the utmost consideration and went to great trouble to assist us throughout.

Christmas day—'Peace on earth and goodwill towards all men.' Well that might be, but why on earth did Coelacanths want to turn up just before Christmas? Christmas! Well, mine wasn't going to be the conventional Christmas, anyway. I waited for what seemed an endless time, but no message came, so I telephoned the Post Office, but they had nothing to report. For seven agonising incredibly long hours that Christmas Day, 1952, I paced that bridge. The gong went for lunch, but I could not go, no great loss to me because I cannot eat the conventional Christmas meal, anyway; my liver revolts. Even the simple stuff they sent up on a tray remained forgotten, and later I saw a deck-hand polishing off the canned peaches behind a ventilator and tip the rest overboard.

In the late afternoon the Post Office telephoned to say that they had tracked Mr. Erasmus (the Minister of Defence) to his farm at White River, but it was certainly an ideal retreat, for the only available telephone was miles away and worked only in office hours and not on holidays. I dare say this was what anyone outside the inner circle would be told, because it seemed impossible to me that a Minister of Defence could cut himself off like that. What if an emergency arose and the Prime Minister needed to speak to him at once and could not? As will be told that actually happened later, but it was from an 'Act of God' (was it God?), for storms had cut the telephone line.

Anyway, there I was right back at the starting-post again, and now the Post Office very kindly suggested that I might try the Chief of something or other. Yes, thank you, would they get him for me, I didn't know his name or anything about him, and so I went back to my thought-steeped pacing of the narrow bridge, in and out of the wheelhouse.

Soon after our arrival in Durban, before we heard of the Coelacanth, we had arranged an exhibition of the head of the Giant Parrot-fish and other related things on the *Dunnottar Castle*, and notice of this had been featured in the press. My wife, who had taken charge of this, was almost overwhelmed by the crowds who came aboard, so that she could spare only occasional moments to dash to the bridge and see if any hope had dawned, but my face as I paced was enough each time. Eventually the Post Office telephoned to say that they just could not find any trace of the Chief they mentioned, and did not think it was any use going on. After all, it was Christmas Day, and late at that. I thanked them very much and the official suggested that they should try again in the morning, to which I agreed. Christmas! I wonder if I shall ever regain any liking for that time?

Though I had little appetite for food and none for festivity, my wife persuaded me to go down that evening to Christmas dinner in the gaily bedecked saloon, where our steward welcomed me like a lost friend after a long absence. The laden tables seemed to belong to another world. I saw it all through a black cloud of frustration and despair. Soup? Yes, but as the first spoon came to my lips, a petty officer from the bridge leant over my shoulder; there was an urgent telephone call. Who? Don't know, sir. I could not afford not to go, and when our steward found my chair empty, my soup untasted, he stared unbelievingly and said, 'What! Gone again?' It was a quaint meal, if one may call it that, during which I was called away four or five times, mainly the press. There were millions to whom that wonderful range of rich and tasty dishes would have been an unforgettable thrill, but I had no appetite and found no pleasure in that gay scene. There were conventional Christmas crackers, and people laughed and joked and put on paper hats. Great Heaven! and the Coelacanth was probably putrefying. We got out at last, some friends had come, but my mind was so distracted that I cannot recollect anything that was said or done, and quite late I went off to another awful night, more nightmares, more fears, many fears, always worry. So much time had gone and nothing had been accomplished, nothing, just back where I was, at the starting-point.

Boxing Day, 26th December, 1952.

At dawn I went for a quick run along the beach, then back to the bridge and to contact with the Post Office, where I had another wait until they again reported failure to find that Chief of Staff. The Post Office suggested another high official I did not know, and there was another long wait, and again a complete blank, so that I went bang once more right back to the start. Then the Post Office suggested the head of one of the armed services. Yes, please, anyone who might help, and this time they got results quickly, and soon I was having exchanges with a distinctly hostile voice at long range. I introduced myself and started off about the East London Coelacanth. Almost at once he interrupted to ask what on earth a fish had to do with him or with the armed forces of South Africa. I asked him if he would kindly be patient for a moment, I was trying to explain, and went on, but he interrupted sharply with much the same query, so now I answered almost as sharply that if he would listen instead of talking he would learn. It was a conversation that should have been recorded, for at times it almost sizzled. I was compelled to ask him if he really believed that a man in my position would telephone one in his at that time of day and on such a day about any frivolous matter. It was far from that, a matter of national importance. 'What!' he barked. 'A fish! Of national importance.' 'Yes! A fish,' I barked back, so firmly that he listened again. After I had finished my main account, I raised the matter of the plane, and at once he said that there was no plane available that could be sent on such an errand and he could not think of such a thing, anyway. I asked him if I might take that as his final official reply to my approach, when he temporised, so I spoke of the Sunderland flying-boat in Durban and said I had heard that it could be got ready in a short time if its use could be authorised. He asked me if I realised what such a flight to foreign territory meant, it might take a week to organise a thing like that. 'Well, God help South Africa if we should be suddenly attacked!' I could not help flashing back. It was a stimulating conversation, but it became clear that with the best will in the world he really was not in a position to do anything, and he was equally emphatic that even the Commander-in-Chief would not be able to do anything without authority from the Minister, and even he might have to get the approval of the whole Cabinet. I suggested that a flight of this type would provide quite exceptional opportunity for the training of young pilots, but the sounds that came from the receiver in response were not encouraging, and I felt as if I had been beaten flat, face down, into the mud of despair. He concluded by assuring me that I had as much hope as trying to get a plane to the moon. That pulled my head out of the mud a bit, and I told him we should see about that and, after expressing my thanks, returned once more to zero point. I have never met this man, nor do I know his name, and I only hope that subsequent events made him think more kindly of my apparent lunacy.

Our friends were most concerned about our obvious state of tension and distress, and had begged us to take some relaxation despite the urgency of the matter. We had therefore agreed, that Boxing Day, 1952, to go to lunch, to tea, and to dinner at three different homes, it being clearly understood that each appointment might have to be cancelled even at the last moment if any Coelacanth development required it. We dared not risk being away from the ship the whole afternoon, so it was arranged that we should be taken back after lunch and after tea as well.

We were probably deadly guests at that luncheon, but our charming hosts were old friends, considerate and expert at making even corpses feel at home. Even so their tasty food almost nauseated me. There was fish, but I could see only Coelacanth. It was a hot day, and there was a specially delicious cold drink; but I could think only of formalin, and all the time my mind kept on switching over from the Comores to Prime Ministers. It looked as if it would have to be that, after all, and was it going to be the same story over again? Anyway, this was the third day and I was no nearer my goal, still at the starting-point, in fact.

We returned to the ship and had hardly got off the gangway when a distracted young Purser's assistant came shooting out of his office and said, with a distinct flavour of reproof, 'Thank heavens, you've come back, Professor. We've been driven almost crazy by people and the telephone wanting you urgently. Please don't leave the ship again without telling us where you can be called up. The Durban Radio Station asks if you will please telephone them as soon as you can. They say it's very urgent'; and he reeled off a list of others who had sought us, some of whom were still aboard and whom I left to my wife while I went to the telephone.

The Radio Office had received a cable from the Comores addressed to me in Grahamstown, which had been duly sent on. Knowing the situation, however, they had kept a copy, and if I wished they would read it to me as they felt it was of great urgency. I asked for it and they read as follows:

> Charter plane immediately authorities trying claim specimen but willing let you have it if in person stop paid fisherman reward to strengthen position stop inspected five kilo formalin no refrigerator stop specimen different yours no front dorsal or tail remnant but definite identification Hunt.

I thanked the Radio Officer for his extremely thoughtful action in telling me of this cable,* as indeed it was, and it is typical of the

---

* Apart from its importance, this cable had an interesting career, which it is worth a diversion to relate. Being Christmas time (Christmas time!), the University offices in Grahamstown were closed and the staffs of all categories were away. An exception was J. Beek, the University electrician, a valued consultant and friend of our Department. He was working at home that day when the telephone called and he found himself speaking to Port Elizabeth. Someone asked him if he would take a radiogram for Professor Smith as they could not track him in Grahamstown. 'H'm,' thought Beek, 'a nice present from somebody for the Professor.' He knew I was far away and did some quick thinking. He replied, 'Yes certainly, send it up and I can keep it in my workshop until he comes.' 'No, no,' said the voice, 'this is a cable, not a machine'; and then asked him to write it down, which he did. He could see at once that it was important, but had no idea where we were. So he set out to find out, and telephoned a member of our staff. No reply. He then had his own taste of Christmas holidays, something like my own, for though he tried the number of every single member of the University staff who had a telephone, it was a complete blank, every one was away. Beek does not give in easily. He had no idea where my Secretary lived; as it happened, it would not have helped him even if he had, for she was away at the sea. He remembered having seen her take part in some play and she had been associated with a doctor's wife, whom he promptly telephoned, found her in, and told her about the cable. It fortunately happened that she had seen a press report that we were in Durban and knew we were on the *Dunnottar Castle*. So back went Beek, and eventually persuaded the Post Office authorities to relay that cable back to us at Durban. Good for Beek!

thoughtful assistance constantly received from all branches of the public services in South Africa. Many people complain about public servants, but that is not my experience at all.

I read those cabled words again. So that had come into it as well, as if there was not enough already; but it was no very great surprise. My leaflet method had tremendous advantages, but it also had certain drawbacks, one of which was that while so great a sum for a fish, just one fish, would certainly arrest attention everywhere, if one were found by its aid when I was not about, in more enlightened people it might well excite natural human cupidity. If this man was prepared to pay £100 each for these fishes at such a distance, surely they must be worth a lot more? I had certainly never concealed my views about the importance and value of the Coelacanth, the leaflet showed that clearly enough, and if the French had had the remotest belief in my views and in the possibility that Coelacanths might live in their waters, they would have done something about it before if there had been anyone sufficiently interested from the scientific side alone. The very fact that the leaflets taken by Hunt had been new to the Comoran authorities and that they had had no reservations in distributing them was clear indication that the leaflets sent to Madagascar had apparently not really interested the French there, scientifically or otherwise, for if they had been interested in any way, surely my leaflet would have induced them to go into the matter on their own, to hunt and to offer a reward themselves. It could have been done easily enough, and no one could have criticised them for it. Yes, whichever way you looked at it that was my Coelacanth, it had been found as a result of my efforts and ideas, and unless it was just another stray like the one at East London, it did mean, as I had strongly suspected, that it had been under the very noses of the French all along, and they hadn't seen it. I realised full well that one does not value anything until it is desired by others, and I suppose that at the back of my mind there had all along been an unspoken fear that all the fuss and publicity might induce the French authorities to confiscate the fish. In the excitement of the moment they might not be prepared to give full recognition to all that had gone before, to all the years of work that had led to this discovery, to the leaflet that had really tracked this treasure. Hunt must be in a difficult position. He could not afford to antagonise the French, since his trading would almost certainly depend on their good-will.

The French 'authorities' mentioned in Hunt's cable must themselves also be in a difficult position. Willy-nilly, Hunt's excitement and actions and all the circumstances of his relations with me must have forced upon them the importance of the issue. It was true that this fish had been found by no fundamental efforts or ideas of their own, and ethically it belonged to the man whose leaflets they had not only accepted but distributed without any indication that there would be the slightest doubt about his rights of ownership if any fish were found. Now that one had been found, however, it had suddenly been revealed as something of tremendous importance, fantastically more than they had ever supposed. They would naturally be in a quandary as to whether it would be wise to let it go into foreign hands, ethics or no ethics. The cable indicated that they were prepared to concede me certain rights of ownership. That might mean that they really were prepared to concede at least some recognition of my claims, but it might also mean that the fish was in so precarious a stage of preservation, that there might be so much doubt about its being preserved at all, that they were unwilling to take the responsibility for its preservation unless they could say they had been compelled to do so because I would not come. This all left so many uncertainties. If I did not go, nobody could ever question the French authorities taking it from a layman, no matter how interested he might be. I kept on coming back to my uncertainty that they might not know how to preserve it properly? They might not have enough formalin to do it. Like fierce tides all these many complications surged back and forth through my mind, and there emerged from all the obscurity and uncertainty only one clear thought, one certain course—it was like a light that encased my mind and my soul and drove me on. I must go myself, I must go and see that it really was a Coelacanth, and make quite certain that it was properly preserved. Looking back, I realise now that I was in a state of mind that is termed 'Possessed'.

In my half-distracted mind I could see the French standing there over my fish, waiting to seize it unless I came in person, as if they knew that I was beating out my life against an immovable mass of holiday inertia, perhaps of official indifference. This new factor had been such a shock that only now did I notice that Hunt's cable read 'inspected five kilos of formalin' (clearly a misprint for 'injected'), about a gallon. That sounded better! But was it concentrated formalin? It had been arranged for Hunt to get a 'bottle' of formalin for that smaller fish, probably about or less than a pint. This cable could mean that he had got about a pint of concentrated formalin which, according to the directions he had been given, would make about five kilos of dilute solution. That was not enough, not nearly enough to preserve a fish as big as that for more than a short time in such heat. If only he had said 'concentrated' formalin; but he hadn't and it was not certain that he realised its significance. So that was still a very big doubt, the fish might even now be going putrid; in any case, because the proper injection of a large fish is not anything a layman can normally do without instruction, especially in places as hot as the Comores. And what in Heaven's name did the statement about the front dorsal or tail remnant mean? All my fears about its not being a Coelacanth at all flared up again in full force. At top speed my mind took me writhing again through all that sea of doubt, though it did help to remember that the fossil record had shown that the small extra tail in Coelacanths gradually became shorter as time passed; in fact, it was apparently absent in some later forms. That in *Latimeria* was about the shortest. Then in the Lung-fishes, which had almost as long a fossil record as the Coelacanths, the first dorsal fin of earlier forms had just disappeared with time. It was therefore within the bounds of possibility that over this past 70 million years such trends had led to a modern type of Coelacanth without extra tail or first dorsal. It was just possible, and beyond that I clung to our faith in Hunt, and tried to feel convinced that even if this was no Coelacanth, it would almost certainly be something just as interesting. If it did prove to be a Coelacanth it must be different from *Latimeria* because that had both first dorsal and extra tail very distinctly. What should I find if I got there? In my exhausted and overwrought condition it seemed indeed as if the dice were being loaded against me with all these uncertainties. Nothing was certain, nothing clear-cut, the identity of the fish, whether there was enough formalin, would I ever get there in time, first before the thing rotted and secondly before the French took it? Through

REMIO £100 REWARD
RECOMPENSE

Examine este peixe com cuidado. Talvez lhe dê sorte. Repare nos dois rabos que possui e nas suas ranhas barbatanas. O único exemplar que a ciência encontrou tinha, de comprimento, 160 centímetros. Mas já ave quem visse outros. Se tiver a sorte de apanhar ou encontrar algum NÃO O CORTE NEM O LIMPE DE ALQUER MODO — conduza-o imediatamente, inteiro, a um frigorífico ou peça a pessoa competente que e se ocupe. Solicite, ao mesmo tempo, a essa pessoa, que avise imediatamente, por meio de telgrama, o profes- J. L. B. Smith, da Rhodes University, Grahamstown, União Sul-Africana.

Os dois primeiros especimens serão pagos à razão de 10.000$, cada, sendo o pagamento garantido a Rhodes University e pelo South African Council for Scientific and Industrial Research. Se conseguir obter is de dois, conserve-os todos, visto terem grande valor, para fins científicos, e as suas canseiras serão bem ompensadas.

COELACANTH

Look carefully at this fish. It may bring you good fortune. Note the peculiar double tail, l the fins. The only one ever saved for science was 5 ft (160 cm.) long. Others have been seen. If 1 have the good fortune to catch or find one DO NOT CUT OR CLEAN IT ANY WAY but get it whole at ee to a cold storage or to some responsible official who can care for it, and ask him to notify Professor L. B. Smith of Rhodes University Grahamstown, Union of S. A., immediately by telegraph. For the first specimens £100 (10.000 Esc.) each will be paid, guaranteed by Rhodes University and by the South Afri- Council for Scientific and Industrial Research. If you get more than 2, save them all, as every one is uable for scientific purposes and you will be well paid.

Veuillez remarquer avec attention ce poisson. Il pourra vous apporter bonne chance, peut être. gardez les deux queuex qu'il possède et ses étranges nageoires. Le seul exemplaire que la science a trouvé ait, de longueur, 160 centimètres. Cependant d'autres ont trouvés quelques exemplaires en plus.

Si jamais vous avez la chance d'en trouver un NE LE DÉCOUPEZ PAS NI NE LE NETTOYEZ AUCUNE FAÇON, conduisez-le immédiatement, tout entier, a un frigorifique ou glacière en demandat a une sonne competente de s'en occuper. Simultanement veuillez prier a cette personne de faire part, telegraphi- ement à Mr. le Professeus J. L. B. Smith, de la Rhodes University, Grahamstown, Union Sud-Africaine.

Le deux premiers exemplaires seront payés à la raison de £100 chaque dont le payment est ga- ti par la Rhodes University et par le South African Council for Scientific and Industrial Research.

Si, jamais il vous est possible d'en obtenir plus de deux, nous vous serions très grés de les con- rver vu qu'ils sont d'une très grande valeur pour fins scientifiques, et, neanmoins les fatigues pour obtan- n seront bien recompensées.

The famous Coelacanth leaflet

Plate 3

Monsieur P. Coudert, Governor of the Comores, near the wharf at Dzaoudzi, 29th December 1952.

Plate 4

"Hunt's trim vessel", at the wharf, Dzaoudzi, showing the Coelacanth box on the left. Only two weeks later this craft was destroyed by a cyclone.

all this there was only one coherent thought in my mind, to which I clung like a drowning man to a life-buoy: I must go myself and see.

Half distracted by this latest complication, we had meanwhile been coping with visitors and the press. The news by now having got to world prominence, you could almost feel the rival reporters growling at one another. Our friends were standing by, and we got away to spend a short time for tea, this latest development naturally almost the sole topic of conversation. Our friends made various wild suggestions for a drastic solution of this problem. They were attractive and even amusing, but while they relieved the tension for a few seconds they were patently impractical. I was nearing a stage of desperation, and it was at that time that I came to veer to my wife's view. It would clearly have to be Malan. In some ways that cable settled it, and troublesome as it was, it was in some ways in my favour in any appeal for help; for it was not only a race against possible putrefaction, but there was clearly a case for my having to go in person. It did help to feel that the French would hardly be prepared to take a step as drastic as confiscating the specimen unless they were almost certainly convinced of its value; but there was clearly no scientist in the Comores, and I could not be certain if the French did seize it that it would be safely preserved for science. Nothing is ever a hundred per cent., and in some ways this cable, worrying as it was, forced the issue.

We got back to the ship again, and the same young officer handed me some telegrams without comment. Among them was the cable that Beek had handled, that the Radio Station had so kindly short-circuited some hours earlier. It was a renewed shock to read the words again. Knowing Grahamstown in holiday time we wondered how it had come back to us so quickly. (See footnote, p. 109.) Nothing of further import had happened, but more visitors and press representatives were waiting. I got away to the cabin for a while and sat, desperately miserable, for time was slipping by and I had still accomplished nothing, just nothing, and here was what seemed an awful blow. I was an experienced and mature man, and yet in this I was failing, not having yet accomplished anything worth-while in this all-important matter. I had beaten my head in vain against this Christmas holiday wall,

a concrete, no! an iron wall. Portuguese friends who had visited the
Union had said to us, 'You may talk of Russia and the Iron
Curtain, but it is nothing to South Africa on a Sunday or a holiday.
That is an Iron Curtain. It shuts down, boom, boom, like that,
and everything is dead.' They were right. It had beaten me so far.
There was only one hope left—Malan! Malan! 'You will have to
go to him in the end,' my wife had said. It certainly looked like it,
though my mind still obstinately rebelled against the idea. Prime
Ministers and fish just did not mix in my mind.

They called me. Our friends were waiting, so I pulled myself
up to go. It was almost as if my body was in bits like my mind,
and as in a dream I went up to the lounge where they stood waiting.
Malan, yes it would have to be Malan, and when we all sat round
before dinner I had nothing else in my mind, and I told them it
seemed now that this was all that remained. I had been forced to
the very last ditch, with little hope. It was now a question of how
to proceed, and someone suggested that Malan might even be at
the official residence on the Natal south coast. This would alter
the situation very materially for, after all, that was within personal
reach, by car; but my first flash of hope soon faded as it was most
unlikely, for that was the winter resort, in summer it would
probably be the Cape. Whom could we ask? I thought of Desmond
Prior, an old acquaintance, sub-editor of the *Daily News* and
deeply interested in all this, and asked if they would get him on
the telephone for me. Wonder of wonders, I was soon talking to
him. Malan? He didn't know for certain, but would soon find
out. My number? Right, he would ring back in a few minutes;
which he did, to say that the Prime Minister was not in Natal, he
was somewhere at the Cape, nobody seemed to know exactly
where. It was as I had feared, the Cape, a darned long way off.
Prior went on and said that if he might suggest it, would I make
contact with Dr. Vernon Shearer, M.P., now in Durban and not
far from the Evans's house, where we were. He not only knew
all about this affair but was anxious to assist if he could, and in
any approach to the Government his position would certainly
help. Shearer would be at home that night, and it would be
possible to speak to him at once if I wished. So I thanked Prior
and told the others what he had said. Frank Evans was enthusiastic, Shearer was a good man, and with my consent he went to the

telephone and in a few moments called me to speak to Shearer, whose obvious deep concern and interest were comforting, and though I was still without any real hope that this might rip the curtain of despair that surrounded me, it was arranged to go to his house after dinner.

Chapter Eleven

I MUST SPEAK TO HIM

MALAN; Malan! Was it to be the same thing as before? This was infinitely worse, for it was Boxing Day, when he would not be in harness, not in his office, but resting, and as this could happen very seldom he was sure to be surrounded by extra concrete and steel walls to guard his privacy. Not only was it pretty certain that those would take some penetrating, but to justify the tremendous request I had to make I could not even say 'This *is* a Coelacanth', only 'I believe it is very likely to be a Coelacanth'.

Dinner was another phantom meal where attractively served and tasty food passed my unresponsive palate and tumbled into a contorted stomach, which pushed it on through a writhing duodenal tunnel. After dinner Frank Evans and I went off and were welcomed at the Shearer home at 8.15 p.m. Shearer is a dentist by profession as well as a Member of Parliament, and is an able and forceful personality as well as a realist.

George Symons, *Daily News* photographer, was there, and we were soon deep in discussion. Shearer knew the main outlines of events, and I gave him a brief account of my attempts to get air transport. I said that I had all along been opposed to approaching the Prime Minister, mainly because he was resting, but that now it seemed the only way. It added to my depression to find Shearer dubious of the wisdom of approaching Malan before it was quite certain that all else had been absolutely exhausted. He said that it would at least be very difficult, for at a time like this there would be a series of extra barriers around the Prime Minister's privacy that only the highest in the Government party would be able to pass, and as an Opposition member, well. . . . It might be best to have one more try for Erasmus, Minister of Defence. So off he went and had a long session on the telephone while we sat dumbly round a table.

My mind was never off that fish in far-away Comores. Time

was passing, so much had gone, and I was yet no nearer my aim
except that by then I knew without any shadow of doubt that
Malan was the only hope, all else would be a waste of time. I must
speak to him. The telephoning now ended in the same way as it
had done all along, for the Post Office told Shearer that the line
to the station nearest the farm of Erasmus was closed until the
morrow, so he booked a call for the earliest possible hour, 9 a.m.
next day. So there I was, right back at the starting-point, and
we went over it all again, only now I no longer had any doubts or
reservations, my mind had veered right over, and I knew that we
must stake all and go for Malan. Only Malan could help, and after
some discussion I said so, firmly; it was too late to wait for others,
I was quite convinced. I must speak to him. Shearer again said it
would be difficult; but he was more than willing to do whatever
was possible, and went off again to the telephone, which was in
an adjoining room. We had decided that it would be best first to
try Groote Schuur, the Prime Minister's official residence at the
Cape.

Mrs. Shearer had come in, and we sat round the table, silent,
concentrating on the conversation at the telephone. 'Dr. Vernon
Shearer. Groote Schuur, Cape. Yes, the Prime Minister, a matter
of national importance. I must speak to him tonight. Yes, thank
you.' And he was back, the Post Office was on the job. I sat
steeped in suspense and apprehension, without much hope, for
which there was good reason. Prime Minister. H'm! There was
Smuts, whom everyone spoke of and regarded as having a real
interest in science, he was even almost a scientist himself some
people said, and look how he had reacted in my case, a simple
one at that? He had not only turned it down flat, he had even refused to see me at all, quite probably a following-on of his attitude
towards the Coelacanth expedition. I had been told that he regarded
the views of overseas scientists as sounder than my own. And
now this other Prime Minister, Malan, what would he do in almost
similar circumstances? It made me turn cold to realise how very
similar they were, for again it was a race against time for fish,
and yet this time everything involved was from my side very much
worse and very much more difficult. From Smuts I had wanted a
plane on what one may term a domestic issue, all within our own
borders; but what I wanted from Malan was so much more, not

only very much farther to go, but mostly over and into foreign
territory, with international complications as well, which alone
might turn the scale against me. Whereas it had been in my favour
that Smuts had had the flavour of science, would it not be exactly
the opposite with Malan, who was far away from science, very
far, a reputedly dour and at one time almost sinister figure in his
deeply religious stern Calvinistic righteousness? He was known
to be utterly indifferent to the criticism or disapproval of those
who opposed him, and once he had weighed a situation and come
to a decision he did what he felt was right, not what others wanted.
During the war, at a time when the Afrikanerdom he lived for
was battling for its very existence and its adherents were rent and
torn by schisms, Malan was not prepared to compromise or ap-
pease. Indeed, at that difficult time he set out to crush a powerful
group in his own camp, a policy that appalled most of his asso-
ciates of that time; but he succeeded, and later, when the fruits
of his policy and victory became apparent, they won him enormous respect for his courage and wisdom. This was indeed one
of the main causes underlying Malan's final spectacular and
crushing victory over his life-long opponent Smuts. Paradoxically
enough he accomplished this in the British way because he won
really only the last victory in that long struggle. It was something
like the tortoise and the hare over again. Indeed, I reflected, mankind may be divided into the tortoises and the hares, I had myself
been like the tortoise this past fourteen years, plodding along
steadily, without encouragement, looking for my Coelacanth,
and now at the end I was aiming to finish off with a spurt no hare
could ever equal, not even a Pegasus. I wondered how Malan . . .
the telephone bell crashed through my thoughts and went on
ringing furiously. Shearer got up and went out hastily, and there
followed a long conversation of which we heard odd fragments.

'Yes, Vernon Shearer, M.P. Member of Parliament. . . . Yes,
yes, tonight. Thank you.' Another fruitless effort, for Shearer
said that the Post Office had told him that the Prime Minister was
not at Groote Schuur, but at his private home at the Strand, where
he was resting, and there were strict orders that he was not to be
disturbed. Nevertheless, Shearer had stressed the importance and
urgency of the matter and we could only hope for the best. He
began to speak of Malan in a manner that interested me greatly,

since I had for many years not heard anything personal about him, only reports and comments in the English press. The 'Dokter' had mellowed with age, and his political antagonisms had been tempered by achievement and success. My mind drifted away and back many years to the time when this man Malan, the 'Renegade Parson' as many of the more English section stigmatised him, had suddenly emerged as a force in the expression and forging of South African nationalism. Minister of Education in Hertzog's Cabinet, represented in the press as anti-British, a solemn, earnest, and troublesome opponent, he was plainly of such unswerving rectitude that no one could ever find even one foot of clay.

Rhodes University College in Grahamstown was in need of funds and had an Art School to open. A Nationalist Cabinet Minister for such a function would in Grahamstown indeed be a phenomenon, but the invitation was sent and promptly accepted. There were comments and speculations. Would he drown everyone in a flood of Afrikaans? In the morning, formal but affable and correct, he inspected what he was shown and made proper response. Grahamstown turned out in force that day, town as well as gown. I shall never forget the course of the ceremony, the rustle as Malan stood to speak, the relief that it was to be in English, anticipation gradually changing to astonishment that this vaunted anti-British politician should be able to roll out such polished phrases. He stood solid, quiet, and firm, and for well over an hour, without any notes, this amazing man held his audience submerged and quiet beneath an eloquent stream of English, perfect in sense and construction, so smooth that it was only from intonation and accent that one could know that this was not his mother tongue. It was by all standards an impressive achievement. Young as I was then and little as politics meant to me, it was clear that this man could not fail to become a force in South Africa, and that while he might be hated for his strength no one could fail to respect him. He radiated honesty, courage, and determination, and even if these were employed as weapons in a field not to everyone's liking. . . . 'Yes, they call him the Sphinx.' Shearer was speaking again, 'and'—his words were cut off abruptly as the telephone went again, and he was off in a flash. 'Yes, yes, Shearer, yes Shearer.' Silence—then in Afrikaans,

'Yes, Madam, Vernon Shearer. How are you, Mrs. Malan, is the Doctor well? Yes, I have with me Professor Smith'; and then a brief outline of the main facts. My heart began to pound so madly it almost choked me. Then there was silence, he was clearly listening, it lasted some time, an agonisingly long time, my body was shaking as in a fever. Then Shearer's voice, subdued now, 'You don't think it could be done now?' Another silence. 'Yes, thank you very much indeed, very much obliged. Good night.' Shearer came back slowly, his face despondent. I had no need of his words, my heart fell from my boots through the floor. 'Mrs. Malan,' said Shearer. 'I spoke to her. The Doctor was already abed and she was emphatic that nothing was to disturb him, for he was unusually weary and they were concerned about him. She would promise nothing but would see how he was in the morning, and if she judged it wise would tell him about it. So that's that.'*

10.30 p.m. of the 26th December of the year of our Lord 1952. It was probably the lowest ebb of my life. The sands of time were running out, fate was screwing me down to the dregs, wringing out the last drops of my spirit from the rags of my being. The *Dunnottar Castle* was due to sail at 11 a.m. tomorrow, and what on earth was I to do, for now there seemed no more hope? Even if Malan was told in the morning and took some interest in it, the Strand was an awful long way off, diagonally across the Union, about as far from Durban as Venice from London, and it was Christmas holiday time when public services are difficult or dead. I could hardly hope to have things settled before the ship sailed, and to retain any last shred of hope I should have to pack and prepare to leave the ship and stay on in Durban. Prime Ministers! Well, detachedly, I could sympathise, for I knew what their lives were like. In another sphere I endure something like it myself, but this was hard to take. I sat almost turned to stone with black despair, and was curiously unable to get up and go as I felt I should. I seemed to be paralysed, when Mrs. Shearer jumped up and said brightly, 'No need to be gloomy. One never knows what the morning will bring. You're not to go yet, Professor, I'm going to make you a nice cup of tea.' And off she went.

* Recently (August 1955) when I spoke again of these events to Dr. and Mrs. Malan at their home, he said to me, 'You actually owe a lot to Shearer. But for his help, as things were, it would have been very difficult to get through.'

I once met a cultured foreign woman of great ability whom I admired (without further designs; she was already married and so was I). Once in discussing the British, who annoyed her, she said that when a crisis arose, instead of tackling it in a proper business-like way at once, somebody would be sure to say, 'Well now, let's first have a nice cup of tea', and you would just have to wait until they had all had it before getting down to business. I had often thought of that since, and those words always flash it up on my mind like a screen. Mrs. Shearer bustled back soon afterwards with a tray full of good things, and put tea and cake before me; but misery destroys flavour and I ate and drank what could have been sawdust and muddy water for all it meant to my palate.

Even when everyone had finished and it was already more than time to go, I had a strange reluctance to get up. Although it really seemed that everything was finished, my mind fiercely resisted such a conclusion, for it meant that I was virtually giving up, even though it was beyond my powers to do more. Though I had actually put my hands on the table, I was hesitating even while trying to bring myself to the effort of rising to my feet. They were all looking at me, obviously waiting for me to move, all this in a strained strange silence, when this was suddenly and dramatically shattered by the loud ringing of the telephone, which in that tense atmosphere was like an explosion. It startled us all so much that for a few seconds nobody moved. Then Shearer and I jumped to our feet—he went off, we heard him say a few words, then silence, then a shout: 'Quick Professor, Dr. Malan! Dr. Malan wants to speak to you!'

I found myself at the telephone with the receiver in my hands. 'Dr. Malan himself,' whispered Shearer. I croaked into the receiver, but it was a woman's voice that spoke in Afrikaans: 'Mrs. Malan here, Professor; the Doctor wants to speak to you.' A click, a fumble, then that slow voice easily recognisable over a gap of more than twenty years, in English too. 'Good evening, Professor, I have heard something of your story, but will you please give me as full a summary as possible.' So I began, in Afrikaans, saying that I hoped he would not mind if I stumbled occasionally in technical terms. 'Speak English, man,' he interjected. I said no, I wished to speak in Afrikaans, and taking a deep breath, plunged straight in. I gave him a brief account of the history of Coelacanths, of the fantastic discovery of the East London fish, the tragedy of the soft parts, my long search, the recent discovery, the heat, the isolation, my fears, and my needs. I emphasised that I could not be certain that this was a Coelacanth, there was a risk for I had only Hunt's word for it, but of all the laymen I knew Hunt was the most likely to know a Coelacanth if he saw one, and I was more than satisfied that it might be the greatest scientific tragedy not to make certain of it. It was a risk and he must clearly realise it. It was a risk for me to take as well, but there was no question in my mind that I at least must take it and was prepared to ask his help to that end. I said that it was not my name that was at stake; in my view with all that had gone before this was a matter of national prestige. While it was of world-wide importance, it was South Africa's responsibility to make sure of that fish, and that was why I was appealing to him for help. I had taken all the cables with me 'just in case', and read him the last one from Hunt, slowly.

He listened all the time and did not interrupt or ask any questions, he was obviously soaking it all in. He was so quiet that at intervals, fearing the line had been cut, I would ask 'Are you there?' and he would say 'Yes, go on'. When I had finished I saw to my amazement that I had been talking a full twelve minutes. There was a short silence, and his first words were, 'I must congratulate you on your Afrikaans. It is excellent.' That was high praise indeed, but what about the Coelacanth? Was this just an unexpected Prime Minister's sugar-coating? I waited in agony, maybe there would be questions, but none came; and after a short silence he said speaking slowly, 'Your story is remarkable, and I can see at once that this is a matter of great importance. It is too late to try to do anything tonight, but first thing in the morning I shall get through to my Minister of Defence to ask him to allocate a suitable aeroplane to take you where you need to go. Where can you be reached by telephone?' I did some quick thinking and said I was on the *Dunnottar Castle* which was due to sail in the morning, but would come to Dr. Shearer's house from 9 a.m. (I looked at Shearer who nodded assent) and wait there for any message. Would that do? Yes, it would. Then I thanked him and we said goodnight.

As I put down the receiver I felt dazed, like a man reprieved on the very scaffold, like somebody suddenly jerked from the hollows of hell to a high hill-top in heaven. A Prime Minister, and one whose educational culture was very far from, some said fundamentally antagonistic to, biological science, and he had roused himself, on a brief holiday, late. at night, on his own initiative, to speak to a scientist named Smith from a notoriously English centre like Grahamstown. He had listened patiently, and though not a scientist had been able to grasp, weigh, and assess the importance of the matter straight away. He had not needed to ask any questions, and had come to an immediate decision. Had my name been Van der Westhuizen, and had I come from, say, Potchefstroom, there would have been those who could sneer, but I knew, politics or no politics, that from then on nobody would speak ill of this man with impunity in my presence. My dazed mind flashed back to Smuts, and then I found myself in the dining-room again, where I was unable to utter a word in response to the silent question that was plain on the faces which for some seconds were all I could see. 'My word, you can speak Afrikaans,' someone said; then, as I slowly regained my equilibrium and full comprehension of what had just happened, they questioned me minutely about what Malan had said, which produced such an air of relief all round it hardly seemed like the same place. Even the faces had changed.

I arranged to return at 8.30 next morning, and Mrs. Shearer told me a room would be at my disposal to work while I waited. We went back to Frank Evans's house, and when I saw my wife's anxious questioning gaze, something choked me and I could not speak, but nodded. Frank Evans made good my verbal deficiency, and soon gave them an animated account of the events of the evening.

It was only much later that I heard the outlines of the story of what had happened in the Malan household that night. When Shearer's call was put through, Dr. Malan was abed and as far as they knew asleep. Mrs. Malan answered. She listened to Shearer, but judged the matter should wait at least till the morning; but as she put down the receiver Dr. Malan called out to ask what it was and would not be put off. She gave him a brief outline of the matter. Dr. Malan nodded his head. 'This man Smith is well known. Bring me that fish book.'

Some time before, since the South African Council for Scientific and Industrial Research, from which most of the funds for my work came, fell directly under the Prime Minister, when Dr. Malan came into power I sent him a copy of this volume, in whose production the C.S.I.R. had played so great a part. (Only three days after it had gone the President of the C.S.I.R. suggested that I should do this very thing.)

Just before Christmas, when they had been preparing to leave for their brief rest at the Strand, Mrs. Malan had assembled a few books, and quite by chance my *Sea Fishes of Southern Africa* caught her eye as eminently suitable for the seaside, despite its size.

So now they fetched him the book and found the Coelacanth pages in it. He read it over slowly and paged through part of the volume. Then he shut it. He called her again, and tapping the book said, 'The man that wrote this book would not ask my help at a time like this unless it was desperately important. I must speak to him.'

Mildly they tried to dissuade him, to wait for the morning at least, but he shook his head and repeated, 'I must speak to him now.' And so the telephones were set going. Thank God for that 'nice cup of tea!' It has helped to win many victories.

Chapter Twelve

DAKOTA DASH

WE went back from the Evans's house to the ship, and I had to try to calm my raging mind to coherent thought. What lay ahead would require the most careful planning, every step, there must be no false moves. This creature that Hunt had was in unknown foreign territory so that I could only guess at what I should find when I got there, and despite the promised plane, the problem still was how to reach the actual spot where the fish was, and quickly. I might have to make a voyage by sea from the nearest landing-ground. To cover that possibility I had to work out all my needs—clothing, food, money, preservatives, medicines, there must be no slip-up with any item. I gave my wife a tablet to make her sleep, but I had much to do and did not get to bed at all. I was hard at work right through that night, and when my wife turned over in the dawn to look hazily across at me, I was pretty tired, but could smile, for my plans were complete.

She was soon up, for we had much to do and discuss. Our baggage and equipment consisted of more than seventy packages, dispersed between the cabin, the hold, the baggage room, the cold storage, on the top deck next to the funnel, and in the magazine. Each bore a number and its contents were listed in a book. Some of the things I needed for the journey ahead had to be dug out of packages lodged in different parts of the ship, and my wife had to be coached so as to be able to take charge of all this diverse material; for in all our expeditions this had always been my own special responsibility, and it was no light task at short notice.

At 7 a.m. I sent a message to Captain Smythe to ask the latest time of departure of the ship and to say I should be leaving her. In a few minutes he was at our cabin eager for news, when I briefly outlined the latest developments. At once he asked if he could help in any way. I asked for the telephone to be kept aboard, and a gangway open, both until the last possible moment, and for an extra hand to stand by to help my wife when necessary. She would remain in her cabin so as to be immediately available for the telephone. One or two items were needed from packages in the hold and baggage room—could they come up soon? I gave him a short list of food required: cheese, dried figs, biscuits, and Brazil nuts, so much of each. He glanced at it and said it would be prepared at once. When agitated or in action, Smythe has a way of flicking his fingers, which is symbolical of the speed with which he can act in any emergency. All I wanted was done with dispatch, and on his own he had a special breakfast prepared for me which I ate in his cabin soon after. Ours looked like a Customs baggage examination warehouse.

After he left, my wife and I went through the detailed list of my needs: one light suit and a nylon shirt, that I was wearing then. Two khaki shirts, two shorts, compact shaving kit, pyjama shorts, a towel, soap, folding primus, a small aluminium pot, an aluminium water-bottle, six boxes of matches, each in a waterproof bag, a torch, light plastic overcoat, nylon head-net, all in a small waterproof case. Camera (my wonderful Rolleiflex), exposure meter and spare films, Nescafé, sugar, slabs of chocolate, plastic cups, my special silver spoon, two knives, and though I do not smoke, several hundred cigarettes, of course, for without those I never travel in wild parts. They are a wonderful open sesame to primitive hearts. Then last but not least my trusty collecting-box. This is quite a famous box, my inseparable companion on tens of thousands of miles of tropical journeys, by land, sea, and air. It is a neat teak box 18 × 12 × 15 inches high, and it has many compartments and trays with divisions. Its contents are the result of years of experience, and cover a wide range, from almost a full medical outfit to tools, spare parts for pressure stoves and lamps, fishing tackle; there are hundreds of items. Some of them have interesting backgrounds. A tube of rubber solution! We once went on a trip from a tiny isolated coastal settlement in northern Mozambique to the Lurio mouth, about fifty miles of the loneliest track in Africa and through an area alive with wild animals. Lurio lions are notorious. The country there just swarms with them. You can follow the road all right, especially through swamps, for it is made of logs; but you can pass only in the dry season, though there seem to be just as many mosquitoes then as at any other time. If you had a breakdown on that road, your chances of surviving a night in the open were remote, but if you did you would certainly emerge with malaria and worse. We had a Government lorry with a native driver, whom I asked if he had all the necessary tools and spares. He said yes. We set off and how that vehicle survived the jumps and bumps is a miracle; but we got to the Lurio, where there is a small house with netted windows, which the Portuguese always have. Soon after arrival the driver came to report a puncture, and I told him to get it mended. He hesitated, and when I asked sharply what it was, reported that the solution was all dried up in the tube. We tried to dissolve it in petrol, but without avail, it was too hot. Then he tried frying a repair patch on some coals, but that also proved useless. What an idiot I had been to trust a native I had not trained myself. We still had four good tubes, but no spare and no repair outfit, and we had to go back over that awful road. We managed it, but that is why I always carry the rubber solution, and some patching as well.

Spare pump washers! We once got to a lonely lighthouse with only natives in charge. I asked for lamps and they brought three mantle lanterns, which I told them to light up. Sorry, Senhor, but the pumps won't work; and they showed me the washers stripped to shreds. No spares in your stores? No, Senhor, nothing. I told them to go and have another search, and when they had left I had a good look, but the lamps really were useless. I had an idea and took out the plunger of our pressure stove, and behold it fitted perfectly. I soon had a lamp going and put the plunger back into the primus, and when the natives came back to report no luck, as it was still light they did not at first notice the lamp. Then one saw it and his eyes bulged; he pointed in amazement and the others stared as well. How had the Senhor done it? 'I blew it up,' I said, and bulged out my cheeks, and their eyes bulged still more. What a man this must be! Would I blow up the others, too? But I said one was enough at a time as it was hard work. We took that secret away with us, but probably left a legend behind. Nowadays I find it less trouble to carry spare washers.

Yes, my 'collecting-box'. I was repeatedly called to the telephone, press and friends seeking information. At 8 a.m. Guy Drummond Sutton came to fetch me, and we were again welcomed to their lovely house by Dr. Shearer and his good lady. Guy Sutton went off with a cheque for £200 to cash and take the money to the ship, where I had arranged with the Purser to change it for East African currency, since that was the nearest I could get to Comoran money, of which there was apparently not a franc available in Durban. I judged that Hunt would use East African currency in his work, and that exchange could be contrived that way.

They brought me the morning paper, and to my amazement and dismay I read there that Professor Smith had last night asked the Prime Minister for help. I was greatly shocked, as the previous night I had particularly asked everyone not to say a word since I had not sought Dr. Malan's permission to do so. I asked for Shearer and showed him the article. He nodded, he had already seen it, but was not at all perturbed. I told him of my dismay as it might upset Dr. Malan if it had leaked out at this end, for I felt that if anything was to be given out it must come from his own office. Shearer said I need not worry about upsetting Dr. Malan. 'He is a tough citizen, believe me, and can take more than most. Besides, this message is marked 'Cape Town' not Durban. It would not surprise me if that was issued by the staff of the Prime Minister's office'; and as it turned out he was probably correct.

I wanted formalin, and what a picnic! It was Saturday morning, 27th December 1952, and the shops were open, but no factories. No chemist had 2 gallons, 2 lb. perhaps. What on earth was I to do? While I was racking my brains, my wife telephoned; George Prior had called and was with her, and I told her my difficulty, which they briefly discussed and suggested Dr. George Campbell. After some time he was located, and undertook to get a friend to go to his factory and have the stuff sent to his own house that day. He would see I got it. Meanwhile, on the *Dunnottar Castle* Prior stood by, for he had undertaken to go and get the formalin by some means himself if all else failed.

Each telephone call saw me jump, but they were all local. How long would it take to get it all arranged? I thought of my Brigadier in Pretoria. Later I learnt that all that enormous amount of organisation for the flight had been completed in less than ten

The landing-strip at Pamanzi, Comores, clearly once a reef
below the sea.

"The Beloved Isle" of Mozambique, P.E.A. Note the
famous fortress of St. Sebastian at the near end.

Plate 5

In the latter part of an unending day, 2₉ December 1952, starting at Lumbo 4.30 a.₥ Dzaoudzi 7.10 a.m., now at Durban 9 p.₥ telephoning Brigadier Melville in Preto₨ hemmed in by the South African Broadcast₨ Corporation and the Press.

"Do you mean to say we once looked like that?" Dr. D. F. Malan examines the Coelacanth at the Strand, 30th December 1952. Mrs. M. M. Smith is equally interested.

The Coelacanth quartet, Nai₨ 24th October 1953. *Left to r* Drs. M. Menache; J. Millot; E Worthington and J. L. B. Smith

Plate 6

hours—route, foreign contacts and permits, immigration, Customs, refuelling, the lot. South African efficiency! Again I wondered what my Pretoria friend thought about it all now, but as time passed my anxiety grew. When would that message come? I telephoned Brigadier Daniel, but beyond having heard that the flight was to be arranged, he had received no further news. The Sunderland was all ready and the crew standing by, the moment he had any news he would let me know. A call from my wife— any news yet? Sailing had been put on to 11.30 but could not be delayed a moment longer. Smythe said I had better be there by 11.15 at the latest, which meant leaving at once, so Guy Sutton and I went to the docks, where the *Dunnottar* was ready to move. I raced aboard, did a quick check through the stuff, and my wife and Sutton and I went down the gangway as they were undoing the lashings. A quick good-bye on the quay and my wife went up again, almost yanked aboard by an officer as the gap opened, and she was gone. I saw the telephone wire, held to the last, snaking over the side. Photographed indelibly on my brain is a tiny figure, waving: my wife on the bridge of the *Dunnottar* as she gathered way out through the harbour mouth.

At the request and suggestion of my friend Dr. George Campbell I went to his house, where I might have some peace and rest. I asked Guy not to give me away, but within ten minutes of my arrival the press had found me. No, no news yet. I was worrying about the formalin, but this came soon after. The Campbells kindly left me entirely alone, but I could not rest or sleep, for it seemed impossible that there could still be no news. I was in a fever. Had something gone wrong? There had, but not the way I feared. We heard later that when Dr. Malan tried to make contact with the Minister of Defence, storms had cut the telephone line at several points and eventually a police officer had to go many miles over bad roads to take a message. It was just typical of everything in this whole affair, constant hold-ups.

At 3.30 p.m. Brigadier Daniel telephoned to say that it had been decided not to use the Sunderland, but a Dakota from Swartkops, Pretoria. It might be possible to get it away by about 5 p.m., but we could in any case expect to get away early next morning. Brigadier Melville telephoned from Pretoria to say definitely that it was to be a Dakota, and gave me a résumé of what had been arranged, the course of the flight and other details. It was doubtful whether they could manage to get the plane away that afternoon, but he confirmed that in any case we could leave Durban early in the morning. Later I was told that the Dakota would leave Pretoria before dawn next day, would arrive in Durban, Stamford Hill, at 6 a.m., and get away as soon as we got aboard.

It was a terrific relief to hear this definite news, and I arranged to be fetched by an army car at 5 a.m. Friends were told of these arrangements and I sent the following telegram to my wife on the ship:

'PROBABLY LEAVING DAWN.'

And it was only then that I cabled Hunt as follows:

'HOLD ON STOP GOVERNMENT SENDING PLANE.'

Within a short time I was being subjected to an intensive bombardment by telephone, from near and far. Would I confirm that the Prime Minister had granted a military plane? When did we expect to leave? etc., etc. Then a new phase started. Would I be prepared to take a press representative? I said that would have to be considered, and then there came a succession of more such requests from cinema, newsreel, television, and other agents, until I began to wonder if there was going to be any room for me on the plane. I told them all that the matter would not rest with me. Would I take it further? So I asked the Military Authorities to get in touch with whatever person or department was necessary and to put the matter to them. I gathered it would be the Prime Minister's secretary, but in any case the answer eventually came back a flat 'No, only Professor Smith'.

At the end of an expedition such as ours, financial matters were often troublesome in many ways, and as ready funds would certainly now be of prime importance, I sent the following telegram to the President of the South African Council for Scientific and Industrial Research in Pretoria:

'GOING COMORES IN PLANE GRANTED BY PRIME MINISTER TO FETCH COELACANTH WILL COUNCIL KINDLY GRANT FIVE HUNDRED POUNDS TOWARDS EXPENSES.'

And so, near midnight I went to bed and actually slept a few hours. Despite my extreme weariness I needed no alarm clock; indeed never do need one, for I can wake at any desired moment, but I beat myself that morning, and woke at 3 a.m. and was in the car at five. Mrs. Campbell was up at four and we had coffee and litchis together; George was already away. Knowing my liking for fruit, the Campbells had put piles of all sorts in my room, especially great bunches of litchis, which we rarely see in Grahamstown, and those I had not eaten Mrs. Campbell helped me stuff into my case.

It was misty at the aerodrome, and we heard the plane circling long before she came into view. When the door was opened three huge Air Force Officers emerged and came over towards us. The local Commander called out, 'Commandant Blaauw, let me introduce you to Professor Smith,' and a powerfully built man of about thirty, in whose strong face shone piercing eyes, came up with hand outstretched. To his conventional greeting I answered, 'I bet when you joined the South African Air Force you never expected to command a plane sent to fetch a dead fish.' His face opened a bit at that, and his brief reply left no doubt that he felt that way. He was clearly a powerful personality, and I soon learnt from the others that he was an ace pilot from Korea, one of our best. They were all covertly scanning me closely; what was in this skinny little fellow to get a Prime Minister to send a special plane to look for a fish? I thought again of my Brigadier in Pretoria. I judged Blaauw a tough who would fight to the very end, a wonderful ally, but a dangerous enemy, even as a prisoner he would be a danger and need special care.

They asked if I was ready, I said yes I was, but were they? This startled them, but after a second's thought they said they were. I asked what food they had? They said iron rations, standard on the plane, nothing else, they would not need any. I asked how they knew that, and they said they were confident that those would be all that were necessary. I smiled inwardly, though with what I had brought, plus those iron rations, I felt there would be enough for emergencies, so left it at that. Then I asked how much water was aboard, and was told about three gallons, in the lavatory. Why? I asked if they knew tropical East Africa, and without waiting for any answer went on to say that if all went well that would do, but if we had an accident I certainly did not want to fight six men bigger than myself for water; we must have more. Was there any portable tank at the aerodrome? How big? At least five gallons. No! But they had some at the Sunderland base. I asked if we could have two and how long it would take to fetch them?

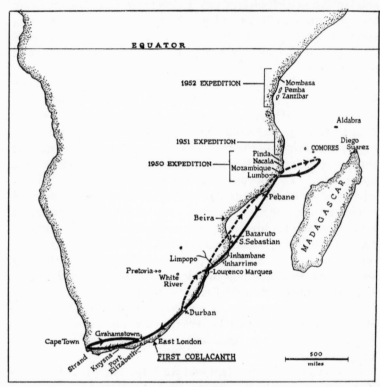

FIG. 4.—Map showing flight of Dakota.

Forty minutes! I refused to leave without that water, and as this flight was for my needs, they did not question this decision and sent a car racing away. That water was never used, and I must record that none of them ever crowed over me on that account. It was not all lost time, for the refueller at the aerodrome gave trouble and needed attention. I thought how everything has its points, even what might seem a disaster at the moment often turns out for the best.

We got away at 7.10 a.m. It was my first experience of a military aircraft. The hull was unlined and she certainly was noisy and not exactly luxurious, while ventilation was provided by 3-inch holes in the sides.

As soon as we had settled on an even keel I went forward and got the names and titles and functions of the crew. They were:

Commandant	. .	J. P. D. Blaauw
Captain	. .	P. Letley
Lieutenant	. .	W. J. Bergh
Lieutenant	. .	D. M. Ralston
Corporal .	. .	J. W. J. van Niekerk
Corporal .	. .	F. Brink

I asked the course, and was told that we should sleep at Lumbo that night, and go on to Diego Suarez on north Madagascar as early as possible next day. After that? They had been unable to find out if there was any hope of landing at the Comores. The South African Forces had made an air strip on Pamanzi during the war, but it was not known if the French had kept this going or whether a plane like this could land there at all. So even the immediate future was still dark and uncertain, just to add to the black cloud of uncertainty and dread that it might not be a Coelacanth after all. This terrible agony, my life blood, all this fuss and bother—just imagine if it proved to be a common fish. How the world would laugh, and even Dr. Malan would catch it from his opponents in Parliament. There was going to be nothing easy anywhere along the line, that was clear, but at any rate we were on the way at last, we were doing something. I was naturally strung to a high pitch of excitement, but spent the time on the way to Lourenço Marques getting to know these six men, fitting them into the categories every mature man has waiting ready-made. When they thought me unaware, which I never am, they studied me with curiosity and interest, nobody saying very much.

Lourenço Marques ahead. Letley grimaced and gestured to a safety-belt, so I returned to the hold and sat down.

As the doors opened I shot out—hot all right, just think of the Comores! A minor airport official ran out and embraced me effusively—at this tense time my response was not very cordial, and I had seen in the hall the South African Vice-Consul Phillip, who now came out to meet me; the Consul, who had suddenly been recalled to the Union, had sent his regrets and regards, and his Deputy would provide or attend to any needs. Then to my great joy I saw my old friends Comandante Correia de Barros, the Governor-General's right-hand man, and his lovely wife, Senhora Donna Maria Emilia. Phillip had kindly told them I was expected and they had been waiting for an hour, and he one of the busiest men in the world. It was one of the brightest spots in that flight. Then there were greetings from various airport officials, all old acquaintances, who had stood aside until Barros and his wife had greeted me. On the way from Durban I had written a brief account of events in Portuguese, and now sent this to *Noticias*, the Mozambique paper of Lourenço Marques, the staff of which are old friends. I had taken the precaution of having a good supply of Mozambique currency, and soon had the crew filling up on hot coffee, soft drinks, and food. Even apart from our own sense of urgency we did not have to stay long, for the machine was refuelled and all formalities completed in rapid time. Anyone who has ideas that the Portuguese are lackadaisical should speak to airmen or to ships' officers, who will soon disabuse that notion. In all the years I have worked in Mozambique, not a boat or a car or a plane provided by the authorities has ever been late, not one. On this occasion everything was laid on with unusual speed, partly because it was by Government orders and partly as an extra bit for me. We heard later that the Portuguese made no charge for any of the services rendered on this whole flight.

Off we went again straight away north, over the land, on a bee-line for Bazaruto, Inhambane far on the starboard side. In the plane we were now less like stilt-legged dogs walking cautiously around and sniffing one another. At the level of Beira I opened my packages and gave each man a small feed consisting of litchis, biscuits, dried figs, and cheese. Eating together loosens reserve, and there was now less tension and even occasional smiles from the crew. I asked Blaauw if I might light my small primus to make coffee for everyone, but he was plainly shocked to the core. It was against all regulations. I told him I had often lit that very stove in a hold full of T.N.T. without any concern, and would do it in that metal hull and guarantee no danger. After all, man, I pointed out, after all I had been through I wanted to get that Coelacanth. But he would have none of it even when I pointed to matches and lighted cigarettes. I could not help smiling, I knew what I was about. I have sat with that stove alight between my knees, balancing it and atop as well a pot of water, in the well of a madly rolling and pitching boat, surrounded by petrol, paraffin, and explosives, and had no fear. Of all the wonderful things of today I rank a primus stove very high, for without it much of our tropical work would be virtually impossible. It is as wonderful as the fact that boiling water kills amoeba and bacteria. Have you ever thought what life would be like if it did not? Anyway, despite my musings we all did without coffee.

I was back in my seat, tensed and taut, when Blaauw came to me and said with a grin, 'This trip is going to make you rich. A radio message has just come to say that the Council for Scientific Research are giving you an award of five hundred pounds.' I could not help smiling at this layman's view and shouted, 'No, my lad, no riches for me. I asked them for this for expenses, to pay for the Coelacanth and other etceteras.' Good old P. J. du Toit, he had acted quickly and well, and I had no doubt that this would be another tasty item for the press.

I told Blaauw and Letley that it might prove not to be a Coelacanth at all, I had gone on Hunt's briefest words. This shook them, and they whistled in astonishment and some alarm. It was impossible to tell them all that lay behind this. They told me that the plane cost about £40 per hour in flight, so even if it were a Coelacanth I calculated it was going to cost at least £20 per pound landed in South Africa, if it ever was. A costly fish indeed, in more ways than one. No commercial fishing this! They wanted to know if I had told the Prime Minister that there was a degree of uncertainty. I said of course, but I had told him that I was prepared to stake my name and reputation on this venture so as not to risk losing this fish if it really was a Coelacanth. They were obviously surprised, but made no further comment, probably because it would have been difficult to express their thoughts politely, but it also made them realise how much greater was the strain it imposed on me.

These men were patently all so capable that I hesitated to interfere in any plans, but I had to come in, for my knowledge and my needs were both important, and must play their part.

There are few who know that whole area as well as I and few with my experience of tropical East African shores. Besides, I was far from happy about going to Madagascar without first trying for a nearer goal. I do not believe in dodging trouble, and those who know me say I often provoke it to shorten a crisis, and that may be true; but to go to Madagascar when it might not be necessary might well set in train a series of increasingly difficult complications and situations that could easily get out of hand for both sides. I could not help feeling that for this South African military plane on this particular errand to land at Diego Suarez might well irritate the scarcely healed wound caused by the forcible seizure of Madagascar during the war, in which South Africa had played so great a part. There would be officials and others there who had not forgotten, and it would not help that that whole affair merely followed the pattern of the British action at Oran. I did not say this directly, but stressed that we all wanted to get back as soon as possible and sometimes there are unexpected delays at headquarters. I soon sensed that on this matter Blaauw and I saw eye to eye, and I suspected that he probably realised the possible effect of that war-time seizure of Madagascar on this affair as clearly as myself. I pointed out that it was worth a bit of a risk to avoid the certain delay that would ensue if I had to make a voyage by boat from Madagascar to the Comores and back. But even if we had to go to Madagascar, I felt it would be better to fly over the Comores, at least to see Mayotte, and if there was no information, we might just look at that airstrip ourselves. Could we not judge its possibilities by flying low down? Screwed-up faces without words were not encouraging, but I was convinced that this would be the soundest policy and said so, firmly.

By the time the island of Mozambique came into view opinion in the plane had veered definitely north of east—if you look at the map you will see why.

In my own mind I felt no ethical uneasiness about going for this fish, rather the reverse, for even though this Coelacanth had been found in French waters, it was mine by every right. Even though I hoped that there would be no opposition, if it came to a matter of establishing that right in the face of official obstruction, while seven South Africans at Diego Suarez might set feelings running high, at Dzaoudzi they would not have that effect. I did not wish to have to point out to the French that this fish had been under their very noses all the time, and they had not known about it. They had had my leaflets, piles of them, for years, and it seemed to be scarcely possible that they had used them to the best advantage. Indeed, from what I learnt later it seemed that my idea had been decried there as elsewhere. This mad South African! A Coelacanth here, preposterous! But old man Coelacanth would have enjoyed the joke.

I went to the hold and tried to rest—what did tomorrow hold? Where time had slipped by before, now it was oozing past with incredible tardiness. I looked out—Mofamede Island near Pebane—phew! that had been a narrow shave, my mind slipped back. . . . We were at Pebane on one of our trips, and went out from the river in a small and ancient tug to work at Mofamede, a tiny island with a large reef, some miles out. We got some fine stuff from the banks at low tide. . . . Then we went bombing out among the coral heads on the seaward side. Quite a strong wind was blowing and the surf was breaking heavily on the jagged reef. Our bombs brought up very fine stuff, fishes of all kinds, many that none of the crew had ever seen before. They all became very excited, for fish is scarce in Pebane, and many big ones came up that day, which the wind and waves drove towards the reef and we had to go close in to collect them. While I was directing operations at the stern, the man at the wheel forgot all else watching fish being netted at the sides. Suddenly my sixth sense made me look up, and I found we were virtually on the reef. It was an awful moment. I dashed forward, knocked the cox aside, took the wheel, shouted 'A ré!' [astern], and held on. It was a matter of inches, waves and wind driving us on, and a slipping reverse gear barely able to withstand them, let alone take us back. It was one of the nearest shaves we have ever had. The surf was terrible and that jagged coral nearly a mile from the island would have cut us to pieces. . . . I went on dreaming. A place of ill-omen, Pebane. Once in a coaster, as we were on the way in at early dawn, I sat watching my wife writhing in agony with acute food poisoning—she was very near death. The sea was rough, the bar shallow, and we bumped and bumped again, and a huge wave turned the vessel so far over on her side that I held my breath. I could still hear the crashes before she righted herself. What a morning that was! . . .

Ralston's head appeared; 'Mozambique,' he yelled. I shot up, and there was the beloved isle, built on the blood and bones of the flower of Portugal. Our wing-tip was near the palms as we banked; Lumbo, 3.30 p.m. As I came out, phew, a blast from an oven wasn't in it, and think of the Comores. . . . There were effusive greetings from the Airport Supervisor, other officials, and the hotel manager. I tackled them at once. Did they know anything about landing on the Comores? No, a complete blank. So I telephoned the Chief of the Radio Station at Lumbo, but he also knew nothing. I asked him to try to make contact with the Comores, but he said it was Sunday, it was impossible. I replied that nothing was impossible really, would he try? Well, he would; but soon after he telephoned to report a complete blank, they would not open till next morning. Shortly afterwards there was a roar and an East African Airways plane from Nairobi touched down. We tackled them, did they know anything about Comoran landing, the possibility of landing anywhere on the Comores? But they knew nothing. We may have looked a mixed and tough lot, but they were restrained and apparently incurious. It was true that we had not been introduced.

I found out that none of our crew had ever been to the island of Mozambique, so by radio telephone I spoke to the Port Captain at the island, five miles across the bay from Lumbo, and asked him to send us a launch. We went to the hotel and had refreshments, and then to the wharf where the launch was waiting. Some of its native crew had been with us on our expeditions, and there were excited greetings for the 'Patrao', and of course as usual he had cigarettes. They shyly gave their news, and I learnt that Salimo's wife's brother had been eaten by a lion. While the airmen went to have a hasty look round the island, I spent a short time with the Port Captain and his family, and gave them a brief outline of what it was all about, the children more interested in some chocolate slabs from my pocket. Then we went back across the bay, a lovely cool trip in the gentle northerly breeze, the stars twinkling.

Dinner as usual was astonishingly good in such a remote place. Iced beer cooled the thirsty crew, Blaauw watching each man's single bottle. The hotel manager whispered quietly in my ear, 'I have the coolest room for the Professor.' I asked Blaauw for a take-off at 4 a.m. There was a general groan, and after a bit of a skirmish we fixed for 4.30, coffee at 3.30 a.m., the cars at 3.45 a.m. Some of them grinned. Would the Portuguese make it? I offered to bet them it would all be on time, as indeed it was—to the minute.

If my room was the coolest, heaven help the others, and if it was like this here, what about that fish at the Comores? I lay and sweated and tossed but could not sleep; for though I had pills with me, I use them as seldom as possible, never when my mind must be at full stretch. At 1 a.m. I got up and smiled as I lit my primus, thinking of Blaauw. I made coffee and almost took him a cup. Once again I tried to sleep, but my mind was too active, so at 2.30 I got up, took my torch, and went to have a look round. I envied the native servants, who were as usual soundly asleep all over the place; indeed, you have to step over them. The night before I had noticed some pineapples in the kitchen, and went to explore the possibilities of the pantry. There were some nice pineapples, bananas, and papaws. I packed a selection in a carton and took them to my room, leaving my card stuck in the brush of one of the remaining pineapples. The owner-manager would smile, for he was an old friend.

At 3.15 a.m., just to be sure, I went round. They were all up, all had coffee, none were effusive.

Lions are not uncommon about Lumbo, and they sometimes ramble round the airport at night; and though for the sake of the crew I hoped we might see one, none were about that morning. It was hot even at that time. Phew! think of the Comores.

We took off at 4.30 to the second.

Chapter Thirteen

DZAOUDZI DRAMA

IT was an impressive dawn whose breathtaking beauty only served to emphasise the threat that lay behind its tumbled masses of red-tinted clouds. This was the cyclone season in one of the worst zones in the world, and if one caught us out over that sea, Coelacanths or anything else would not matter any more. As we took off we plunged straight at tier upon tier of gigantic columns that reached up into misty heights, giving the impression that we were approaching an enormous and fantastic tinted marble temple of ever-changing aspect and form. The clouds looked so solid I found myself tensing up each time we plunged into a whirling face, half expecting the plane to be crushed flat. We climbed steadily and I had repeatedly to clear my ears, but could not take my eyes from the wonderful scene that lay before and about us. Never before had I seen such spectacular cloud effects, their size and grandeur were almost beyond description. A tap on my shoulder made me jump, and there was Ralston holding a type of bulging greyish overall. 'It's going to be very cold up here, sir; you'd better get into this Mae West'; which was something new to me, a thick padded overall suit, at which I looked dubiously. 'You float in this,' he added with a grin. That made me think at once of Tiger Sharks; floating in that sea wasn't much use, it just prolonged the end. Twenty minutes on the average was all you had with those brutes about, but Ralston knew nothing about that; yes, and I hoped he would not need to learn, certainly not in my company. He helped me get it on, and it certainly was comfortable, for we had gone up fairly high and it was bitterly cold, the occasional brilliant sunshine deceptive.

I came back to the present and went forward to Blaauw and Letley. Our course was straight for Mayotte. It had been agreed that we should keep on trying to get Dzaoudzi by radio to know if we could land, but so far there had been no response, though

Bergh and the operator van Niekerk were at it all the time. I could see the regular and repeated movement of van Niekerk's arm as he sat hunched over the table in the tiny cubicle.

I went back to the hold and got out my supplies. First I took each man a kind of fruit salad of my Lumbo-foraged pineapple, papaw, and banana, sprinkled with sugar and dried milk. They looked at this with astonishment, and Blaauw at least cocked a speculative eye at me, but nobody asked any questions. Then I gave them a round of biscuits and cheese, and in a loud voice so that all, especially Blaauw, could hear, pictured the delights hot coffee would have added. Blaauw sat like a rock without moving a muscle, but Letley flashed me a quick impish grin.

All this time my brain was buzzing like a machine round the main themes of whether we should be able to land and was it a Coelacanth? As the time grew nearer, I became more and more tortured by doubts and fears. Had I not been an incredible fool to trust a layman's opinion? Hunt had the pictures and all the information we could give him, but those not expert can easily be mistaken, as we know from hundreds of experiences. The situation was typical of most of my life, either hell or heaven, seldom anywhere between. When I asked my wife to marry me, I said I did not know if I could bring her happiness, but I could at least promise that she would never be bored; and she has eased many a tight corner by reminding me of this with a smile, often a very grim one.

Here it was again. Could anything be more ridiculous? In my maturity I had staked virtually my whole life on the identity of a fish I had not seen; but I tried to push these doubts and fears away, for there was nothing to be done until I got to the fish itself, and that was the present problem. Could we land at Pamanzi? Bergh must have got weary of shaking his head in response to the question on my face that there was no need for my lips to utter.

Cyclones were never far from my thoughts. I asked Blaauw what hope we should have if one came on. He said that in the air we might manage as long as we had fuel enough to get up and out of range and reach some safe landing; the greater danger lay in being caught on the ground. Surely the plane could be anchored, I suggested; but they said it just did not work, time and again it had been tried but the wind always won. As the wind

increased so the anchored planes would first rise from the
ground and 'fly', held up by the wind, but when it became really
strong the machines were doomed, they were torn and smashed.
Well, there were so many worries and anxieties and uncertainties
in all this that another didn't matter very much. Compared with
this, walking in the dark in a jungle full of wild beasts was just
nothing; for I had done it, so I knew. We could not do anything
but just go on. We hardly spoke, everyone was tensed up, this was
a most critical time for us all. My eyes alternated between the
piled-up clouds ahead and that ominous elbow whose hand plied
the key. Again and again it went, and my hope and disappointment
rose and sank in steady succession like the waves that lay so far
below. Suddenly Letley pointed ahead, to what appeared no more
than another dense cloud; but my vision is no longer young and
I screwed my eyes. 'Mayotte,' he said, and my heart turned right
over. So it was there, somewhere there that this fish lay, this fish
in whose identity much of my life might be buried. Suddenly the
blurred mass turned into a cloud-topped island. Surely now we
were so near we should get a reply to our constant battery of sig-
nals; but still nothing came.

We were diving down at a steep angle when the clouds parted
and drifted aside, giving a clear picture of steep rolling hills and
conical peaks whose densely tree-clad slopes rose almost abruptly
from the sea. There was obviously little or no flat country here.
Could we ever land? We passed at about 3,000 feet over the extensive barrier reef that lies west of Mayotte. It was a marvellous
sight, a multi-coloured riot of blues and greens, which for some
moments diverted my thoughts. What a place for a fish, a maze of
channels and water of all depths, with clearly abundant coral, and
even at that height it was possible to see plainly many shoals of
fish of all sizes. Whatever the outcome of the Coelacanth, this was
a place where we ought to work, for if a fish as large as the Coelacanth had been there all this time unknown, what other treasures
might not be hidden there as well? We must come some time, and
I was already planning to this end when my thoughts were shattered by a shout from Bergh, who said 'O.K.', and first jerked his
hand, thumb up and then down. I suddenly felt queer and shaky.
We were actually going to land. By this time we were circling to
lose height and had a panoramic view of the whole island, and

although it was misty and hazy I took a number of photographs through the small air-holes. We saw Pamanzi and the houses of Dzaoudzi and a small lake, and had a passing glimpse of a tiny toy vessel close to the wharf that something told me was Hunt's. My heart was pounding madly, and they had almost to force me to sit down and tie myself in. I had seen the air-strip. It certainly was small and looked rough, a rounded bit of the island sticking out to the south, obviously not long ago it had been a coral reef under the sea, for it was almost at sea-level now. The waves had showed a north-easter of force less than two; we had to land from the sea and in front was a high hill.

Bump, bump, bump! It was a wonderful landing on that rough surface, but the instant we came to a stop the heavens opened and the rain just poured down in torrents. Everything was blotted out and visibility reduced to a few yards. The roof of the plane leaked like a sieve, and I had to rush round to get my sleeping-bag and papers to dry spots. I was curiously indignant about this, as I hate leaky roofs; but idiotically I also felt a sudden splash of comfort, for it was as if this was a last effort of fate to try to keep me back from the true end and reality, and I had a queer flash of hope.

The rain stopped as abruptly as if turned off by a tap, the mist parted and figures came running across the flattened coral rag. The door opened and through a blast of hot air I saw Hunt's face looking up at me. For a moment I just could not speak; then with a rush of pent-up emotion the words 'Where's the fish?' burst from my lips like an explosion. With extraordinary intuition Hunt replied, 'Don't worry, it's a Coelacanth all right'; and this had a strangely soothing effect on me, but I was still in a fever. I found myself on the ground, various French officials were introduced to me; but I saw hardly anything, I wanted to see that fish. 'It is on my boat,' said Hunt, and that at least was a terrific relief, for it meant that even in French waters, on Hunt's boat it was not strictly in French territory and technically at least it would be less like taking it from the French. At the same time this was my Coelacanth (if it was one) by every right, and in my almost insane obsession at that moment I knew that those six South Africans who were with me would be prepared to stand by me in support of that right if it became necessary.

I checked that I had my camera and the necessary accessories, and we moved over to the small house on the edge of the field

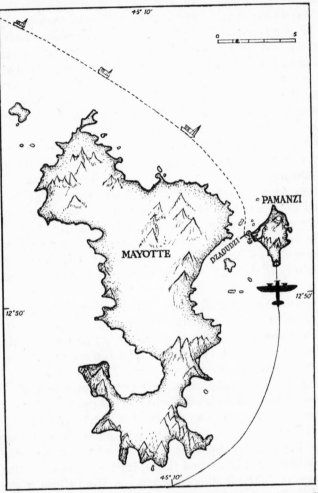

Fig. 5.—The islands of Mayotte and Pamanzi, Comores, showing small projection where the Dakota landed.

where a few cars were parked. 'Where is your boat?' I asked Hunt. 'At the quay,' he said, 'but we shall have to go first to the Governor's house, as he is waiting to meet you. We'll just have to do that,' he added quickly when he saw my reaction. 'For my sake, at least

It won't take long.' I have often suffered from the necessity of paying tribute to officialdom, but this was probably the hardest I have ever endured. It was agony and torture, and I raged inwardly, my mind a searing flame. Blast these formalities! I had not endured all I had been through or come so far to exchange polite words with a Governor at that critical moment. I wanted only one thing, and that was to see that fish, to know if I was a fool or a prophet. But civilisation won, the flames in my mind subsided, and I became *homo sapiens* again. We passed houses and trees and a curved drive, pulled up below a tall, two-storied wooden residence, walked up steep sun-drenched steps, through the front verandah, and into the relative gloom of a large shady room, where dim human figures were waiting. I was formally introduced to the Governor and his lady, and through one of his suite who spoke English I presented our crew. My French is satisfactory for scientific use, but I have little conversation. Most Portuguese speak French, so I wondered if the Governor might perhaps know Portuguese, not very good reasoning I know, but I tried it on him and he did not understand. I thought it better not to try German; so we used Hunt and the official.

They drew our attention to a big table along one end of the room that I now saw was laden with bottles and dainties of all kinds. We were directed towards this, but I could endure no more, and said politely but firmly that while we were more than grateful to His Excellency for all his courtesy and hospitality, I had endured much and come far and wished first to inspect the fish. Would he kindly permit us to return so that we could all the better enjoy his bounteous hospitality a little later, we should not be long? There was a flutter, but my face showed that I was going, so all of us went, the Governor as well, but not Madame. It was only a moment in the car and there below the concrete wall was Hunt's schooner. The place was jammed with idling natives, who delayed our passage down the steps. (See Frontispiece.) Hunt pointed to a large coffin-like box near the mast, and I knew it must be in there. They picked up the box and put it on the hatch-cover, just in front of me, a foot above the deck, and Hunt pulled away the lid. I saw a sea of cotton-wool, the fish was covered by it. My whole life welled up in a terrible flood of fear and agony, and I could not speak or move. They all stood staring at me, but

I could not bring myself to touch it; and, after standing as if stricken, motioned to them to open it, when Hunt and a sailor jumped as if electrified and peeled away that enveloping white shroud.

God, yes! It was true! I saw first the unmistakable tubercles on the large scales, then the bones of the head, the spiny fins. It was true! Malan would not suffer for his action, thank God for that! It was a Coelacanth all right. I knelt down on the deck so as to get a closer view, and as I caressed that fish I found tears splashing on my hands and realised that I was weeping, and was quite without shame. Fourteen of the best years of my life had gone in this search and it was true; it was really true. It had come at last.

Suddenly my mind cleared. Time was passing. Blaauw had told me that we must leave as soon as possible, for in his opinion if the weather shut down we might not be able to get away at all, and I could not but agree with him. I knew those seas. This was something that must go round the world like a tidal wave, and I must work quickly and efficiently. I got them to get the fish out of the box, posed us all and took several photographs. Then I spent about five minutes in rapid inspection of the fish; which was not easy, as my excitement was naturally intense, the sudden release of fear and strain was almost more than the human system could endure. It was certainly staggering to find no first dorsal fin and no extra little tail such as all Coelacanths have had; but it was a Coelacanth. It was probably different, probably a different genus and species from my East London fish, but still a Coelacanth. I must name it quickly—no more risks like the last one. Malan, yes certainly first Malan, genus *Malania* sounded good. *Malania hunti* seemed to be clearly indicated, since each had played so prominent a part in the final act of this long drama. I told them to pack it away. Hunt had been talking animatedly to my airmen, and he now invited Blaauw and myself to his cabin. He produced a bottle of whisky to toast the occasion, and Blaauw who would probably have liked more, took the minimum for politeness, while I put a drop in my water to be matey. I wanted information and kept up such a rapid running fire of questions to Hunt, asking him to answer quickly, that Blaauw, solid as he was, just faded away. Hunt has a keen brain, and it was not long before I had the main outlines of the story from his end. The Governor had several times looked into the cabin, but we did not see him, and Blaauw returned twice to say that we must get off as soon as possible. The clouds were certainly low and threatening, and there was rain at intervals.

I told Hunt that I should be giving this animal a scientific name, and that I proposed *Malania hunti*, the latter to honour him for his important part. He asked if I could not somehow bring in the French, as his relations with them were important, his living depended on that. I said the only way would be for him to drop out, when we might call it *Malania comoroae* or *anjouanae*; and after discussion he said that while it would be very flattering to have his name figured that way, could it be *Malania anjouanae*; to which I agreed only with reluctance and only because he was quite emphatic that he preferred it.

It was clear even then, and it became much more so later, that Hunt was in a difficult position: and in view of all he had done I was prepared to go as far as possible to alleviate this and to aid him. I told him that I was prepared to continue the offer of a reward of £100 for another Coelacanth, through him as my agent; and that if he got another in their waters that way, it was to be offered to the French. I intended to say this to the Governor before I left. Hunt was very appreciative of this suggestion, which he thought would go far to smooth any ruffled pride or hurt feelings.

It was only about 500 yards to the Governor's residence, and I elected to walk as I wanted some photographs. The precious coffin was put on a lorry and Hunt arranged that it would be taken direct to the air-strip to await us there. I hated to let it out of my sight, but felt they knew I would kill anyone who tried any tricks.

At the top of the steps I turned and took one more long look at Hunt's trim schooner, which had played its part, an important part, in this fascinating story. It was his home and his life; he obviously kept it trim and neat and cleaner than most such craft are. I had a queer feeling that had he lived in earlier times Hunt would also have lived on the sea, but he would probably have been an explorer rather than a trader. He and Blaauw had 'clicked' at once, and Blaauw told me, almost wistfully, that he would not mind a voyage with Hunt. I wondered, for I know what it is like to live in a small boat in the tropics, but there would have been something natural in their association. They would make a formidable pair at any time, and in earlier centuries would probably have made history of their own. I looked hard at that schooner, not suspecting that I should never see it again: for a bare two weeks later they were caught in a cyclone and the boat was destroyed and sunk. Our plane did not escape by much. Did Coelacanths bring destruction in their train? I remembered that Goosen's trawler *Aristea* that had caught *Latimeria* was wrecked and destroyed not long afterwards.

I looked about me. Pamanzi is only a tiny island separated by a narrow strait from Mayotte, which is much larger, mostly hills and mountains. I saw canoes and lines and nets, and asked about fish supply. Shoulders were shrugged, and screwed-up faces with few words told their tale. Yes, there was fish, but not much, not nearly enough; the natives were not very industrious fishermen, they got some but were satisfied with very little. During the war there had been plenty, hand-grenades and depth-charges did better than lines, and sometimes brought up a whole shoal. There was little fish close in, those who went out to the big reef did better; but often when they got in the fish was too far gone for European taste.

I told them how impressed I had been by the large reef I had seen from the plane on our way in, and Hunt said he had done some goggling there, and that he had never seen so many fish anywhere, nor so many kinds; the reef was far richer than any about Zanzibar, for example. I said that I was contemplating returning to work on the fishes.

The Governor was enthusiastic. I would be welcome; he had no children there; I could have half his house; they would be delighted. I was touched by this offer, and I got the interpreter to explain how overwhelmed I was at his generosity, but that we could never dream of imposing so uncomfortable a situation on him, as our lives were of course governed by the tides and we were up and about and out at all hours. We had to live by ourselves; was there any other house available? Oh yes, that could be arranged; anything I wanted that was possible would be granted. I found out about the rainfall, the winds, available food supplies, vehicles, and boats. French waters were a big gap in our studies of the fishes of the western Indian Ocean, and I made full use of this opportunity to learn all I could for our work.

The soil was clearly good, and with abundant rain the growth was everywhere luxuriant. I knew there was malaria, dysentery, and hookworm, and other tropical plagues. The houses were not netted in like those of the Portuguese, and the natives were plainly lethargic. The Governor said that this was due not only to climate and disease, but the natural indolence of the natives was much increased by the ever-present cyclones. It was almost impossible to get them to construct decent houses or to carry out long-term planting of palms and trees, when a cyclone could destroy the work of years in a few moments. One result was that whereas fruit in such a clime should be most abundant, the supply was in reality not very good and at times there was little. He indeed spoke prophetically, for only two weeks later a cyclone hit Dzaoudzi and the devastation was terrible.

On the way up they showed me with pride one of my Coelacanth leaflets (Plate 3), with the write-up in English, Portuguese, and French, and the picture, prominently displayed on the public noticeboard of what looked like the equivalent of a magistrate's office. Hunt proved unexpectedly coy about being photographed in its company.

We got back to the Residence. This time I saw it properly, a typical French colonial structure, very high for coolness and shade. Apart from the inconvenience of sharing with others, I would not have cared to live in it; certainly not in the top storey, for anything, for it was all wood and a tinder-box. The furniture was lovely, and there were many antiques and curios. They put us to table, and there were speeches and toasts. A bottle of very precious old brandy of a famous vintage was opened for this occasion, and it was hard to endure their disappointment that I had less than a teaspoonful, while Blaauw's stern eye on his crew reduced them to tasters rather than participants. There was ample wine as well, but no takers on our side. I had coffee. The crew had none of my inner infirmities or restrictions about food, and their inroads on the dainties concealed a good part of my deficiencies, though Madame was concerned at my lack of appetite. Right in front of me was a schoolboy's dream, an enormous cake spread with sticky chocolate icing, the mere sight of which made my liver throb. I had not yet eaten anything that day, but could not risk any upset now, not even for the sake of policy or politeness. Although Blaauw shot several short warnings about time across to me in Afrikaans, he had no need to speak, I was as anxious as he to go. The younger members of the crew were enchanted by the place, and would have rejoiced at any, even enforced, stay; but it would have been criminal folly to delay. I had got from these friendly people as much information as could be contrived in less than a stay of days, so as soon as politeness permitted I rose and said we must unfortunately tear ourselves away, and, speaking very slowly, expressed my gratitude to His Excellency for his very kind assistance and co-operation in this matter, which I appreciated very greatly, as I most sincerely did. I appreciated only too well that he was in some ways in a difficult situation, and he had handled it most gracefully. Because of that I went on to say that I would never have come for this fish had I not felt it was mine, because it had been found as a result of my search. Even though I was so interested in Coelacanths, I would not have lifted a finger to fetch one that had come as a result of efforts of someone else. But this one, I told the Governor with a smile, and asked the official to translate carefully, if this one had been found on the steps of your Residency, sir, I would have come for it, for it is mine. However, because you have all been so kind I have asked Captain Hunt to act as my agent here, and he is authorised to offer a further £100 as a reward for another fish, and the very next one he obtains that way in French waters will be given to you as the representative of your nation. It was clear that this was greatly appreciated by them all.

We parted with cordial adieux from the Governor and his lady, with hopes of return at no distant date. I got all their names and titles and occupations. There was still one more thing to do, and I sent off brief cables to my wife, to Dr. Malan, and to the President of the Council for Scientific and Industrial Research, to say that it was a true Coelacanth.

Then we hurried off to the air-strip. The box? Yes, there it was, safe in the lorry in the shade, and soon it was in the Dakota, where I opened the lid and looked inside as well, just to be sure. We had spent barely three hours on Pamanzi, and yet it seemed almost an age. It had been one of the most critical periods of my life; but this whole affair had been just one crisis after another.

It was in many ways really a kind of nightmare, and though I kept on telling myself 'It is true; it is true', my inner self was like an obstinate animal that would keep on stupidly turning back towards the doubts and fears that had torn and tortured me all through those long days and nights.

I took Hunt aboard and paid him the £200 E.A. I had; £100 for the reward to the native and the rest to cover his own expenses. In the few hours before leaving Durban I had got friends to get me as many as possible of the newspapers that covered the affair, as I knew Hunt would value them. I now gave the bundle to him, and they clearly were a treasure.

I reflected that not only he but all these people had shared an event of which they would be able to talk with profit, or at least I hoped so, all their lives.

Chapter Fourteen

UP IN THE CLOUDS

I LOOKED again to make quite sure. Yes, the box was really there. So Hunt and I got out and, lining everyone up against the plane, had several photographs taken. We said our last adieux to all those present and climbed aboard, the doors were shut and the motors started. I got into that 'Mae West' suit.

I looked hard at the air-strip, as I had seen Blaauw doing several times before we got aboard. It was short, all too short, and the little wind of the early north-west monsoon came directly over the not inconsiderable hill whose steep southerly slopes marked its northern end. We must take off running straight at that hill, and I did not see how a plane of this size could hope to achieve sufficient elevation in so short a distance. However, I was no pilot and Blaauw clearly was one of the very best; so I strapped myself in and reflected that if we did hit the hill it would be over very quickly. It would certainly be a spectacular way to die, and, anyway, I had seen the Coelacanth.

10 a.m. on Monday, 29th December 1952. The engines roared in their test, slowed down, and suddenly we were off in a tearing rush of sound. I found myself gripping the seat and staring through the small air-hole. We left the ground and suddenly the sea and the slopes of the hill tilted so sharply that I caught my breath. Blaauw was banking steeply and the wing-tip was so near the trees I expected it to hit all the time; but we were safely away, and by screwing my eyes I could see the last of the tiny figures on the edge of the strip. One stood out in front waving. I assumed it was Hunt, and hoped that he would not be left to face unexpected repercussions, though he seemed to be very much at home and at ease among the people there. We went westwards and up, up, up, into the towering cumulus clouds whose marbled summits Blaauw estimated to reach up to at least 30,000 feet. They certainly were awe-inspiring and disquieting, great tumbled mountains of

dense whirling vapour with little clear air between, white and grey and black, some with electric storms inside their piled-up masses, so that they were at intervals lit up in sections by concealed discharges. We plunged into almost solid-looking clouds, inside which it was almost dark; then out again into narrow shafts of brilliant sunshine, sudden transitions which were as vivid as the intermittent flashing of a floodlight in a darkened room. We were so high that it got very cold, and I felt it even through my 'Mae West'.

At about 15,000 feet we steadied down. At that height and in such conditions navigation was to some extent guesswork, for there was obviously wind but no means of estimating either force or direction. I could not rest, for the weather looked very bad, and all the crowded events of the recent past hours had keyed me to a pitch of intense excitement; it was almost an intoxication. I went to the cockpit and stood behind the two pilots, who wore earphones. Suddenly Letley made some signs to Blaauw, and started to write down a message, which he showed to Blaauw, who flashed a quick glance at me and then read it again. Letley handed me the slip, and on it I saw: 'Managed to intercept a message stating that a squadron of French fighter planes left Diego Suarez before we took off from Dzaoudzi with orders to intercept us and to compel us to turn back to Madagascar.' My heart missed a beat. The two pilots were staring intently at me, while I did some rapid calculations in my head. 'What speed can they do?' I asked. 'Don't know exactly,' said Letley. 'But they are very much faster than we are.' 'Do you think it possible for them to overhaul us before we get to Lumbo?' I asked. Letley nodded. We were in a clear patch at that time, running between a series of piled-up mountains of cloud, with occasional glimpses of the sea, and where I had disliked those clouds before now there could not be too many for my liking. My mind was racing. 'Any hope of escaping in a cloud?' I asked. 'Radar,' said Letley. 'Well,' I said, speaking slowly, 'I don't know how you chaps feel about this, but I'm not going back. I don't believe they would dare to shoot us down if we refused to turn, but I would be prepared to chance that rather than turn back.' Letley suddenly burst out laughing and Blaauw grinned. So deeply had I been engrossed in weighing every aspect of the situation that it was some seconds before it penetrated my mind that this was a hoax. I made no comment, I was not even angry, it was such a terrific relief, and I went inside, put my sleeping-bag on the icy floor near the box and tried to rest. My eyes would stray to that box. They would not have got me to turn back. This was my Coelacanth. I lay there, going over in my mind again all I had learnt, especially what Hunt had told me, and how it fitted into the background of my life and work all those long years in these parts. It is an amazing story.

In the western Indian Ocean, which embraces the East African coast, Madagascar, and other lesser islands, it is normal to find deep water close to land. There are only a few places where the bottom shelves gently from the shore, in most parts great cliffs beneath the sea plunge abruptly to the depths, and here the clear and lovely green or blue of the water changes to an ominous black. An echo-sounder chart from such parts is most interesting, for it shows the profile of the bottom of the ocean in miniature.

The coastal natives over most of that area have almost everywhere a seafaring and fishing tradition, often derived from the Arabs, whose southerly penetration in exploratory voyages commenced so long ago that its origin is lost in the remote past. Line-fishing of different kinds is common to them all, and partly because the water is too clear for fishing to be successful where it is shallow, in many parts they fish where the water is relatively deep, from 50 to 100 fathoms. With proper tackle and ample fish, the many problems of deep-line fishing can be overcome to make this a commercial possibility, but when you see the clumsy tackle used by most East African natives for this purpose you wonder how it pays; and it continues only because their economic level is so low, their catch per man per unit of time could never be competitive in any efficient civilised community in temperate climates. Those who fish in this way generally use a lump of coral the size of a man's head as a sinker. In some parts they go out with dozens of such lumps, and have a special knot so that when the sinker reaches the bottom or the desired depth a quick jerk shakes it loose from the line, which method at least saves hauling this extra weight several hundred feet to the top. Others find it less trouble to prepare only a few such sinkers, and use them all the time, hauling one laboriously all that way to the surface each time they need to pull up the line; but pulling up one fish and letting the line out again may take twenty minutes or more.

At that depth, 50 to 100 fathoms, the water is colder than at the top, and quite often the fishes down there are different from those commonly found in the surface layers. On parts of the Kenya coast, for example, natives who learnt the trick from visiting Japanese fishermen haul up from this deep, cooler water numbers of fish of kinds that it is astonishing to see in such tropical climes.

The people of the Comores have apparently always practised deep-line fishing. At least that is what you learn on inquiry, but one has to be cautious in accepting statements about the past from natives in those parts, since the average East African native has a much poorer sense of time than any European. Once a thing has happened it is past and done with, and we constantly found that it is exceedingly difficult to establish whether a past event had taken place last week, last month, or last year. In that area the Comores are almost unique in structure, for beneath the sea they apparently slope steeply and uniformly down, in many cases at an angle of 60 to 70 degrees, which is very steep indeed. As a result, there is deep water close to the shore, except only off part of Mayotte, where there is a large reef to the west. It is therefore possible to fish in quite deep water without going far from the shore, which is a great advantage, because it means that on the leeward side of the island such fishing can be carried out during even the windy seasons, which cover most of the year.

The Comoran natives are not distinguished by great energy; indeed, in that respect they fall below the average, already low, and they are not uniform in performance—those on Anjouan being considered the most progessive and energetic, while those on badly disease-ridden Mohilla are notoriously lethargic and hard to move. This is reflected in the proportion who will take the trouble to go fishing and in the time they give to it, so that it is not surprising that the Coelacanth story featured Anjouan, where the most energetic Comorans live.

In this deep-line fishing at the Comores they catch distinctive, well-known fishes, like certain large Rock Cods, some specialised species of the Snapper family, and the cosmopolitan 'Oil-fish' (*Ruvettus*), a rather elongate Snoek-like fish with peculiar scales. This fish is very oily and in some parts has an evil reputation, it being said that the oil is strongly purgative and even poisonous, and there are many records of ill-effects and even deaths following the consumption of its flesh. In other parts, however, as apparently in the Comores, it is a valued food fish and commonly eaten without harm. It is interesting to note that this fish is oily, for so is the Coelacanth, very oily.

By late December 1952, the leaflets that Hunt had taken in the previous October had, by orders of the Governor, been distributed to all the islands and by special runners about them, so that the more intelligent natives at least were aware, even if they could not believe, that the enormous sum of 50,000 Colonial francs would be paid for one special fish.

According to what has been told, some at least of the European officials read the leaflet with scepticism if not with amusement, and I was told that though a visiting scientific officer from Madagascar was shown the leaflets Hunt had brought (he may have seen them before on Madagascar), he attached so little importance to them that he apparently did not indicate anything special to the local authorities nor did he mention the matter on his return.

On the night of the 20th December a native, one Ahmed Hussein, of Domoni, a small village on the south-east coast of Anjouan, with another fisherman, went out in his canoe to fish. First they went to his palm-leaf-strip traps, close to the shore, from which they took small reef fishes that are used for bait. Then they went somewhat farther out, and let out their long lines. Hunt had heard that the depth was about 20 fathoms.*

In the night Hussein hooked a large fish, which he eventually subdued at the canoe by battering its head, a merciful way of killing a fish, but scientifically a shocking tragedy. Nobody seems to know if he caught anything else, but from what I gathered of the Comorans, one such large fish would have been more than enough to satisfy any of them, so they went back to shore and to bed.

* The French later gave this depth as considerably more; indeed, stating that they had been able to find the exact spot and take soundings, and they quoted the depth to a metre. This indicates work of unusual precision, for it would depend on the memory of a native to find the exact spot where he was when he hooked the Coelacanth, on a dark night in a drifting canoe without any anchor. With the bottom sloping as steeply as in this area, even a few yards out would make a considerable difference to the depth. However, a few fathoms more or less are not important. What is important is that where the Coelacanth was hooked was emphatically not any 'inaccessible depth' of the sea.

This is in many ways an immoral story, for what was bad proved good. Even in our colder climate I have taught my sons that when angling it is a crime not to clean any fish you have caught before taking it home, even if you get in cold, wet, and sleepy, and no matter what hour. Thank heaven, these Comorans had not had a training of that kind; for they apparently threw the fish down at

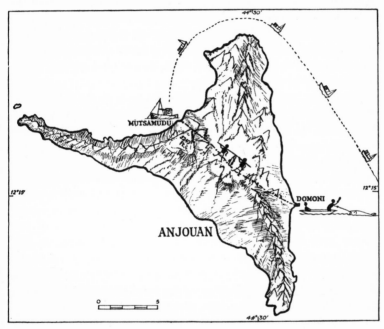

Fig. 6.—The island of Anjouan, Comores, formerly known as 'Johanna', showing where *Malania* was caught and position of Hunt's schooner.

Hussein's hut, just as it was, without scaling or gutting it, despite that oven-like climate.

Next morning Hussein took it to the local market for sale, and it was about to be cut up when a native who looked at it advised them not to do so because it looked like the fish on the leaflet, Hunt's paper.* While the French authorities did a tremendous amount, it is clear that Hunt was always hunting, so that the natives came to connect him with the fish. One could imagine the

* It later became apparent that this surprisingly intelligent behaviour on the part of the native was due to his being of a higher class, a trained teacher.

debate that ensued. The instructions on the leaflet were clear: 'Do not cut it or clean it or scale it, but take it at once to some responsible person'; and who more so than Hunt, whose schooner, by a miracle, was known, as natives do know such things, to be anchored at that moment at Mutsamudu on the other side of the island, about twenty-five miles away. But what a twenty-five miles, the path mostly through deep, densely bushed valleys and over high mountains.

It still remains in my mind as one of the most astonishing things of this whole story that anything could stir people like the Comoroans to the stage of even considering carrying that 90-lb. fish that terrific distance over such hard country in that blazing, tropical heat. That they actually came to do it shows the tremendous power of money. It was only a fabulous sum like 50,000 francs that could have got them to do it, but it would have been an achievement in even a temperate country, in any country. They did it. My blood ran cold when I heard the story, the uncleaned fish first in the close tropical night, and then that whole long day in such torrid heat. It is a miracle that it had not liquified in putrefaction long before it reached Hunt. It may be the preservative nature of its oil that saved it.

According to Hunt, when those men reached Mutsamudu they came straight to him, and he recognised the fish at once as a Coelacanth. It was already putrefying and he had no formalin; so he went posthaste to the office of the local doctor, but found he was away. Remembering Mrs. Smith's instructions, Hunt told his crew to cut it for salting, in a hurry, and unfortunately while he was getting the salt they cut it as they were accustomed to do in salting such fish, hacking it open along the back, through the body and head like a kipper. Next time you see a kipper, look at it. That is how my precious *Malania* was cut, but of course by Hunt's instructions the insides were left intact, most of them.

Hunt realised the full importance of this find, and wisely questioned the natives. Was this fish known to them? Oh yes, they knew it well, they were rare but caught regularly. They called them '*Kombessa*', and they were not much valued as food when fresh, but were good salted. When cooked fresh the flesh became soggy and jelly-like, and was not very good to eat; but they were eaten. They were nearly always caught with the Oil-

fish in the deeper water and on flesh bait, using Squid or any kind
of fish. They fought hard on a line, were difficult to kill, and some
were lost after being hooked and pulled up. Hunt found out
afterwards that a good many people there knew these curiously
rough scales, for they were used to roughen bicycle tubes in mend-
ing punctures. These fish were usually caught in cyclone time;
that is, towards the end of our year. Most of them were big fish,
more than 30 kilograms, some very big, but there was another
and smaller kind occasionally seen. Some of this might be doubtful, but Hunt was satisfied that they really knew the Coelacanth,
and that though it was rare, it turned up regularly. When he told
me all this, I was worried by the name '*Kombessa*', because in
East Africa the rather rare large Kingfishes (*Caranx*) are called
'Kambesi', and to the undiscerning eye they might well appear
not so very unlike the Coelacanth. They have the same ferocious
appearance and a large, powerful mouth.

Hunt had to act, and he did so with speed. It was not clear if a
radio message was sent or could be sent from Anjouan to Dzaoudzi,
but Hunt set out in his schooner and arrived at Pamanzi on the
following day, the 22nd December 1952. He at once informed the
Governor of his find, the local doctor willingly gave all the formalin available, and Hunt himself injected this into all the parts of
the fish, and from what I saw he did it well. Hunt had a metal-
lined box made to hold the animal. He sent me the cable mentioned
before, expecting me to be at Grahamstown, but realised from
my reply that I must still be on the *Dunnottar* at Durban.

The French can scarcely be blamed if they were at first somewhat sceptical of the great importance Hunt attached to this fish;
but his intense excitement had its effect, and a cable about it was
sent to the Scientific Institute of Madagascar at Tananarive. Not
only was this cable so mutilated in transmission by the native
operators as to be undeciperable there, but the official to whom it
was addressed was absent at that time. Christmas time! (See
p. 88.)

If I had endured many difficulties and uncertainties, those at
Dzaoudzi had had their own. Hunt was shrewd enough to realise
that the importance he attached to the find was having an effect
on the French authorities, and he eventually had to face the
situation that, despite their initial scepticism, he might well have

to surrender the fish to them. He was in a most awkward situation, as his trading depended on the good-will of the French authorities, and he could not afford to offend them. Not one of them would apparently believe that anyone would come from so far off as South Africa just to fetch a fish, certainly not in a special flight such as Hunt visualised and obviously expected. Hunt got the Governor to promise that if I did come to fetch it in person that way, no difficulties would be raised about its being handed over to me. Even when my final cable came there was apparently still scepticism; they were not finally convinced until the roar of the Dakota brought them all running from their homes to look at the skies. It must indeed have been sweet music to Hunt's ears. . . .

I must have dozed off, for I woke with a start to a shout in my ears. Ralston's head was poked through the door and he was gesturing ahead. 'We can see land,' he shouted and withdrew. I was up in an instant and went forward. Yes, there was the African coast and north of us was a bay, but it was not the bay of Mozambique. We all stared. It proved to be Mokambo, south of Mozambique. The wind up top had been northerly after all, and we had been driven southwards. Swinging round in a wide arc, we soon picked up my beloved isle of Mozambique, and I could see right beyond Fernao Veloso, which is the northern point of Nacala Bay, to the wreck on the end of the Pinda Reef.

Pinda! I have told you something of our life there and of the lions. Pinda! Where I endured unspeakable agony and nearly died from the stabs of the dreaded Stone-fish; but all that is a story by itself.

As the air was fairly clear just then and the light good (11.55 a.m.), I asked Blaauw to circle close north of Mazambique which enabled me to take the photograph reproduced on Plate 5, showing the whole island, with the famous fort of St. Sebastian at the near, north, end. At 12.05 p.m. we landed on Lumbo. The 'Chefe' of the airport ran out and eagerly sought my news. I told him we had got it and he stared at the box. 'Could he see the fish?' I shook my head, for on the way over I had resolved that not a single person was going to see that fish until I had shown it to Dr. Malan.

It was baking hot, the wind from the land almost scorched the skin. I asked the crew their needs, and they voted for iced shandies.

So I telephoned the hotel and asked the manager to send the necessities, 'muito muito depressa', with plenty of ice, and, as is usual with the Portuguese, it was all there in record time. We did not stay long and, after hasty but cordial adieux, took off at 12.55 p.m. into a mizzling north-wester. Although weather reports stated that it was cloudy with rain most of the way south, Blaauw said he hoped to reach Lourenço Marques by 6 p.m. and to get to Durban that night. It seemed ambitious, but he was the expert. I calculated that my wife, due at Port Elizabeth early that morning, should already be at home, though I naturally knew nothing of the road breakdown she had in reality endured on the way.

This was almost the worst part of the flight. We went up to 15,000 feet again, and there was nothing to see but cloud. It was beastly cold in that unlined metal shell, so I lay down on the floor wrapped in my bag and tried to sleep, but despite two restless, wakeful nights my mind was still racing madly, weighing up all that had happened and planning all that still had to be done. I must not let my exultation lead me astray, for I knew only too well that enthusiasm can end in a long and painful walk back, and this was a peak of achievement I had not before attained. Virtually alone in the scientific world, I had held to my conviction that the Coelacanth was to be found in the reefs of the East African region, and if what I had learned at Dzaoudzi was correct, the fish I now had with me was not just another stray, like the one at East London, but a homebird at home. It should be only a matter of time before others were found. Yes, I was exulting. It had not been pleasant to have one's deductions just pushed aside. I thought again of Smuts, with his ready ear for the overseas experts.

It was strange to look back on how almost all other scientists had been united on that issue. It was almost a kind of conspiracy between them. There was the opinion of the British Museum that the East London Coelacanth was obviously a stray from the deeper parts of the ocean. . . . The Danish deep-sea expedition had gone hunting hoping to find the Coelacanths in the great depths; palaeontologists in America and other countries! They were satisfied that Coelacanths lived in the 'Inaccessible depths of the ocean'. All of them knew it was ludicrous to go fishing for

Coelacanths with hooks and lines. It could not be done. And now it appeared that malaria-soaked, worm-ridden, bone-headed blacks of the Comores had been doing exactly that for centuries past, and not all the learned deductions of museum scientists could unsay it. What is more, Coelacanths were no strange food on the Comores. It was not even impossible that ancestors of these very scientists may have eaten Coelacanth, for in the early days of sail many British ships engaged in the spice trade with the East called regularly at 'Johanna', as Anjouan was called in those days. One British captain liked the place so much, he settled there and had a famous garden. At Mutsamudu, deep water close to land gave complete shelter from the hellish wind, and here the ships revictualled and filled their tanks, while the crew banished incipient scurvy with vitamin-rich tropical fruits. Slabs of salted Coelacanth may well have been among the stores they took aboard.

Thinking of food brought me back to the present, and I got up and gave the crew a snack of biscuits, cheese, and dried figs, but could not eat myself. The cloud was still so dense that neither land nor sea was visible. Though I was restless and overstrung, I compelled myself to lie down again, and made a stern effort to sleep; but a sudden stab of intense pain brought me to a sitting position. From before we left Durban my ears had been troublesome, and now, after several severe spasms, this settled down to a steady toothache in my right ear. This was a predicament, for before the advent of penicillin I had once had an abcess there, and it had not been a pleasant experience; and with all that lay ahead another now would be a disaster of the first magnitude. With anything of that kind treatment is a matter of hours, so I went forward and told Blaauw of my predicament, and asked to light the primus to sterilise a syringe for a penicillin injection, for which everything was in my 'collecting-box'. Blaauw was shaken, but I would not press the matter too strongly, as the plane and our lives were his ultimate responsibility, and of course the Coelacanth was with us now. It probably would not have helped even if I had gone on, it was clear that I would have to stick it. The agony was considerable, and I could scarcely sit, let alone lie down. So I turned to a resort I have often employed in such circumstances, which is to keep the mind so busy that it does not register pain, and decided to use the remaining time to write notes on the events of the past few days while they were still fresh in my mind, especially what I had learnt at Dzaoudzi. Soon I became so engrossed in getting the many points into their correct order that I forgot all else, and was brought, not to earth fortunately, but to look at it, by Ralston, who shouted 'Bazaruto', and there it was far beneath us to starboard, the clouds at that time being wispy and thin. We cut across inside Cape Sebastian, when the cloud over the land shut down again, and the plane became once more just a noisy box encased in cotton-wool. I went on with my notes.

My ears suddenly told me we were at a lower altitude, and looking out I saw the lakes about Inharrime, with glimpses of the sea between the ragged clouds. We dropped to only a few hundred feet above the dunes, and in quick succession passed the Limpopo mouth, then along the chain of coastal lakes about San Martinha, Chefina Island, and the Incomati mouth, and there was the Polana beach and the bay of Lourenço Marques, all old friends.

We touched down at 6.20 p.m. Our Vice-Consul Phillip was waiting at the airport, and there were greetings and inquiries from the various Portuguese officials. My chief concern was refreshments for the crew, who again alternated between coffee and cool drinks with sandwiches.

Despite my great stress, I had always kept in mind the Brigadier's request that the crew should not be driven too hard. This had been a long and trying day, and eager as I was to return I put this to Blaauw and suggested a night in Lourenço Marques; but like horses scenting home they were all eager to get on and to reach Durban that night. I asked Phillip to telephone my friend Dr. George Campbell in Durban to find me an absoutely trustworthy photographer to meet the plane, for I wanted to have my precious films developed at once.

It was raining as we took off at 6.45 p.m., and in the gathering gloom it seemed a flight that would never end. I had discovered that the crew had all been on holiday when they were abruptly recalled for this flight, and while they had not offered any account of their reactions, it was only natural that there should have been some degree of resentment. I spoke of this, and said that some compensation for them would be to have participated in what would remain an historic flight. Being curious about this matter, at about 8 p.m. I wrote on a sheet:

'Will you kindly write here what you said, when you heard you had to come on this unusual flight to go hunting a dead fish near Madagascar. (Leave out unprintable words.)' This was passed around in turn, and it is interesting to record their comments, which are given below:

1. *Commandant J. P. D. Blaauw*
   It must be a pretty important fish if the Prime Minister is prepared to give an aircraft and crew to some hare-brained scientist to fetch it.

2. *Captain P. Letley*
   The first time that I knew we were going to fetch a fish (DEAD) was when the Orderly Officer told me. My reply, as you requested, cannot be written down. Anyway, I enjoyed the trip.

3. *Lieutenant D. M. Ralston*
   Not very impressed at first and was doubtful whether it was the correct fish. Professor Smith's enthusiasm is infectious, and I have found this an extremely enlightening trip.

4. *Lieutenant W. J. Bergh*
   As I was all set to go on a special visit (my girl friend) for the week-end, I did not like the idea very much at first. I had to cancel all arrangements by phone and said, 'Somebody caught a fish that should long since have been dead!' The trip was, however, so enjoyable that I was all for staying at Dzaoudzi.

5. *Corporal J. W. J. van Niekerk*
   When I heard about the fish story, I thought that we were going to have chips with it, too, but I enjoyed even the smell.

6. *Corporal F. Brink*
   Although I made arrangements to visit some friends on Sunday for a swell dinner, I had no idea that I would have to come on a fishing trip for a fish that was dead already. But the trip was very enjoyable, and the Professor was like a nurse to us, feeding us all the time.

I suddenly realised that the pain had gone from my ears and the enforced inaction had produced relief from strain; but only to merge into an incredible weariness, and I could think of nothing more wonderful than getting between cool sheets in a quiet room. Though what I had already planned meant a very early start next day, I might manage to snatch some sleep at Durban; for the few friends who knew of my return would soon leave when they saw how weary I was. It is quite amusing to look back on my ignorance of what lay ahead.

'The lights of Durban,' Ralston again, it would not be long now, but it was a full half-hour before we could land. Round and round we buzzed, because a stubborn aerial refused to come in and eventually a plate of the hull had to be unscrewed and opened before it could be retracted. We went down. As the door opened I was first at the steps, and was immediately blinded by a battery of flash-bulbs. In that fraction of a second's vision I was appalled to see a seething crowd whose dimensions enlarged as further flashes flared. How on earth had all these people got there? My bewilderment and dismay increased when that human dynamo George Moore of the S.A.B.C. at Durban grabbed me by the arm and pushed a microphone with trailing wires under my nose and started to question me. The sounds from my lips were more frog-like than human, and, indeed, later that night when my son in Grahamstown heard those words from our radio set, he said to my wife, 'But, Mom, that's not Dad.' His mother's sole retort was a terse 'Shut-up', as she sat tense before the machine.

In this confused milling crowd I was moved across the ground towards the office. I needed a drink badly and asked for coffee. A Customs officer pushed a form under my nose, put a pen in my hand, and asked me to sign on a line. The officer in charge said the Commander-in-Chief in Pretoria was waiting on the telephone, would I speak to him, and so I made my formal report and received his congratulations (Plate 6, facing p. 129). He asked if I was now finished with the plane or should it take me to Grahamstown? So I told him my plans, could the plane take me to Cape Town in the morning as I wished to show the animal to Dr. Malan? Would he kindly make contact with the necessary authorities as soon as possible to say that I wished to bring it? All this he promised to do. I then told Blaauw that we might have to go to Cape Town in the morning and why. He was by then clearly resigned to anything and told his crew. Only later were they able to get my wife on the telephone at Grahamstown, when I gave her a brief account of events and told her my plans.

My coffee had got cold, so they fetched more, and it was scarcely easing my parched throat when George Moore brought me to earth with a bump, saying that they wanted me to say something over the microphone, as the whole of South Africa was waiting for me. It was only much later that I discovered that all programmes had been dislocated that evening for this purpose. This was terrible. It was already 9 p.m., we had provisionally arranged to take off at 3.30 a.m., and I was so weary that it was an effort to utter any word at all. I looked at him in dismay, and said, 'What must I say, man?' 'Anything you like,' he said. 'Even just a message.' I sat back and thought. If people were waiting and had been waiting, a mere message was a poor return; they would want to know what it was all about, and it was emphatically not a story to be told in a few words. Suddenly I remembered my notes, and told Moore I had made them and could use them to give an outline of events, but that it would take at least twenty minutes. Instead of saying, as I hoped, that that was far too long, to my dismay he shouted, 'That will be fine, Professor, you take as long as you like'; and there was no doubt that he meant it. The notes were still in the plane, and with my directions one of the crew went to seek them while I drank more hot coffee and tried to compose my mind to the ordeal ahead. I must not make a hash of this. Those notes were merely a sketchy scrawl. The man came back, the sheets were pushed into my hand, and I sorted them out while those who filled the room shuffled and pressed tight around me like a wall, though I could scarcely see them through the black mists of weariness that enclosed me. I began to speak, or rather to croak at the microphone, my throat muscles almost refusing to function, and then suddenly I was no longer aware of my surroundings but almost miraculously back in it all, living it over again, the strain and agony and suspense. It was so real that when I told how I had found myself weeping at my first sight of the creature on Hunt's vessel, I was there again and even though I knew that tears had again run from my eyes, I did not care. Once from sheer exhaustion my voice failed completely, and I had to stop and gesture for more coffee, then went on. At the end I felt like a pricked balloon, and just sat hunched up while whirling black mists shot with points of light submerged me, but Moore brought me up by asking if I had any idea of the name I intended to give this creature. I said, yes, to honour Dr. Malan, the genus *Malania*, and from the island Anjouan, where it was found, so came provisionally the name *Malania anjouanea*. There was dead silence, then a sudden burst of applause. Someone seized my notes and said 'Let me see those notes'; I was too weary to care what anyone thought, it was enough that it was over at last. Perhaps now they would leave me alone; I wondered if I would ever again know what it was like not to be unutterably weary. But that merciless Moore pushed the microphone nearer and said, 'Now just something in Afrikaans, Professor. You must not disappoint our Afrikaans listeners.' Only half conscious now, I tried to rouse myself, and from far off, speaking of this same event in Afrikaans, heard a strange voice that it was hard to realise was my own. The words came without volition. I have never had the courage to ask to listen to that part.

Chapter Fifteen

MALAN AND MALANIA

As I lay back, my friends swam into my consciousness and took hold. I could not speak, but tried to smile thanks for all they said. Photographer George Symons took my two precious rolls of films, and swore to let me have them before 3 a.m. 'When can we see the Coelacanth?' my friends asked, and this was drowned in a chorus from the press, who asked to photograph it. There was near consternation when I shook my head, then explained that Dr. Malan was to be the first to see it; until then, no one else. They tried all they could, but I was adamant. Then came a telephone call from Pretoria, to say that in the matter of taking the Coelacanth to Cape Town to show Dr. Malan, it was felt that as he was resting and on holiday, and in view of his age, having need to conserve his strength, it would be too much for him to come all that way in from the Strand. They had obviously mistaken my intentions. I asked if the matter had been put to Dr. Malan himself, and the answer was 'No,' they did not want to disturb him, but he had been told of our safe return. So I said that I appreciated all their kind concern for Dr. Malan, but I certainly had as much myself and had never expected him to come to Cape Town and certainly did not want that. I wished to take the Coelacanth to him wherever he might be, and unless he expressly forbade it, would do so. I added firmly that if all else failed I would push the thing there on a wheel-barrow myself. At any rate, that could be settled later. Would the Commander-in-Chief kindly authorise the flight to Cape Town, and the issue could be put to Dr. Malan in the morning; but it must, please, be put to Dr. Malan himself, for whatever else might happen I intended to go and find out myself if it had been. He very amiably said go ahead, and he would pass on my message. Then they put through a call to my wife in Grahamstown, when I told her what had happened and asked her to bring all the necessaries for coffee and food for seven to the

Grahamstown aerodrome for 6 a.m., also four copies of my *Sea Fishes of Southern Africa*, each inscribed with the name of the officer concerned, and as follows:

WITH MY COMPLIMENTS, IN MEMORY OF THE 'COELACANTH' FLIGHT TO PAMANZI, COMORES, 29TH–31ST DECEMBER 1952.

Would she also find and bring along a large square of white cloth, a piece of clean plank about a foot long and 10 yards of string? My wife knows me and confined her curiosity, merely saying 'Right.' I realised that all this meant no sleep for her. Could she cope? 'Yes.' Then she asked, as we intended calling at Grahamstown, could not she and our son William come to Cape Town as well? Phew! That was a poser. I said I would see what could be done, and after ringing off spoke to Blaauw, who at once said it was quite impossible as women were never permitted on military aircraft. So I telephoned Brigadier Melville in Pretoria again, 12.20 a.m. A weary voice spoke and I said, 'Smith here again. Are you married?' when weariness gave place to surprise. 'Then you will perhaps understand better why I am disturbing you again at this unholy hour'; and put my request. He whistled, there was silence for some seconds, and when he spoke again he seemed to be pulling reluctant words from his lips: 'It would be highly irregular, of course, highly irregular, and I do not remember that it has ever been done before; but everything about this flight has been highly irregular, so I suppose you can do it. O.K.' And so at what had now become an early hour of the morning, they made another call to Grahamstown to warn my wife to be ready to leave at six. Then I thought I might get a little sleep. They asked where I wished the Coelacanth put for safety, and when I said in my bedroom of course, they were not surprised. I was escorted to my room by the press still asking to photograph the fish, and even when I started to undress, that did not discourage them; they went on firing questions even when my shirt concealed my head. Had I any photographs? I nodded. Any hope of getting any? 'No.' One by one they faded, but Natalie Roberts of the *Daily News*, an old press friend, still stayed on. Though I was clad only in shorts, she sat on the bed and talked, and when I pointed out how scandalous it was, she just laughed.

At 2 a.m. George Symons came in with the negatives, which were a real thrill, for they were perfect. Mrs. Roberts begged hard for one, and I told her what had happened in the matter of the pictures of the first Coelacanth; but eventually relented to her persistence and handed over one negative with the condition that the scientific name *Malania anjouanae* had to be printed with it, and that it remained my copyright. Within twenty-four hours that photograph had appeared in every newspaper of any rank in South Africa, and within forty-eight hours in most others throughout the world.

We took off at 4.50 a.m., and for once it was nice and clear; but above East London we ran into low cloud, and Blaauw doubted if we should be able to land at Grahamstown. It was only by flying below the cloud in a long valley from near the sea that we managed it, and we were mighty close to the trees much of the way. We touched down at 7.05 a.m. Aided by Mrs. Hester Locke, one of our earlier 'Book' artists, my wife, a sleepless night's ravages skilfully concealed, served coffee and food, and we all got aboard and were off at 7.40 a.m., emerging from the clouds only west of Port Elizabeth.

My eldest son was on holiday at Knysna, where I have a riverside house and a laboratory. On the piece of board I had asked my wife to bring I wrote a message, and attached this to the cloth shaped to a parachute and asked Blaauw to fly down over the place, which I pointed out to him the first time we passed. Then we made a long circle out to sea to lose height and zoomed down low over the house, and Blaauw dropped the 'bomb', with perfect judgment, for we heard later that it fell only a few yards from the fence and safely reached my son; but the huge Dakota coming back to pass so low down caused a near panic among the coloured folk who live in the valley behind. They expected bombs.

Over Bredasdorp I was in front with Blaauw and Letley, discussing our possible return flight for that day. Letley suddenly interrupted by pointing to his earphones and wrote down a message which he showed to Blaauw, then handed to me, 'Message from Dr. Malan, he thanks you very much for having taken the trouble to come so far, but he does not wish to see the fish and wishes you a safe return to Grahamstown.' This was a shock. Was it the old business of evolution? There was continual trouble

about it in America, for example; and all those letters I had received! I did not let them see a thing, but nodded, put the paper
into my pocket and said, 'Oh well, now we are so far we can lunch
in Cape Town and go back early this afternoon.' Privately I decided that I was going to make quite certain there that the message
really came from Dr. Malan. I looked down to see them both
grinning somewhat impishly, and this time knew at once what they
were up to and could cheerfully have killed them. They knew
full well that only Dr. Malan himself could have turned me back.

10.35 a.m., Ysterplaats Airport. The Cape Commander-in-
Chief, Colonel Louis du Toit, and other officers were there to
meet us and a lorry with guards was ready for the Coelacanth.
Dr. Malan's compliments, and would we spend the day and lunch
with them, and a function had been arranged for tea-time with
numerous guests. So there was to be no return that day.

To his partial disgust, William was left behind, but the promise
of looking at jet planes consoled him. We were soon at the Strand,
where we were warmly welcomed at their holiday home by Dr.
and Mrs. Malan. He can best be described as a grand old man,
greatly respected, admired, and loved by his people. No man can
ask more. She is a gracious and dignified woman whose life is
clearly centred on the care and service of this man. The bond
between them is almost tangible, and their home breathes serenity
and peace. Once formalities were over, refreshments were offered;
what would I have? Prominent on the tray was a bottle of whisky.
Whisky for the Professor? When I said we did not use alcohol
except to preserve fish, there was something of a silence, then
laughter. The Malans take no alcohol, but when I was on the
way some discussion doubtless took place. The life I lead, going
to many remote and wild parts and enduring adventures I would
avoid if I could, has gained for me the reputation of being a
pretty tough person, and those who do not know my ways would
almost certainly credit me with a taste for whisky and strong
tobacco. I use neither, except cigarettes, and then only in our
work as bribes for fish or as presents, which is probably why my
relatively frail body is tough. Yes, whisky was clearly indicated
for this English Professor from Grahamstown, so as it is no light
undertaking even for a Prime Minister to get a bottle of whisky
early in the morning in South Africa in a place like the Strand,

a real hunt took place. I have often wondered what happened to that whisky, and must ask Dr. Malan some time. Their young adopted daughter Marietjie was intrigued by all the fuss and followed me around. She called me 'Oom Vis' (Uncle Fish).

The box containing the Coelacanth was put under a tree on the lawn. I had it opened and showed the fish to Dr. and Mrs. Malan, and to my wife as well, for she had not seen it before (Plate 6). Dr. Malan looked for some moments, especially at the head, then turned to me, and with a twinkle in his eye said, 'My, it is ugly. Do you mean to say we once looked like that?' I replied, 'H'm! I have seen people that are uglier.' Then I gave him a scale from the animal, which he handed to his wife with instructions that it was to be put in the family archives. The press photographers had a good time with us all, and I noticed that Mrs. Malan was always on the watch to see that they did not worry 'The Doctor'.

Word of our arrival soon got round, and crowds of curious sight-seers were constantly passing. Despite the guard under the tree, I kept a wary eye on the coffin myself, and soon noticed a secre-tive-looking man moving about the drive and along the fence. I watched him for some time, and eventually told Colonel du Toit I couldn't help feeling suspicious of that chap. He was greatly amused and said there was no need to worry, he was the Prime Minister's special guard! After lunch Mrs. Malan, aware of my exhaustion, insisted on our resting awhile in their own room for comfort and quiet. But sleep would not come and I wondered whether I should not after all have had some of that whisky.

A request came to Dr. Malan that the Coelacanth should be put out on exhibition in a public place for everyone to see. He passed this on to me and I considered the matter. I had brought this fish so far for the special purpose of showing it to Dr. Malan. He had already selected those he considered would have excep-tional interest in seeing it. I had refused to show it to the crowds in Durban, and felt it would not be fitting to do more now. From the scientific point of view, it seemed wiser to refuse at that special time. Any public exhibition needs careful planning, and with little time for that would then have involved a degree of risk I was not prepared to undertake, and I did not want the animal exposed more than was necessary. I told Dr. Malan I would prefer not to have any public exhibition then, and gave my reasons; but added that if he wanted it done we could go into the matter. He at once said that the decision must be mine alone, and I trust that those who were at the Strand at that time will understand my reluctance.

In the afternoon some hundreds of guests from all over the south-western Cape, invited by telephone only that morning, assembled at tea-time. Dr. Malan had asked me privately if I would address them, to which I agreed, but said also that I was so exhausted it would be a terrible strain to speak in Afrikaans. He patted my arm, and took it on himself to announce that he wished me to speak in English. After several speeches the company, composed of leading scientific and public personalities of the Cape, filed slowly past the Coelacanth bier, while crowds assembled outside in the street, and their cameras constantly clicked and buzzed.

After that day of intimate contact, we left the Strand knowing that behind the solemn, stony face of the newspapers lay a warm humanity and an active if dry sense of humour. It left us with more. Back at Ysterplaats my wife put into words what had been filling my mind; she said, 'That man could do no wrong to anyone.'

We learnt that night that the *Dunnottar Castle* was due at 7 a.m. next day. Early transport was arranged, and we arrived at the docks as the ship was being made fast; but as the Port Officials had not yet arrived, there was no entry. Time was precious, and I was raging at the gangway when a door opened in the side of the ship near by and Captain Smythe jumped out and hailed us, naturally dumbfounded that we could be there, as may be understood. One of the officers had seen us on the quay and had hastened to tell him. In spite of the guards, we all went aboard through the same hole.

On our voyage in that ship from Mombasa southwards I had found 8.30 a.m. very late for breakfast, and had had occasional passages with the head waiter, for I much preferred having my simple meal at children's time, 7.30 a.m. I left my wife and Smythe and went to the dining-saloon, now just 7.30, and seeing this head waiter coming from the kitchen, stood at the side of the door, and as he passed said, 'Would you mind if I had breakfast with the children?' He started, and with bulging eyes stared speechless at me and almost dropped his load. He obviously thought I was a ghost. It could not possibly be me, in the flesh, for the last he had heard was that I was careering about somewhere off Madagascar.

When we got off the ship we discovered that our car had vanished, so we had to find a taxi, no light task in that area, and eventually discovered one, far from new, with a coloured driver, also an older model. I told him to go to Ysterplaats, and as our speed did not satisfy my haste, after a while asked him to hurry as a plane was waiting. A second or two later the car swerved alarmingly as he jerked round to look, and he said, 'My God, sir, you aren't the genilman with the fish are you?' I said, 'Yes, I am.' He said, 'Oh, what a honour, what a honour for me and my taxi.' There was silence for a while, then with agony in his voice; 'But the only trouble is, sir, no one will believe me. Can't you give me something to prove it, sir?' I found all my cards had gone, but my wife had hers so I autographed one of those and he left a very happy man.

We took off at 8.30 a.m. First we went north, low over the *Dunnottar* at the docks to see Captain Smythe waving his arms from the bridge. Then we circled and cut across the Cape Flats to the Strand, where I got Blaauw to circle the Malans' house twice low down. Judging by the effect on the hastily emerging populace, they also expected bombs, but we saw the Malans come out on the lawn and wave. We 'bombed' them with several copies of the early morning papers, then turned east and up, over the high escarpment that soon blotted out the line of surf where their house lay.

There was more bad weather with low cloud-ceiling all along the coast; once again there was grave doubt as to whether we should be able to land at Grahamstown. But Blaauw was equal to the emergency, and we got in to find Mayor McGahey and numerous citizens there to meet us. It was a great joy to see Miss Latimer there, too, with G. G. Smith, the present Chairman of the Board of Trustees of the East London Museum, who had come over from East London to welcome our return. Her presence brought back poignant memories of the first Coelacanth. Then she was a young girl, finding her feet. Now she was a mature woman of established position, her Museum famous, her Chairman and Board well aware of her value to the Institution. She kissed me before them all, and nobody was embarrassed, not even myself. The crew of the Dakota had got the box out and were standing round politely, but clearly very conscious of the compass needle pointing northwards. In a brief ceremony each of the four officers was presented with one of the inscribed volumes my wife had brought, while the others each received a special memento. They were soon aboard and off, and we watched that huge machine fade to a minute speck, then she was gone. As she vanished it was as if a curtain had suddenly been dropped at the close of a tense act.

It was fitting that Malania was loaded with Miss Latimer into G. G. Smith's van, and we all went off to the laboratory. Before the cars had stopped we heard the telephone ringing madly, and as I got out Mrs. Locke's head came through the window, calling 'Trunk-call, Professor.' It was prophetic.

BOOK III

THE WAVE RECEDES

Chapter Sixteen

FLOTSAM AND JETSAM

A CHAOTIC account of a chaotic time.

The days and nights that followed our return to Grahamstown on the last day of 1952 were something of a nightmare, of which it is difficult to give a coherent account. My Secretary had gone on holiday with her family and left no indication of her whereabouts, nor should I have worried her had I known them, for the Christmas–New Year period in South Africa is dedicated to release from work. She was due to be away for another two weeks. At that time even the Prime Minister rests, at least he tries to, but of course unexpected events like wars or Coelacanths may intrude.

Despite efficient handling in my absence, there was the usual accumulation of troublesome matters, reports and queries and inescapable financial commitments and payments. I find myself constantly grateful that while I have enough to eat and a comfortable dry bed to sleep in, I am free from those cares that great wealth brings. There is more than enough to do besides.

From the moment we arrived, telephone calls came constantly from far and near. Would I confirm this or that? Were we going to remain in Grahamstown? Could such and such a representative, press, radio, television, cinema, publishing, and others, come for an interview?

In normal times pressure of this kind would have been hard to bear, but now it was almost unendurable, for I had been virtually without sleep for a whole week. Fortunately even in normal times I can do with less sleep than most, and my body and brain are rather like a worn engine whose minor deficiencies are concealed when it functions at high speed. My wife was equally overwhelmed, and tore herself into bits, acting all at once as secretary, buffer, and general assistant. Even the laboratory boy was away enjoying a restful holiday!

The last day of 1952! My weary brain shot occasional probes of worry into the future. Could we stand this pace and pressure?

A trunk-call. The London *Times* wanted an article. When? At once, please, its point would otherwise be less, and if I would write it, it could come by cable. I said it was doubtful if it could be done, as life was more than full, and would not promise, but said I would see how things went and if at all possible would do it. I would let them know by next morning at the latest. They asked if they could make provisional arrangement meanwhile? Yes, but it must be understood that this did not bind me, and at the moment there seemed no hope. This was the afternoon of our return, the 31st December 1952.

This story is told partly to show the wonder of modern communications and partly because this article played an important part in countering the unfortunate effects of that 'Missing Link' appellation that had been tacked on to the Coelacanth.

My brain often annoys and sometimes alarms me, for it has a part that works secretly, even when I am hard at work at something else. Although exhausted that night, I knew I would have to write that infernal article, but put it from me then. Telephone calls pursued us to our house, through a meal, and until we had to ask the Post Office to draw the curtain. I slept like a log for five hours, and at 3 a.m. found myself fully wide awake with that confounded article clear-cut in my brain. I slid out of bed, though probably not even a bomb would have wakened my wife, crept downstairs, and had a cup of Nescafé. I can never condemn those who are addicts to alcohol or tobacco, for I am just as bad with that stuff and turn to it in every crisis. 'A nice cup of tea!'

I wrote steadily until daylight dimmed the electric lamps, and by then most had been got down on paper. This was only the first part. It is doubtful whether those who hear a good broadcast or read an interesting article know how much labour lies behind it. I put a call through to say that the article would be ready by noon, and learnt that though it was a public holiday, 1st January 1953, when all public services are dead, provisional arrangements had been made with the Post Office at Grahamstown, and a telegraphist would be waiting to send this off by cable to London. This would now be confirmed: he would be on duty from noon, and would I make contact and send it to the Post Office?

Typists! They are normally scarce in Grahamstown, and this was New Year's Day. At the aerodrome Mayor Patrick McGahey had said that if he could assist us, privately or officially, would we ask. I had that in mind and telephoned him now, 5.30 a.m., and he answered, clearly without ill-feeling, from his bed. Two typists at 9 a.m., please? Without hesitation, yes! he would see to it, he believed two of their staff were still in town. More Nescafé, and to the laboratory at 6 a.m. First a quick look at the Coelacanth; yes, it was still there, a good solid fish, there was nothing imaginary about that. It was real.

At 8 a.m. Mayor McGahey telephoned to say that he had managed to find two expert typists,* and that they were prepared to forgo the holiday to help us, and would accept no payment for their services. They arrived at 8.45, and worked all the time until 11.30, when it was complete, the final clean copies. At noon it was at the Post Office, and next day I got a cable from London thanking me for the article and saying that it had been published that morning, the 2nd January 1953. Only four days later a copy of that paper was in my hands. Such are modern times! (This article is reproduced in Appendix D, p. 243.)

During this same morning, 2nd January 1953, there was a trunk call from the press. Had I heard that the night before Dr. White of the British Museum had broadcast over the B.B.C. to say that it was nonsense to speak of the Coelacanth as a 'missing link', and it certainly was not the ancestor of man, and did I agree with him? It was the same Dr. White who in 1939 had relegated the Coelacanth to the abyss and reproved me for naming that first one after Miss Latimer. That 'Missing Link' caption was a great trial, especially as some overseas reports had virtually tacked it on to me (see p. 87). I knew that White would already have been answered by my article which had appeared in the London *Times* that morning, but told the press now that while it was doubtful if the Coelacanth would ever be proved a direct ancestor of man, it must be pretty close to the main evolutionary stem. It is interesting to note that a day or two later, Julian Huxley, the famous British biologist, took up the whole matter in a broadcast over

* Miss R. M. Koen and Miss M. Goetsch—of Grahamstown.

the B.B.C., and in this he expressed views rather like my own, saying indeed that the ultimate vertebrate ancestor of man was probably something like a Coelacanth. He said that when Dr. Malan asked his rather whimsical question about the Coelacanth, 'Do you mean to say we once looked like that?'—the answer really was 'Broadly speaking, yes.'

We could barely find time to open the constant series of telegrams and cables from all over the world, and the sheaves of letters were piled up and treated in rotation. Post Office revenue for that period must have been very considerably augmented by the Coelacanth. There was a constant succession of visitors from far and near, all eager to see the Coelacanth, and it was difficult to cope with them, so an illustrative exhibition was hastily prepared. Everyone was so full of questions that, as we all had only one voice each, I dictated a brief outline of the main points of the whole affair, and had this posted up as well.

Press representatives and photographers of papers and journals from all over the world kept on coming, new arrivals being viewed with disfavour by those earlier on the spot, and at times I wondered what we should do if the almost open general hostility broke its bounds. They reminded us of a pack of bristling dogs waiting for one to start it off.

Mayor McGahey came to ask if he could arrange an official welcome, and as the public would like to see the Coelacanth, could we have it exhibited in the City Hall, and combine the two? We agreed to do all this on the 9th January 1953, and this was duly carried out with a record attendance.

At the request of the authorities of the East London Museum, we later took *Malania* there, and with *Latimeria* alongside it was exhibited for two days, which were a repetition of the earlier historic times, for thousands of people in lengthy queues pressed in constantly all the time. The fish was also exhibited by request at Port Elizabeth, and attracted great attention. Many further requests for exhibition of the fish came from far and wide, but these had to be refused, as was also the generous offer of a Port Elizabeth business magnate who offered to fly the fish and myself to the Rhodesian Centenary Exhibition: neither the C.S.I.R. nor I felt the risk justifiable.

A Coelacanth can do strange things to scientists. My wife and

I posed for photographs and became ciné and television stars. I would leave broadcasting engineers fixing a tape machine in my office to face more flash-bulbs or to wave the Coelacanth's fin for a ciné. We were told that within three days a television record from our laboratory had been shown all over America, and later we got letters from scientist friends in remote places like Japan, Alaska, and Timor to say they had seen us on the screen. We were, in fact, carried along by a kind of tidal-wave we could scarcely control, a wave that went right round the world many times, to its uttermost corners, and the backwash still keeps on coming back to us even after this long time. In this process an obscure and highly technical scientific term became part of the common speech of mankind.

When I snatched a moment for a closer look, it was a most unpleasant shock to discover that the first cutting of the fish to save it, as told by Hunt, had been a crude hacking open as the natives do when they wish to salt any big fish. So far from its being a complete animal, the whole brain was missing and much of the viscera had been badly hacked and torn. This was indeed a bitter blow. Once again it was not a complete fish.

On the morning of the 3rd January 1953 my Secretary appeared, ready for work. Hearing of my predicament only the day before, she had summarily cut short their holiday and swept the whole family back home. It was a fine gesture, for she came at a critical time when we were almost desperate with all that was besetting us.

No sooner had the movie and television people gone than there came a flood of requests for articles, popular, informative, and scientific, about the Coelacanth, of which only a small part could even be considered.

During this time we estimated that not less than twenty thousand people came to look at old man Coelacanth. Not many humans have achieved that in death. It reminded one of Lenin in his glass coffin, or dead royalty in state.

A bright spot in that difficult time was the arrival of three young coloured men* at the laboratory. They stood for some time quietly watching and, when asked if they wanted anything, said, rather shyly, that they were graduates of Fort Hare, the non-

* F. Backman, B.Sc., L. Backman, B.Sc., and N. Dennis, B.Sc.

European University College, they had heard we needed assistance, they had taken Zoology and could they help in any way?

Our enormous collection of fishes from East Africa stood untouched, in sealed bottles and tins, packed in crates that were piled up in the laboratory, an angular tower that reproached us every time we passed. So we set the three young men to unpacking these treasures and putting them into more suitable containers. It was no pleasant task, formalin is stifling, and it was hot. They laboured for many days and would accept no reward. We remain grateful for their kind thoughtfulness and service.

Even though the Coelacanth had been so badly mutilated, most of the soft parts were there, and so, as before, I made a thorough but more or less general investigation so as to be able to give information that was eagerly awaited by scientists everywhere. As was mentioned previously, the gills of the first Coelacanth were lost, but these were intact and they were remarkable. Most fishes have gills of cartilage (gristle), relatively soft, with 'gill-rakers', soft finger-like projections, above. The gills of the Coelacanth proved to be bony and hard, and instead of soft gill-rakers there are teeth. In fact, stripped of the soft filaments below, they looked almost like jawbones; they could easily be mistaken for them. They showed at least that jaws and gill-arches had the same origin.

I found in the intestines a structure known as a 'spiral valve'. If ever you open a Shark or a Ray, run the intestines through your hand and you will come to a peculiar, rather hard, purplish part, which you will see clearly has a spiral structure. Cut it open longways and you will see that it is a device to make a short bit of gut do the work of a much longer straight part. The digested foods must go round and round, and so are exposed to longer absorption. This structure is characteristic of Sharks and Rays and not of modern fishes, though it is found in one or two of the more primitive types that still survive. The study of fossils had progressed so far that some workers had come to suspect that Coelacanths might have a spiral valve, and here it was. (Some other things suspected to be present, like the internal nostrils, were not found.) This type of intestine clearly carries one back to the very earliest beginnings of vertebrate life or even farther. In the intestines I found fish remains, a few scales and the eyeballs of a fish. Fishes' eyes vary in size, but, taking an average, those were from a fish of about 15 lb. in weight. A 15-lb. fish is quite a size. This confirmed my views about the way a Coelacanth fed. Clearly he pounces and grabs. His powerful jaw muscles would enable him to hold the struggling prey, and it seems likely that the toothed gills would come into play and rasp that struggling fish's flesh and life away. Then it could be pulped and mashed and broken up, and swallowed just as a big Rock Cod does it. Degenerate! Deep-sea refuge to escape competition! Not this fish.

To my great sorrow, this was a male. I had, of course, hoped for a female with young. We are still waiting for that.* There were many other points observed and noted, but they are rather technical.

Scientific publications normally take some time to prepare and appear. Even in 1939 it took a month before my first account of the Coelacanth appeared in *Nature*, and another four weeks before I saw a copy. In 1953, on the 2nd January, two days after our return, my wife and I set to and worked all that week-end, furiously, and a seven-page manuscript and photographs were sent by air on the 6th January 1953. This appeared in the issue of *Nature* of the 16th January, and a copy was on my desk in Grahamstown on the 19th, by which time it was in the hands of scientists all over the world as well. Modern times!

Several letters came from Hunt giving further news. Some days after we had left the Comores, the ceremony of presentation of the 50,000 francs took place. I have no record of events, only that bare statement. Hunt wrote to say that some photographs had been taken and he hoped to send prints later, but the cyclone finished that. This presentation payment of so vast a sum must have had a profound effect, the kind of effect we had hoped for, and we waited and waited, hoping to hear of more and other Coelacanths.

After these events, Hunt returned to Africa, and soon after set out again on his Comoran round. By a strange trick of fate, when he returned to Pamanzi, only two weeks after we had left, a cyclone caught him there, and after what he describes tersely as 'a terrifying experience', he and his crew escaped with their lives; but the

* See p. 237, Appendix C.

schooner was smashed and sunk, beyond any salvaging, a tragic sequel to its eventful participation in the Coelacanth adventure. Hunt apparently lost everything, though, providentially covered by insurance, he has since found another vessel. For a time he stopped trading about the Comores or anywhere in French waters, but recently he has written from there again.

Regrets for Hunt's misfortune are of added poignancy, for had such a cyclone caught us at Pamanzi, we might have had more of the Comores than we bargained for. It was a close enough shave.

Dzaoudzi and the whole of Pamanzi and Mayotte from the air were pleasant to the eye, but the damage wrought by this cyclone to buildings, plantations, gardens, and the vegetation was, according to reports, both devastating and heartbreaking, and will take many years of labour, and many years of persuasion and encouragement by the officials, to repair. In such parts you see men labouring earnestly to administer the territories they control, living in discomfort, far from their real homes and congenial company, in constant danger of deadly or crippling, often almost incurable, diseases, and one wonders why on earth they do it, quite often when the peoples for whom they labour clearly do not appreciate this or desire their presence. They are the last of this passing phase of 'Colonial' administration, the condescending gesture of White superiority that is arousing increasing resentment in the awakening consciousness of existence that is stirring in the backward ebony mind. Where will it all end?

I have told previously of my voluminous monograph on what remained of the first Coelacanth, and which would have been even more ample had the specimen not been recalled for exhibition. Even with what had been lost in this second specimen, the full investigation of the various parts of the body would mean many years of careful investigation. Such work is slow, for it involves the most delicate manipulation. Our knowledge of structure and life comes from many years of intensive study by a series of leading experts. It has progressed so far that the proper study of a whole organism has really got beyond the powers of any single man. Scientists have therefore specialised, one man often devoting his whole life to the study of only one organ such as the eye, the kidney, the pituitary, or the liver.

It will therefore be understood that to reap the greatest advantage from this wonderful opportunity of an almost complete Coelacanth, it would be desirable for each organ to be examined and studied by an expert who already had in his brain a full knowledge of that organ in most or all other creatures. This therefore ruled out an examination only by myself, for, despite all I know about fishes, it would take years before I could master all the existing knowledge of each organ in turn; and besides that, it would have been selfish and unjustifiable. My chief aim was to extract the utmost scientific value from the Coelacanth. In addition to this, now that there was a real hope that the true home of the Coelacanths had been found, I wanted to get on with what had become my greatest work—the investigation of the fishes of the whole western Indian Ocean.

It is a curious paradox that while the fishes of most seas have been almost fully investigated, before my work there commenced, those of East Africa had hardly been touched. Our series of expeditions had indeed shown this to be one of the richest and most interesting areas in the world, and our discoveries had astonished ourselves as well as the world of science.

I put my view about the study of the Coelacanth to the South African Council for Scientific and Industrial Research, and suggested that we should invite specialists to apply to be included in a panel of workers to carry out the whole investigation. This was approved by the Council.

There was another aspect to be considered. This was the only reasonably complete specimen of a Coelacanth. What if no others were found? Full study of the fish meant that it would have to be cut up; dismembered. I wished to put that off until there was no further hope of more specimens. In my own mind I decided to wait for another eighteen months, which would cover a full intermonsoon period, and if the Comores proved to be the real home, there was every hope that others would turn up or be found within that time. Another important point soon emerged, which was that for the proper study of certain organs, formalin-preserved material was useless, quite fresh tissues, treated in various special ways, were necessary. So the full study was, in any case, going to depend on finding more specimens.

As a result of this, the following letter was published in *Nature*, on the 28th February 1953, over my name:

INVESTIGATION OF THE COELACANTH

It was my privilege to carry out detailed investigations on the first Coelacanth, and to have discovered what appears to be the area where those fishes still live.

The recent Comoran Coelacanth, while mutilated more than was at first realised, nevertheless retains most of the soft parts, including the abdominal viscera. This extends enormously the scope of the investigational work that may be carried out on the specimen. There will be still more that can be done only on parts, exudates, and secretions from an untreated fresh specimen, which it is hoped to seek before very long.

It is in keeping with the importance and scope of the investigations on all parts of this fish that they should be assigned to leading experts in the field in which they fall. I have advised the South African Council for Scientific and Industrial Research, and have requested the Council's approval of, and co-operation in, this matter.

Application to be included in this scheme should be sent either to the South African Council for Scientific and Industrial Research, P.O. Box 395, Pretoria, or to me personally at Rhodes University, Grahamstown. While every possible facility will be granted to selected visiting specialists, it should be noted that there is no possibility of financial aid from this end.

The ownership of the next specimen or specimens is of less importance than their proper preservation for scientific purposes. As certain organs and body fluids require special treatment and preservation, it is intended to compile a set of special instructions to be issued to those in areas where it is possible that a fresh Coelacanth may be obtained. It will be appreciated if those interested will kindly furnish detailed special instructions composed in language as simple as possible, giving full directions, and not only the names, but also the actual composition, of any materials to be employed.

Since there is a hope that more Coelacanths may be found at the Comoro Islands, it is desirable that all such materials should be available there.

This elicited a widespread response from scientists all over the world, and as a result my wife was able to publish a composite account giving detailed instructions for the care and preservation of a Coelacanth, so as to enable the maximum to be obtained from investigations.

Among the general letters we received in all this time were many different types. The clerical staff had a fat file of letters which they privately and irreverently termed the 'Crackpot' file (which I did not see until later), in which they housed letters to which that term could be applied. As in the case of the first Coelacanth, there were many letters from apparently religious persons of a certain type which came from virtually all English-speaking countries. Some of these correspondents were really shocked that a man like myself should so misuse his position as to mislead the public by talking of millions of years. One man, whose attacks editors had refused to print, published a denunciatory pamphlet about my views. In some missives my worldly end and my future in another sphere were vividly portrayed; I was told that it would be better for mankind if people of my type had never been born, and there were even threats of personal violence. One good lady in Grahamstown called in some indignation with an issue of a well-known paper from England, in which somebody quite scurrilously 'Gave me blazes'. She expected I would write to pulverise the author, and was surprised when I laughed and said that I never replied to anything like that, nor would I permit her to do so on my behalf. A day or two later she delightedly brought me a further issue of the same journal in which somebody else (in England) had pulverised the author. It generally happens that way.

An R.A.F. officer who had been at the Comores during the war wrote to say that he hoped I would not be shocked at the tale, but as food had been a problem at that time, depth-charges were used to get fish. Many queer creatures came up that way, and after seeing the picture of the Coelacanth he was almost certain that there had been several in the catches they had made about those islands. I need hardly record that I was not shocked by this disclosure; in fact, if he felt that way I wondered what his reactions would be to what I could tell him.

The descendants of a missionary who had lived near Mount Kilimanjaro wrote from Germany giving a good deal of information about flying-dragons they believed still to live in those parts.

The family had repeatedly heard of them from the natives, and one man had actually seen such a creature in flight close by at night. I did not and do not dispute at least the possibility that some such creature may still exist. A man of foreign birth reported having seen a dragon at a place on our own south coast. It had left clear tracks on the ground before it vanished in dense bush, and though he had told the police, nobody had succeeded in tracking it. I suggested a Leguaan (a big lizard of South Africa). People from many countries wrote to tell of Coelacanths they had seen there. An American soldier stated that they were common in the fish-markets of Korea. A woman in Bermuda was positive one had been offered to her by a fisherman there. One somewhat politically minded person wrote to reprove me for naming the fish after Dr. Malan, and said that it would have been much more fitting to have honoured in that way the native who had caught it. Several natives did the same. An American who wrote about the Coelacanth, concluded by sympathising with me for having to live in such a dreadful country as South Africa, a visiting native professor had told them all about it. I concluded my reply by saying that many years ago I had heard a talk by a visiting American about life in his country which had left us all very thankful that we lived in South Africa, and that what they had been told was probably as accurate as the story we had heard. An American ichthyologist wrote: 'Now I can die happy for I have lived to see the great American public excited about fish.'

The broadcast from Durban about the whole matter had apparently been greatly appreciated, though friends laughingly reproved me for having made many others weep from my emotion. My young son certainly disapproved of that part. Anonymous letters are normally despised, but we received some that do not fall in that category, and one is reproduced on p. 254, at the end of that broadcast.

The whole affair had some peculiar consequences. All over the world it led to greatly increased sales of books about fishes; in Britain especially of one by a late member of the staff of the British Museum. I had sent a scale of the first Coelacanth to an American museum, and this had been kept for safety in the strong-room. Now it was brought out for exhibition, and thousands of people filed past to see it. A prominent member of the British

Parliament, in attacking an opponent, called him a 'Coelacanth' on the grounds that from his long silence in that august assembly it was a surprise to find him still alive. The able retort was that the Coelacanth lived long, had great endurance, and never spoke unless it had something to say. At least a thousand people told us personally that while it had been very good of Dr. Malan to do what he did, it was only right that he should have, and of course everyone knew that General Smuts would have done at least the same if he had been there. We just smiled! It is significant that literally a flood of letters and telegrams of congratulations and thanks had been sent to Dr. Malan, not only from South Africa; and among them were many from persons, from angling and other clubs, societies, and institutions, composed mainly of those opposed to his political principles. Many of those who had done this told us personally or wrote to say so.

When the general election early in 1953 showed the trend of public opinion by returning Malan to power with a greatly increased majority, one close but very sore old friend, to whom this represented almost the end of the world, wrote in accusation that 'you and your darned old Coelacanth helped this on', and this view was very widely held. But in that form it was certainly not correct. If Dr. Malan gained any advantage from the Coelacanth affair, it was because he had earned it himself; it was entirely his own doing. Not only did he put himself out on my behalf when no one could have blamed him if he had not, but he took the decision alone and the very considerable risk that this entailed entirely alone. It was a risk, especially at that time. It was very different with Smuts, who would not have had to take any risk to help me, but who would not even spare a few moments to hear me.

The series of events which had compelled me to seek assistance from both Smuts and Malan had been almost fantastic in their similarity, not only in the subject of my appeal, but in each case by the most curious coincidence the climax had come not long before a critical general election. It was even more fantastic that each of these two men had, almost dramatically, within a very short time afterwards been himself treated by his own people almost exactly as he had treated me—the one spurned, the other supported. One could not escape the conclusion that this indicated that the manner in which each man had behaved in my case was symbolical of the way he had treated his own people, and once again it showed clearly that, though this may take a long time, in the end, if he lives long enough every man reaps what he sows.

Chapter Seventeen

FALLING THROUGH

EVEN though the discovery of this second Coelacanth at the Comores, and the information gleaned by Hunt, appeared to pin-point that area as the home of those animals, it was clear that they could scarcely be abundant there. Although it was true that this Comoran Coelacanth had been found in the type of environment which satisfied every condition I had deduced and predicted, I knew only too well that a Coelacanth in any place does not necessarily mean that it is at home.

Most of Hunt's information was got from natives, and South Africans know from bitter experience that the average native attaches little importance to factual accuracy or to veracity. Their approach in such matters is very different from ours, and when questioned a native will almost invariably tell you what he thinks you want to know, rather than what he knows about what you ask, or even if he knows nothing at all.

At the same time, however, the evidence that Coelacanths were caught occasionally indicated that if their true home was not at the Comores themselves, it would not be so far off this time, and there was all the more likelihood that this might be found more easily. The field of search would certainly be greatly narrowed down.

It had long been one of the main objectives of my existence to establish or to see established the certain home of the Coelacanth. Even before my return to the Union with the animal, and on the flight itself, my mind was busy revolving this matter and exploring possibilities. I hoped that the discovery of the Coelacanth would abate the scepticism of the French and stir them to action, in the Comores at least, but at the same time nobody had studied this matter as deeply as I and nobody else knew as much. While I know only too well that nobody is unique and nobody is irreplaceable, this had become a matter of personal honour, and before I died I wanted to see it completely tied up and tidied away in its proper niche in the halls of science. This desire was greatly increased when I discovered that, after all, we had not yet got a complete animal. That also I was determined to get or see made available for science, and though tired of the tropics, I was quite ready to go again, and as often as need be, now that this more than encouraging discovery had been made.

It had long been my ambition to catch a Coelacanth alive so that the ordinary man could see it in an aquarium, and be given the opportunity to look back to the kind of creature that lived hundreds of millions of years ago. There is probably no other true scientific story which has given the ordinary man so clear a vision of what is meant by time, and to have a live Coelacanth on view would round it off in a way that H. G. Wells would certainly have appreciated. It was in one sense his idea of a 'Time Machine' come true.

There were many other things as well. Was there still another species, the small one Hunt had mentioned?* In addition, the startling difference from *Latimeria* observed in *Malania* raised difficult problems. Was *Malania* really different, or was it just an exceptional, perhaps extreme, variant?

Any species reproduces itself with comparatively small variation between individuals, but I had long held the view that this 'mass production' would tend to weaken or slacken in the course of time, that in a relatively broadly unchanging type like the Coelacanth, while the general form remained constant, after long ages there would be increasing variation in characters of lesser importance, like the position or size of the fins and other parts. There is one curious, rather primitive, rare type of fish (*Tetragonurus*), which is like this. Though it has been known for centuries and odd specimens have turned up over almost the whole globe, comparatively few, less than thirty adults, have been found in all that time. What is amazing is that hardly any two specimens agree in minor characters, like fin counts, and to this day scientists do not really know if there are a dozen species or only one. It will need hundreds of specimens before this can be settled.

* I have since come to believe that this is actually the Oil-fish (*Ruvettus*) that the Comorans catch in the same way as the Coelacanth.

In the case of the Coelacanth it was clear that problems like these could be solved only with more, probably only with many, specimens. There was also the strong possibility of mutilation or of deformity, or both, to account for these differences, but one needs to be cautious in seeking to explain things that way. We had one striking lesson.

When working in the northern part of Mozambique, in a canoe-catch one day I saw one of the peculiar Unicorn-fishes, a type of fish that has a long horn on its head, and this one even more peculiar because it had a hump on its back as well. You often see humped-back fish, a result of being either deformed or mutilated, usually when young. I looked at this one closely and decided it was probably a deformed specimen of the large Unicorn-fish that is quite common up there; but at the lighthouse that night my wife remarked that she had seen a deformed '*Naso*' that morning, it had a humped back. That made me sit up, and I questioned her. Next day I watched for that 'deformed' fish, and within a week we had got a dozen; and what is more, while all had humps some had no horns. It did not take long to discover that this was no 'deformed' fish at all, but a true species, and I found that while the males had horns the females had not. I described that fish in scientific literature and named it '*Naso rigoletto*'. Following the publication, from scientists over a great part of the world came a series of letters, many quite amusing, some chagrined, to say that they had had that species in their collections many, many years, and had just dismissed it as an abnormal or deformed fish. So I was wary about 'deformed' fish. It is risky to decide anything like that on one specimen, and in the case of the Coelacanth it all pointed clearly to the need for more, for many more, specimens.

I wanted to clear up all these points; it was something I wanted to see settled before I died, and I was prepared to go on myself. The Governor had given a most cordial invitation to return to the Comores, where it was clear that no scientific work like mine was in progress; nor had it probably ever been done at all. Coelacanths were apparently caught near the end of the year; the best time, with little wind, for any work on fishes. We could do our normal work and hunt Coelacanths as well, as we had been doing for years. We must get an expedition going.

Even when I composed that early article (p. 243) for *The Times*, most of this was in my mind, and it led me to insert the concluding paragraph as a venture, in which I asked if some yacht owner would make his vessel available for this search. There was little possibility of the large and perpetually busy South African Government Fisheries research vessel being seconded for such a project, but there have been a number of wealthy men, owners of sea-going yachts, who have rendered great service to science by placing these at the disposal of biologists over wide areas of the ocean. One of them might be attracted by this venture.

In the nightmare weeks that followed our return to Grahamstown this matter had to be relegated to a temporary background, but it pushed itself right to the front with the receipt of a most interesting letter from Jersey, Channel Islands. Dated 16th January 1953, it came from W. J. Stuttard, who represented himself as owner-master of a 150-ton twin-screw yacht, *La Contenta*. He offered this vessel, himself, and crew. He had a photographer, and stated that their expedition was not a profit-making concern other than what they might make out of travel-films, and he mentioned their thirst for knowledge and adventure.

The Channel Islands! The place, we are told, to which people of means or those with enough to live on without working go to escape British income-tax. This looked like the answer, but even though with our resources this seemed the only way, it is almost always cheaper in the long run to pay in cash for what you get rather than in other ways, and anything like this would need the most careful handling, and even then endless difficulties and complications can arise that had never been foreseen. No matter what terms or conditions might be agreed upon in advance, should any dispute arise in a case like this my party would be under most severe handicaps. The possibility of trouble is much greater when arrangements and agreements have to be made by correspondence.

So I replied with gratitude but without committing myself, and immediately put the issue to the Prime Minister's Department, as a matter of policy, and because this gave a sounder approach to the possibility of a Government vessel of some kind being seconded for this purpose, one which despite its global interest had acquired so clearly a South African national character. The reply indicated that there appeared to be no valid reason for refusing the offer of the *La Contenta*. The issue was then in turn submitted to the South African Council for Scientific and Industrial Research, and from them was received a recommendation to accept what appeared a generous offer. The Council also generously voted a thousand pounds towards the expedition, and I set about raising funds from the public. Thanks mainly to handsome contributions from a group of Johannesburg business magnates, this was rapidly achieved.

After having taken what seemed satisfactory precautions, I wrote on the 7th March 1953 to accept this offer of Stuttard, and it was settled that the sole direction of the scientific work should be in my hands. It was my intention at that time to manage by some means to make a short visit to Jersey, to meet Stuttard and his crew and to inspect the vessel, but this proved impossible, as there was too much that always needed my personal attention.

Arrangements for any such expedition as was now visualised to hunt further Coelacanths involved negotiations in widely different fields. First there was the critical matter of a vessel, now apparently solved by Stuttard's offer of *La Contenta*. There were all the special equipment and stores necessary for our work and maintenance. Thirdly, there was the matter of participation by other scientists and contribution by other institutions. Since at least part of our work would be in French waters, it would be necessary to seek permission and possibly some type of co-operation from the French.

Of all these, transport was the most troublesome, and once that was settled it seemed at least possible that no matter how many other obstacles might arise, they could probably be overcome. Even if the French were not co-operative, there were other parts not far off where we might have as good a chance of finding Coelacanths, and there are many things one can get done on the spot that volumes of correspondence will not even loosen. So transport was undoubtedly number one.

Museums and other institutions in various parts of the world had been asking if I intended to go to seek more Coelacanths, and some were eager to have at least some part in any such venture. Some were anxious to have Coelacanths. The press published a statement by a member of the staff of the British Museum that they were prepared to support an expedition for this purpose if I got it going. Although Stuttard was apparently prepared to offer his vessel and crew without payment, and I had sufficient to cover fuel for his vessel, as well as for food and equipment, as I well knew there is always an element of uncertainty in the cost of such ventures. We had some financial reserves, but there was no harm in having more, and no harm in permitting others, if they were eager to do so, to make contributions, provided no uncomfortable terms were attached to them. I wanted to find Coelacanths, not for myself but for science, and if science would help financially, all the better.

After weighing the matter carefully, I decided to select a limited number of the leading institutions in the world and to send to each the following proposal, namely that the payment of the sum of £500 towards the expedition would secure the right to purchase a Coelacanth for a further £500. This meant that a specimen would cost £1,000, which was very considerably less than it might be expected to cost any individual institution if it conducted the search alone, while it limited liability to £500 if none were found. In the event of there being fewer Coelacanths available than participants, they would be left to settle the allocation between themselves. It was to be accepted, however, that the first Coelacanth taken in French waters was to be given to France. The money subscribed in this way was to go to Stuttard for expenses.

The British Museum and several others replied that they did not wish to participate, a large American institution apparently found £500 too large a sum to risk, and indeed only two of those approached hoped to be able to do so. Fortunately, however, as far as it was possible to judge at that time, we apparently had enough for our purpose without any such extra aid.

We shall now follow the course of negotiations with Stuttard.

Even before I accepted his offer, he had informed me that he intended to come via the Cape, giving sound reasons for that course. In letters dated the 17th February 1953 and the 12th March 1953 respectively, he visualised leaving in good time, stating in the latter his intention to leave in the first week in May (1953).

Knowing what I did about preparing for expeditions, I wondered whether he would find it possible to do this, and was not surprised to receive a letter, dated the 15th April 1953, in which he reported difficulty in getting equipment delivered in time.

This difficulty evidently increased, for in a letter dated the 30th April 1953 Stuttard reported that the delay in getting equipment might mean that he would have to go via the Mediterranean.

In my reply to this, dated the 5th May 1953, was the following:

> If you should go through the Mediterranean it will I think cause the very greatest disappointment out here as there will be great numbers of people, especially those who are supporting us, who are hoping to see the vessel. Pictures of the vessel have appeared in all the leading papers. I would not let them have any of you without your special permission, and in any case felt that it would be better when you are actually in South African waters. Another great drawback of your going through the Mediterranean would be that you would be compelled to battle southwards against the monsoon, which I can assure you is really appalling, and the run from the Red Sea downwards would be something of a nightmare at that time. In addition, I am planning to provision the ship very largely here, but that is no insuperable matter if you can get sufficient foodstuffs in England. You are likely to encounter difficulty in getting things in Kenya. If the foodstuffs we are planning are to be taken, then I think it will be advisable for you to load them here, as to get them round to Port Amelia in time will be more than a nightmare. With regard to all this, I should stress that we shall be more than content if we get to the Comores by September. There is no hurry, and we get the best tides then. If you leave England even as late as the end of June, assuming that it takes you 25 or 30 days to the Cape, you should easily get to Mozambique Harbour well before the end of August. I think it would be advisable for you to make Mozambique Harbour our point of departure from the African mainland, as it gives us a real northing in our crossing which we may be very thankful to have.

Stuttard considered this matter and wrote several letters about it. Eventually, in a letter dated the 13th May 1953, he stated that he would sail not later than the first week in July and come via the Cape.

That seemed definite and satisfactory, and in the meantime Dr. Eigil Nielsen of Copenhagen, one of the foremost palaeontologists of Europe, had written to say that he was waiting for a final decision from his University about participating in our expedition, and that he was, in any case, planning to go and hunt for Coelacanth fossils on Madagascar.

With this in view I wrote to Stuttard and suggested that if Nielsen came in he might perhaps travel on the *La Contenta*, which would be of benefit to all. Stuttard welcomed this, and stated that he could easily be accommodated.

In a letter dated the 23rd May 1953 Stuttard stated that I could take it that he would definitely be sailing within the first few days of July, and that such small items as could not be got aboard in time would be sent on to Durban.

On the 5th June 1953 came a letter from Nielsen dated the 28th May 1953:

> Today I got the welcome news that the money had been granted, which means that I now am in the position definitely to accept your most kind invitation to contribute to the Coelacanth venture as well as to carry out my work on Madagascar.
>
> I am extremely glad to know that it seems possible to arrange for my actual partaking in part of your expedition, and as to eventual inconveniences I am accustomed to rather much in that way from the life in our small crowded Greenland vessels, which often spend more than a month in covering the distance between Denmark and Greenland. The further possibility that an arrangement could be made so that I could join the yacht already in England sounds of course perfect to me. My equipment does certainly not take up much space, as my first plan was to go by airplane. I beg you ask the owner of the yacht to be so kind as to inform me as to time and place for the departure, and to thank him on my behalf for his invitation.
>
> As to my contribution to the expedition, please instruct me as to the deliverance. I can send the money to England or to you or deliver them personally, I don't know which method you prefer?
>
> I shall be very grateful for your advice as to what sort of camping outfit, clothing, and photographic equipment is necessary for work in Madagascar. I suppose that it is possible to buy much of the things on the spot, Leica-films (i.e. Kodachrome films), etc., probably can be had out there?

On the 5th June 1953 I wrote to Stuttard as follows:

> I have this moment received a letter dated 28th May 1953 from Dr. Nielsen of Copenhagen, to say that he has been granted the necessary funds and that he wishes to be a contributor to the expedition, also that he would be very pleased indeed to travel with the *La Contenta*. He had originally planned to go out to Madagascar

by air. He is delighted at the opportunity of coming out with the *La Contenta*, and says that he has not got very much equipment. He asks that you should make the earliest possible contact with him, especially to notify him of the date of departure. I am enclosing a copy of my letter to him, which goes by this same air post, and you can see that I have told him that the payment of the original £500 can be by arrangement between you and him, because I feel that should go to you. Please make your own arrangements. In addition, he should pay for his keep. I suggest that you work out some reasonable sum like 10s. per day to cover the cost of food, etc., even more if you think it wise, as he would otherwise certainly have to pay quite a considerable amount to get out. He will doubtless have to make his own arrangements for the return journey.

To avoid any possiblity of misunderstanding on that point, I had quite early sent Stuttard an explicit account of my resources and had said that this was the limit from my side. The financial aspect had in the later correspondence begun to obtrude itself, and in a letter dated 4th June 1953 Stuttard wrote that as he feared in the beginning for the financial success of this venture and could not himself afford to purchase all the equipment required, he considered it necessary to seek further funds on my behalf. He had indeed approached the Nuffield Trust.

From this and other matters, on the 9th June 1953 I sent the following cable to Stuttard: 'If financial burden too heavy you better cancel everything writing unable assist further.' To this Stuttard cabled in reply that he intended sailing as planned and that he had written to Nielsen.

On the 10th June 1953 the President and Vice-President of the South African Council for Scientific and Industrial Research visited Grahamstown and called at my Department. I gave them a résumé of all that had occurred, showed them the correspondence, and told them that in my opinion a distinct element of uncertainty about the whole project had arisen.

We had a full discussion and it was their opinion, as it was mine, that it would be inadvisable to spend money on the project unless all the arrangements were quite sound and satisfactory to all parties concerned.

Stuttard wrote again on the 11th June 1953, enclosing a copy of a letter of the same date from himself to Nielsen, in which he informed Nielsen that he was planning to sail about mid-July, the date being dependent upon the delivery of a large deep-freeze essential to my requirements. He stated that the route would be via the Cape.

Although the date of sailing had been moved from the first week in July to mid-July, this still fell within my time-limits, but all my anxieties were aroused by a letter from Stuttard dated the 2nd July 1953, in which he stated that he had reluctantly come to the conclusion that it would be out of the question to come via the Cape if he could not leave before the 15th July. He undertook to try to decide early the following week and to advise me by cable, so that I could get all my stuff up to Mozambique if he had to come via the Mediterranean. When this issue had arisen earlier, on the 12th May 1953, I had written to Stuttard as follows:

> I am indeed pleased that you have abandoned the Mediterranean approach. Not only would it have caused me endless difficulties at this end, but for you to have gone battling into a four- and sometimes five-knot current against a southerly monsoon as well would certainly not have been pleasant. It will be quite bad enough going up the Madagascar Channel against the current, though you will have the wind with you in the southerly part, and proper use of eddies can avoid a good deal of trouble (north of Madagascar the current runs north). All that we can go into here, and it may be possible to arrange for you to have a discussion with the Captain or Mate of one of the Portuguese Coasters at Lourenço Marques. Regarding the explosives, I have heard from the Portuguese Authorities, who state that it will be almost impossible to arrange for them to be sent to Port Amelia. I think it will be quite clear for them to go to Lourenço Marques and be stored in the Government magazine there, and the Port Captain has promised every facility and aid in this matter. So after what you say I am going ahead.
>
> I wish to emphasise again that as far as we are concerned, it will suit us quite well if we get to the Comores by the beginning of September. The four best tides of the year for reef work are the 24 August, 8th and 23rd September, and the 9th October. If we can contrive things so that we do the circumnavigation of Madagascar in November, that will probably be best of all, as we can expect the least wind and slowest current at that time.

In South Africa both persons and firms had donated a wide variety of goods and supplies for the expedition, and it had been arranged for them to be sent to the nearest port. At Cape Town, Port Elizabeth, East London, and Durban there would be generous consignments ready for *La Contenta*. At Lourenço Marques there was more equipment and that ton of explosives, whose part as essential to the expedition had been established between us before I accepted Stuttard's offer. In addition to all this, our Government had kindly conceded a number of special concessions for *La Contenta's* visit that would mean a great deal to Stuttard as well as to the expedition.

At that stage, 8th July 1953, it was clear that even to attempt the by then enormous task of getting all this dispersed stuff to Port Amelia within six or seven weeks to meet this abrupt change of plans was too much. The Portuguese authorities had been quite explicit that it was virtually impossible to arrange for the transport of the ton of explosives from the Government magazine in Lourenço Marques to a port in the north and to store them there. I knew what transport along the East African coast was like at that time, and short of chartering a special vessel or by other expenditure on a quite unwarranted scale, it would have been virtually impossible to do so. I should have to consult those who had provided the money, but on general principles I was opposed to the risk of spending in that way so much of the funds that had been donated, for even if I succeeded in this formidable and apparently impossible task and got the essential goods there by the stated date, sea travel in a small vessel is so uncertain that there could be no guarantee that Stuttard would arrive in time to carry out the expedition, or indeed at all. With the best will in the world he could never guarantee to do so. I could picture our party perched on top of a pile of partly perishable baggage in the humid torridity of a remote East African port, while this small vessel battered its bows southwards against the powerful monsoon-impelled waves and the current of the long stretch down the East African coast. We should have no redress if Stuttard did not arrive, it might prove beyond his powers or control, and all that tremendous effort and expenditure would be wasted. From my experience and knowledge, I was quite firm in my opinion that what Stuttard now asked would be almost impossible without unjustifiable expenditure, that it lacked certainty as justification, and in short to attempt it at all would be folly.

Serious as it was, this was not the only complication that arose from this proposed abrupt change of plans. Stuttard had apparently not succeeded in obtaining all the items he had hoped free of charge. Notable among these was a deep-freeze unit, to which he referred in almost every letter. According to his letters, he could not leave without it. Owing to the unexpected but obvious concern Stuttard had revealed about finance, I had got interested friends to agree to cover the cost of the deep-freeze unit (the intention being to sell it on their behalf after the expedition), and wrote to Stuttard as follows on the 22nd June 1953:

Following on our recent correspondence I have taken further action with regard to finance, going to certain friends who are in some ways a reserve I do not easily care to tap. At any rate, the result is that they are prepared to pay for the deep-freeze, on condition that at the conclusion of our association it shall either pass to my possession or be disposed of and the amount returned. This should relieve you, especially as you have indicated that the deep-freeze is not a piece of equipment which you will greatly value for your vessel.

In the letter dated the 2nd July 1953 Stuttard wrote that he was pleased to note that I was accepting the responsibility of the deep-freeze, and as there was a twenty-five per cent. discount I should not experience difficulty in disposing of it at a profit.

As no cable (see p. 202) had arrived by the 8th July 1953, the date on which Stuttard's letter of the 2nd July was received, I consulted the friends who had offered to sponsor the deep-freeze, and told them of the situation that had suddenly arisen. When they were originally approached about this, I had explained that the vessel would come via the Cape, as that was clearly understood from Stuttard at that time. After full consideration they now stated that they were not prepared to continue this offer under this sudden drastic change of conditions imposed by Stuttard, and the following cable was sent to Stuttard:

Sponsors prepared refund cost deep-freeze only on arrival here and in time carry out full operations. Unless come via Cape impossible co-operate.

Three days later I received a letter from the Jersey Electrical Co. Ltd., dated 6th July 1953, the concluding paragraph of which was as follows:

We shall be pleased to receive your remittance at the very earliest opportunity and in order to prevent any further delays, we are assuming that this will be coming forward and consequently, we have asked Frigidaire Ltd., to get the equipment down immediately as we understand from Mr. Stuttard that he wishes to leave Jersey by the end of July.

Even by this date, 11th July 1953, there had been no cable from Stuttard, and now this letter had disturbing implications. It implied that by the 6th July, when this Jersey firm wrote, Stuttard knew that he could not leave before the 15th, and so, according to his own statement, if he came at all he intended to take the Mediterranean route.* Nielsen was due to join Stuttard on the 10th July, and I doubted whether he would be prepared to wait at Jersey until the end of that month, which this last letter indicated as sailing time.

Nothing further happened until the 16th, which brought a letter from Stuttard dated 9th July 1953 in which he informed me, among other matters, that Nielsen was due to arrive next day, and that he would be informed about the situation (see p. 206). He went on to say that to prevent an absolute fiasco he advised me to send everything to Mozambique and he would be there in ample time.

On the 16th July 1953 I sent a cable to Stuttard as follows: 'Letter ninth received confirm ending co-operation writing Smith.'

On the 23rd July 1953 a letter dated the 18th arrived from Stuttard, in which he informed me that he was in touch with the French and Danish Embassies with a view to participating in an international expedition, and that he had made a statement to the President of the South African Council of Scientific and Industrial Research and to the Acting Secretary of External Affairs.

On the 21st July 1953 a letter dated 16th July arrived from Nielsen, in which he stated:

The 10th July I arrived at Jersey expecting to leave from there one of the next days with *La Contenta*. Mr. Stuttard informed me, however, that the actual departure would not take place before the end of July, and that moreover the boat would go via Suez instead

* See letter from Nielsen, p. 206.

of the original route via Cape Town. I was somewhat troubled both because of the altered route, firstly on account of the rainy season starting in Madagascar some time in November, and secondly because I had been looking forward to seeing you in Grahamstown.

I therefore altered my plans by booking a passage to Port Elizabeth in the *Edinburgh Castle*, Union Castle Line. I leave Southampton today and expect to arrive at Port Elizabeth on the 1st August.

In this way I get a whole month more time for the work in Madagascar, and, moreover, I get an opportunity to see you in Grahamstown one of the first days in August.

Nielsen arrived at Port Elizabeth on the 1st August 1953. He had arrived at Jersey on the 10th July 1953 and went to *La Contenta*, where he met a few men and women on board, introduced as the crew. Later he went to a maternity or nursing-home with Stuttard, who introduced him to his (Stuttard's) wife, still abed, having a few days before given birth to a child. According to Nielsen, he was informed of the delay in sailing and of the change in route, but nothing was mentioned about the possible severance of connection between Stuttard and myself. After weighing the situation Nielsen eventually decided to leave, as outlined in his letter. It was only when he got a cable from me at sea that he realised that something had gone wrong in the arrangements between Stuttard and myself.

So, after all those months of strenuous work, there I was in late July right back at the starting-post again, and once more rapid action and decisions were called for. A vast amount of material, equipment, and stores was waiting, including a ton of explosives, and while the idea of just abandoning everything was hateful, to go on meant finding a ship in a hurry. We must be at the Comores for October and November at the latest, which meant leaving before the end of August, barely a month.

As will be outlined in the following chapter, I had other troubles, for negotiations with the French had not been settled.

It was suddenly announced over the radio that I had cancelled the Coelacanth expedition. This I immediately contradicted. My first move was to telephone Minister Paul Sauer, to whom I outlined the position and asked him if there was any vessel in the Harbour Administration that would be suitable for my project, and if so how could I set about getting it. He said his staff would find out, and within twelve hours the answer came back that there was no vessel they could recommend or release.

Meanwhile I had telephoned prominent people in the shipping world at all the ports and others in Johannesburg and Pretoria, asking them to try to locate some vessel in South Africa that could be diverted to our project. A few doubtful prospects were notified, and on the 27th July 1953 I set out by air in the forlorn hope of finding at that late date some vessel that might still enable us to do what we had planned. I wanted to hunt Coelacanths, but had no intention that we should fill a Tiger Shark's belly by going in an unsuitable vessel. I ransacked Port Elizabeth, but found nothing suitable; then left by air and got to Durban that same evening, where within an hour of arrival I was inspecting vessels. One or two were possible, but were ruled out either by cost or by the time needed for essential repairs. On the 29th July 1953 I went to Cape Town and was whisked off at once on arrival to a conference. It was bitterly cold at that time, but I could visualise East Africa and the Comores. One vessel was hopeful but very costly, and when I telegraphed to explain the situation and to ask the South African Council for Scientific and Industrial Research if they could manage another thousand pounds, the answer came back: 'Yes, but we strongly recommend postponement until next year.' I could not ignore that, and with all the other difficulties not yet solved it spelled 'Finis', there was too little time.

Nielsen's ship arrived early in the morning and I went to meet him. We had only a few brief moments, in which I gave him the main outlines of the story and told him my wife would meet him at Port Elizabeth.

I had asked to see Dr. Malan—once again I was in that office where I had sat in such discomfort before. I told his Secretary that my need was past, and if the Dokter was very busy I should go; but he said no, he knew he would like to see me. When I went in Dr. Malan rose at my entrance and smiled as he held my hand. He asked what I wanted, but I said I would not burden him with my troubles. I wished just to greet him again, though I told him briefly that my Coelacanth hunt was off.

I slept most of the time in the plane on the way back to my wife and Nielsen at Port Elizabeth, from where we took him to Grahamstown, to the laboratory, and of course first to the

Coelacanth. Nielsen had worked on Coelacanth fossils all his adult life. He had baked in heat and frozen in terrible cold hunting them from the equator to the Arctic circle, so that they were not mere fossils and academic abstractions to him, but an intimate part of his life. On his way to South Africa, Nielsen had been staggered by the comparative lack of interest in Coelacanths he found in an important institution in London. One scientist, indeed, had said he was 'Sick of Coelacanths'. It was beyond Nielsen. When we got into the room where old *Malania* lay, Nielsen walked all round and looked for some time in silence. Then he said, almost breathless with emotion, and with deep sincerity, 'How beautiful.' And so he is, old man Coelacanth, to a scientist, a wonderful and beautiful thing.

Nielsen is, of course, a Scandinavian, and we heard later that before his arrival our staff speculated on his appearance. It was decided he would be huge, blond, and genial, but instead Nielsen is small and dark, active in mind and body, and has a rapier-like humour. His English is excellent, as we learnt when he gave a public lecture we had requested on his work. He is no soft laboratory worker, but as tough as a scientist in his field has to be to get anywhere. He would have been at home on the shores of a Triassic swamp.

When he got to work on *Malania* it was interesting to see that he went first to examine that extraordinary puzzling cavity and channels in the nose, next to look for traces of the air-bladder, exactly as I had done myself. Smoking is not permitted in our highly inflammable Department, so that Nielsen got to know the outside of our building quite well.

After a week of intensive study, Nielsen was due to leave. Early that morning, at his special request, we went for the last time to the laboratory. He took the Coelacanth's pectoral fin in his hand and shaking it, said solemnly, 'Good-bye, Malania.' It was very sincere and quite touching.

It is interesting to record that by courtesy of the French authorities in the Union, we managed to send Nielsen's heavy baggage to Madagascar on a French warship that happened to be passing. Nielsen went over by air, and later wrote to tell me that he had got more than two thousand splendid Coelacanth fossils in Madagascar. One could hardly describe them as anything but valuable scientific material, but he did not indicate that there had been any difficulty in taking them from French territory.

The following is quoted from the *Evening Post* of Jersey, issue of 2nd February 1955.

END OF LA CONTENTA'S *THREE-YEAR STAY* COELACANTH SEARCH RECALLED.

The 160-ton motor yacht, *La Contenta*, which has been in St. Helier Harbour for nearly three years, left this morning for St. Malo.

This former Admiralty Fairmile Class craft came into the news in May 1953, when she was being fitted out to undertake an expedition in search of that extraordinary fish the Coelacanth. A specimen of this supposedly prehistoric fish had been found in the Indian Ocean, leading to arrangements being completed between the noted Professor J. L. B. Smith and the owner-captain of the *La Contenta*, Mr. W. J. Stuttard, to equip the craft to search for another specimen. However, after a period of time this expedition fell through and it was understood that *La Contenta* would then be used to search for treasure in the China Seas. This venture also fell through.

Only Once Put to Sea

In a stay of two years nine months in St. Helier Harbour, *La Contenta* only once put to sea, and that was to Gorey on the occasion of the regatta there in 1953. Recently *La Contenta* was thoroughly overhauled and successfully underwent tests in St. Aubin's Bay.

Mr. W. J. Stuttard stated shortly before leaving, 'We are bound for Vigo in Spain and from there we shall cruise in the Mediterranean where we shall stay. We are tired of Jersey.'

Chapter Eighteen

PORTCULLIS AND DRAWBRIDGE

THE global reactions to the extraordinary culmination of my long search for the Coelacanth had profound effects in France, where widespread and somewhat hysterical propaganda in the press aroused public feeling. I was denounced as a robber who had pounced on their national treasure. As a result, there was widespread agitation, and it was urged that the French Government should demand the surrender of the Coelacanth to France.

This could scarcely have arisen had the matter been presented to the French nation in its true perspective, for apart from my initial intense anxiety to see that it really was a Coelacanth and that it was safe, it had never been my intention to keep it to myself in any way. I intended the fish to be available to expert scientists of all nations. It was indeed my hope to be able to find more specimens for that purpose myself, and the expedition had of course been planned to that end. All specimens were to be for the benefit of science generally, not to belong to me or to be confined to the scientists of any one country, but for all.

Nothing of this outburst was communicated to me officially, but it was natural to expect that its effects would not be without repercussions in higher circles. As I wished to do scientific work in French waters, it would be necessary to request formal permission from the French Government, and those who had to consider my request could scarcely be unaware of this degree of national resentment that had been aroused against me, while they would almost certainly be unaware of the true circumstances.

As I had no direct contact with any personality in French Government circles, on the 15th January 1953, as a preliminary, I wrote as follows to Dr. Millot, who was then in Paris:

> I wish to record my great appreciation of all the assistance and co-operation we received from the authorities of your country, not only through their representatives in South Africa, but also

those in charge of the Comores Archipelago. The Governor, M. P. Coudert, did everything in his power to make our all too short stay on Pamanzi Island as pleasant as possible, and both he and his officials, realising the significance of this great discovery, gave us every assistance.

As a scientist I know that you will rejoice that this has occurred, and it will naturally be of added interest to you that the discovery has been made in waters under the charge of your Government.

I may inform you officially that although the knowledge of this has come via our leaflets and constant propaganda, I have requested Captain E. E. Hunt that the next Coelacanth he might get in French territorial waters should be handed over to the French Authorities. Even though the present specimen is considerably more damaged than I had hoped, and a complete fresh specimen is essential for the full study which is contemplated, I shall be happy to know that you get into your possession the next, and I trust complete, specimen.

Will you kindly accept, my dear Sir, once again my sincere thanks for the co-operation of the French Authorities and a renewed expression of my belief that all of us who are scientists in Africa must work together for science.

I received from Millot in Paris a cordial reply, dated the 19th February 1953, in which he expressed the hope that we might work together, and that he would later outline steps to that end. He also stated that the resentment which had been aroused in France had resulted in a decree prohibiting the export of scientific material of value, including Coelacanths, save with the authority of competent local scientific organisations.

To this letter the following reply was sent to Millot on the 23rd February 1953:

. . . the reactions and objections in France . . . were surely made in the absence of knowledge of the true facts of the case. Only today have I had a letter from another source quoting some of the events you mention. For that reason I am enclosing a statement which I shall be pleased if you will kindly hand to the proper authorities, and to the press if you judge it correct to do that.*

At the moment I am engaged in the preliminaries of arranging an expedition to the Comores and Madagascar. This involves very much work and a fairly large vessel (150 tons) which has to be

* I have not yet received comment from any source on this memorandum.

carefully arranged many months ahead. Will you kindly let me know specifically as soon as possible if we shall be permitted to work at the Comores and about Madagascar; we plan to come from about August–October, first at the Comores and then to voyage round Madagascar.

You may not know that I am engaged on a large-scale work on the fishes of the western Indian Ocean. During the past seven years we have made a number of expeditions to East Africa, covering the whole coast of Mozambique, Zanzibar, Pemba, and Kenya.

In order to use our time as efficiently as possible, we need to employ explosives and Rotenone poison, and have everywhere received permission for that purpose. Will this be permitted in your territory also?

We have got together very large and important collections from the east coast for our final study, and it will certainly be a great pity if the French Territories are not included in this work, which is expected to run to a number of volumes.

An early reply will be greatly appreciated.

The memorandum which I enclosed was as follows:

I have heard with great surprise that there has been strong resentment in France against my fetching the Coelacanth fish from the Comoro Islands.

May I present the facts. From the time that the first Coelacanth was found in 1938 I have constantly sought to find more and if possible where they live. My deductions led me to think that this would be on the east coast in the neighbourhood of Madagascar.

Immediately after the war I started an intensive campaign, one of the methods being a special leaflet in English, French and Portuguese, showing a picture of the Coelacanth and offering a reward of £100 for each.

By various means these were distributed along the East Coast. In 1948 I was in Lourenço Marques arranging this distribution with the Portuguese authorities, and with a Portuguese official called on the French Consul in Lourenço Marques, and explained the importance of the matter to him. He readily agreed to send a batch of the leaflets by air to the authorities of Madagascar, and assured me that they would be distributed there as requested. Neither then nor later was there any suggestion that if a Coelacanth were to be found, its removal would not be permitted by the French authorities.

Since 1945 I have made a number of expeditions to the east coast of Africa, always seeking the Coelacanth. A great deal of time and many thousands of pounds have been spent in this search.

The Coelacanth at the Comoro Islands was saved chiefly because of my search and propaganda leaflets. I regarded and regard that fish as ethically mine. Had it been found by purely French effort, I should have made no effort whatever to get it.

It may be recorded that I asked Captain Hunt if he got another Coelacanth in French waters, as a result of my search, to hand it to the French authorities.

I do not regard this fish as belonging to me personally, or even to one country, but to the world of science. I have already told the South African Council for Scientific and Industrial Research that it should be examined by a panel of International Experts, and we are at present considering how this may be arranged. Scientists in France will have an equal opportunity with those of other countries. A statement about this will appear in the journal *Nature* (London) on February 28 next.

Early in March 1953 I submitted a memorandum requesting from the French Government permission to hunt fishes in their territories,* exactly as we had been granted permission by all other foreign governments in Africa. Time was of course a vital factor, and it was disturbing that only in May 1953 did I receive in reply a request for further information relating to that application.

On the 8th May 1953, to acquaint him with what was happening and hoping that he might be able to assist, I wrote to Millot as follows:

... I now enclose a copy of a statement about the poison and explosives we wish to use. To you personally I stress again that we are exceedingly careful in our use of these from every point of view. Not only do we always aim at causing the least possible damage to natural life, but we are fully aware of the effect of such methods on the minds of primitive people. We have our own ways of impressing on the Natives that both these methods are not for the ordinary man, and that, especially in the case of explosives, disaster will almost certainly follow their use.

It is not only in your territories that these methods are forbidden, but in all, and it is because of our reputation and the great care that we always exercise that all the other Governments have given me this

* Up to September 1955 no specific reply to this request has been received.

free permission. Not a single one of them has ever had cause to regret this in any way whatsoever, and I am confident that at any time in all the Territories where we have worked we shall continue to be able to enjoy these special concessions.

In the matter of the Coelacanth I wish to emphasise to you that we are not coming on this venture with any sense of competing with you and your nation. Not at all, we are coming because I feel that no effort must be spared to find further specimens. We shall be only too honoured to be able to collaborate with you to the fullest extent. I have probably more experience of getting fishes under East African Tropical conditions than any other living scientist, and it would be foolish not to use that for this great hunt. We can indeed offer to share any methods or materials that we may have with you on the fullest basis of co-operation.

At the moment it does not appear likely that we shall be able to commence operations until the end of August at the earliest. That should enable you to work for some time before we come, and I shall all the time hope to hear that you have caught a Coelacanth. As you possibly know, we have decided that the specimen here is not to be dissected further until other specimens become available. It would, in any case, be desirable to keep this intact unless we get another specimen of the same type.

I do hope your Government will see its way clear to getting Captain Cousteau to assist in the Coelacanth hunt, as that deep diving will almost certainly be a most useful method of hunting. It would be a very great achievement if one of your countrymen could report on live Coelacanths in the sea, and the whole world would certainly take the greatest interest in anything he could tell of their habits. From what I have read of the method, in those clear waters it would appear to hold out one of the greatest hopes in our search, and I shall be greatly obliged if you would kindly send me your comments and report on this.* We ourselves use goggles and diving, but have of course nothing comparable with the magnificent equipment developed by your countrymen.

I appreciate your difficulties fully, but know that together we shall be able to overcome them all. The important thing is that we must secure more specimens for science. It does not matter to me who gets them, except that it would give me the greatest satisfaction for your country to have a complete and perfect specimen, whether by your own expedition or any other. I am hoping daily to hear that you have already found one.

* No reply was received on this point. But see p. 223. (Nairobi meeting).

And so my dear Sir, I do trust that you will be able to remove from the minds of any of your countrymen the idea that I am intending to go to your area to compete with you in these matters. I do certainly feel that it would be a very great pity if the fishes of the French Territories were not to be included in my large planned monograph, and feel that I can rely upon the same freedom and facilities for collecting as all the other countries where we have worked.

There was other correspondence with Millot, but nothing further from the French authorities until August 1953, when I received notification that they had decided not to grant authorisation to search for Coelacanths in their waters during 1953. It was stated that various French and foreign scientific organisations had made proposals similar to mine, and it was feared that if all were permitted to operate it might have undesirable results. Instead of separate expeditions, the French Government intended to invite the 'Scientific Council for Africa' to consider the amalgamation of proposed expeditions into an international expedition, under French leadership. During the second week of August 1953 a statement more or less to this effect was issued officially by the French authorities, and appeared in the press in various parts of the world.

The ending of negotiations with Stuttard and this decision of the French put an end to my hopes of working in the Comoro-Aldabra region in 1953. The exclusion from French waters at that time was an action I found regrettable in science, even with the prospect of an international expedition ahead. It had earlier been reported in the press that two expeditions (Italian and Swedish) were in East African waters to hunt Coelacanths, the leader of one had indeed written to me from East Africa. After the decision of the French, I wondered if these expeditions would do as I had planned under this ban, i.e. work at other likely places. Shortly after this (late August 1953) there was a report that at least one of these expeditions had gone over to Aldabra, and then it was stated that one had gone to the Comores and was actually working there. As this was apparently contrary to the decision of the French Government, both as published and in the form communicated to me, I doubted the accuracy of the report. It was, however, later confirmed that not only had the Italian expedition been working at the Comores, but when they returned to East Africa early in November 1953 it was with the startling news that they had succeeded in photographing a live Coelacanth under the water, and at the Comores themselves.

On the 9th November 1953 the following statement, emanating from Dar-es-Salaam, appeared in the press of the world:

> Only French scientists will be allowed to search for the Coelacanth off the French Comoro Islands, in the Indian Ocean between Mozambique and Madagascar, for the rest of this year.
>
> French authorities there have declared a complete ban until December 31 on expeditions by foreign scientists—two days after an Italian zoological expedition secured the first photographs ever taken of a living Coelacanth.

Another report of the 10th November 1953 emanating from Dar-es-Salaam, stated further:

> An Italian expedition which has been working at the Comoro Islands is convinced that there are many Coelacanths there. . . .
>
> This expedition was compelled to suspend its operations* because the French authorities placed a ban on further search for Coelacanths until the end of this year.

On my 1954 expedition to the Seychelles I made a long voyage in the same vessel that the Italians had employed. The owner confirmed that they had indeed worked in Comoran waters after the French ban of August 1953, and he told me that the Italians had handed over to the French authorities part of the collections made, which had been a condition of their being permitted to work there.

* In November 1953, at the Comores.

Chapter Nineteen

MARCHAND DE BONHEUR

By the end of June 1953 the course of negotiations left little doubt in my mind that the French would not grant me permission to work on my own in their waters. Despite all I had learnt at the Comores, it was disturbing that no further Coelacanths had been caught although I was pleased to hear that the French were apparently offering the same reward for Coelacanths as I had paid, namely £100 each, to induce the native fishermen to bring them in. I felt that more than this was necessary, and in the absence of information about the precise measures being taken by the French could not shed the responsibility of feeling that I must go after Coelacanths myself, to make sure whether they really lived in those parts or not. Had the arrangement with Stuttard not broken down or if a suitable vessel had been available in time, I should certainly have gone to work in the western Indian Ocean. There were many places outside French territorial waters where profitable work could be done. I should never be able to rest until the home of the Coelacanth was surely found.

My chief recollection of that tense and difficult middle half of 1953 is of the weight of the terrible responsibility that pressed down on me. Not only was there this matter of the home of the Coelacanth, but the possession of this Coelacanth *was* a terrible responsibility. It was the only relatively complete specimen in the world, it was the first virtually complete specimen ever to be found, and for those reasons it should if possible be kept intact as an historical relic. I had to consider the needs of the world of science, but if others were found then this one could be kept intact. On the other hand, if no other specimens were found I could scarcely justify merely hoarding this one in that way. I was torn between these two considerations, and the only clear solution was to find another, more, as many as possible, and soon. Day and night this worry clouded my brain and my life, and when all hope of a proper Coelacanth expedition of my own for 1953 was finally abandoned, I felt like a wild bird in a cage, not broken but badly battered.

My mind always framed that story the Mozambique native had told about the fish he got at Bazaruto. There was no valid reason why it should not have been a Coelacanth. While I was prevented from going to the Comores at that time, the Portuguese are my very good friends and I could certainly go to Bazaruto. I had already been there, but many years before, and had indeed never worked over the area as thoroughly as its richness deserved. It would repay closer investigation. So I sought and received from the South African Council for Scientific and Industrial Research permission to use some of the Coelacanth expedition funds for a small venture to the Bazaruto area. The Portuguese authorities, as always co-operative and prompt, at short notice arranged the requested facilities for work in September and October 1953.

Before we left for Mozambique I received a letter, dated the 3rd August 1953, from G. F. Cartwright of Salisbury. He wrote to say that he had been goggle-fishing at Malindi in October and November 1952, and that he had seen us at work there at the close of our stay. Later when out over deep water on a reef one day, equipped and armed with spear-gun, he suddenly saw not far below him a large fish whose appearance gave him a shock. It had a huge mouth and a 'baleful and ancient appearance'. To quote further:

> It was a large fish, heavily built, and from 100 to 150 pounds in weight. It was totally unlike any fish I had seen or ever saw afterwards. It looked wholly evil and a thousand years old. It had a large eye and the most outstanding feature was the armour-plate effect of its heavy scales, scales so heavy that it was set quite apart from other fish I saw.

Although its appearance was rather terrifying, he decided to try a shot, but the harpoon just glanced off the scales and the creature disappeared.

On the return to shore, Cartwright told of this fish and questioned other anglers and spear-gunners. The nearest they got was to suggest a large Rock Cod, but Cartwright had had wide experience of diverse Rock Cods and was quite positive it was not. The scales alone ruled that out, and the identity of the fish remained a mystery.

Soon after returning to Rhodesia, in some periodical Cartwright saw for the first time a picture of a Coelacanth, and was at once struck by its resemblance to the fish he had seen. Shortly afterwards he visited the Centenary Exhibition in Bulawayo, and to his satisfaction found a full-size model of a Coelacanth (from the East London Museum) on view there. Its close resemblance to the fish that had startled him was even more striking, and by contriving to put himself into the same relative position as he had been to his fish, as far as he could judge this appeared to confirm in every respect that the fish he had seen had indeed been a real live Coelacanth. What did I think? Well, it was clear that if the Comores was the home of the Coelacanth, Malindi was much nearer and much more easily accessible in every way than East London, which one Coelacanth at least had actually reached. Bazaruto fell in between these places, and Cartwright's experience at least lent colour to the Bazaruto idea. Furthermore, from my wide knowledge of the fishes of the western Indian Ocean I could think of no species that fitted Cartwright's description as well as a Coelacanth. Not one.*

Meanwhile, arising from the refusal of the French to permit any foreigner to work in their waters, this alternative of an International Coelacanth expedition had been taken up by the Scientific Council for Africa, one of whose functions is to co-ordinate scientific effort in Africa south of the Sahara. This body appointed a Committee consisting of Dr. Millot (France), Dr. Worthington (British), and myself to consider the matter. The meeting was arranged to be held in Nairobi during the last week of October 1953.

Early in September 1953 my wife and I and a scientist friend, H. J. Koch, set off for Mozambique. Our work about Bazaruto and the other islands, and at Ponte de Barra Falsa, proved extremely interesting and rich in results, as far as fishes generally were concerned, but not of Coelacanths. That was naturally only

---

* It may be noted that it has been pointed out that it was unlikely that the fish that Cartwright saw was a Coelacanth, because the French have reported that the first live Coelacanth to be caught showed such fear of light. (But see p. 242.)

a forlorn hope, but each Coelacanth-blank day only served to add to the severe mental depression that clouded my life. Would this two-fold responsibility of the Coelacanth, the decision about the fate of this animal, and the suspense of waiting to hear if more had been caught at the Comores, never end? I did not look forward to the meeting in Nairobi, for I had a premonition that my frantic desire to get on with finding Coelacanths was going to be side-tracked, wrapped up in official and technical cotton-wool. It had happened before, but this was much worse, for the Comores were foreign waters and closed against me.

Living on a small vessel and on the islands at that time, we were completely isolated except for an occasional visit to the lofty lighthouse at the northern end of Bazaruto, and when we went to work at sea we had no contact with the rest of the world. Towards the close of our work in that area, we landed one day on the mainland opposite Bazaruto, and found the people there very excited, for at low tide a man had gone probing into the dirty water at the base of an eroded mushroom-like coral lump and had found hidden there an enormous 'Garrupa', or Rock Cod, which he eventually managed to kill. It was well over 200 lb. in weight, a terrific fish to have remained in what was only a puddle. As we stood by looking on, a Chinese who spoke Portuguese came up to me and said that there had been a radio report the night before about a curious large fish that had been caught by the French. He had heard my name mentioned, and that had made him take some notice of it, as he knew I was working among the islands. We certainly jumped at this. Had they mentioned where it had been found? He thought it had been Madagascar, but was not sure. Was it a Coelacanth? Yes, that was the name.

It was like the burst of a bomb to me, but although we questioned him closely he could tell us no more. We rushed round to everyone who had a wireless-set, but found out nothing much besides. Although it was not quite certain, for they might all have been mistaken, I felt many years younger. We could get no other information of any kind, for when newspapers reached that part they were at least six days old. It was not until we got back to civilisation a week later that we learnt that it was indeed a Coelacanth, and that it had been taken at the Comores and at Anjouan, the same island.

I shall always remember the sensation of terrific relief this gave me, as if a crushing burden had been lifted from my mind. So it was the right spot, they were there! I could see the end of this great strain, I could keep my *Malania,* and it would be only a matter of time now before all those high specialists were each and all wresting the secrets of the life of the long ages past from the tissues and structures of fresh Coelacanths. I could see in the near future long queues of eager sightseers filing past a tank where a living Coelacanth stared scornfully at his equally 'degenerate'* near descendants.

Two in the same place. It must be their home, so that my enduring aim had been achieved, and most of my burden would now fall on the French. Their exclusion of myself from their waters was based on mistaken ideas, for in doing so they had tried to keep me away from something I had never wanted for myself but for science.

As soon as we could get to a Post Office, I sent Millot a cable conveying my warmest congratulations.

Now that one home of the Coelacanth had been found, the Nairobi meeting took on a new aspect, and I looked forward to it more with interest and anticipation than with concern.

Cartwright's story had been constantly in my mind. From my wide knowledge of the fishes of South and East Africa, I could still think of no species of fish known from there that fitted his original spontaneous description as well as a Coelacanth. I wanted to question him further, so arranged my flight north from Lourenço Marques so as to be able to spend a night in Salisbury, where I met Cartwright and we talked at length. It is significant that nothing emerged from our discussion that made it in any way less likely that his fish had been a Coelacanth; rather the reverse.

When I got to Nairobi, it was to find that Millot and Worthington had invited Drs. Menaché and Wheeler to attend our meeting as well, and it certainly was interesting.

Despite my now relative detachment, my technical instinct was naturally to further the catching of Coelacanths, soon and many. As the proceedings developed, it was almost uncanny how they followed, only in much more condensed fashion, almost exactly

---

* This term is applied by some scientists to those forms which do not or are not likely to give rise by evolution to other forms. Thus the Coelacanth and *homo sapiens* both fall into this category.

the pattern of the A.C.M.E. expedition talks of six years before. Once again I was apparently alone in my Coelacanth single-mindedness, and to me they all appeared less interested in catching Coelacanths than in seeing how much else they could hang on to it. I listened to a commendably elaborate scheme for carrying out oceanographical investigations covering an enormous range of scientific effort. Most of the first day I listened, and it certainly was an impressive project, but to me pure phantasy and of little value as a Coelacanth-hunting venture. Next day I had my turn and talked a good deal, casting doubts on the feasibility of so extensive and costly a scheme and on any possibility of raising the relatively large sum such a project must cost. We had a battle about estimates and got to a compromise figure, and even that was far outside my ideas of practical finance. Though South Africa might be prepared to assist towards hunting Coelacanths I could not see our country financing extensive oceanographical work in seas so far away. I told them it seemed impractical to visualise such a scheme when we now knew at least one place where Coelacanths lived. I wanted to concentrate first on the Comores alone. I wanted to see Coelacanths caught for science, and outlined the simple, direct, and relatively inexpensive scheme I had in mind.

However, I was assured that the Scientific Council had expressly directed that this expedition should have the oceanographical character that was now outlined, and that the Council did not want any other. They did not share my doubts as to whether the necessary funds would be forthcoming.

Certainly of all the accessible parts of the oceans near populous countries, the region of the Mozambique channel is probably the least known scientifically. Oceanographical investigations there are highly desirable and would probably pay handsome dividends. But my common sense told me that if the French caught more and more Coelacanths in their closely preserved waters, no foreign Government was going to spend large sums of money on an expedition to find Coelacanths. I had no faith in this international project purely as far as hunting Coelacanths was concerned.* If

* It has recently (June 1955) been announced that the International Expedition to hunt Coelacanths has been postponed, but that Dr. Millot is going on an expedition of his own, equipped with special cages to keep Coelacanths in deep water, and with a type of bathysphere designed by French experts so that he may go down and study live Coelacanths in their natural home.

they wanted to do general oceanographical work, that was quite another matter; so I let it go, but told them that I at least could see no part in it for me, and did not intend to participate. I had plenty to do besides. I wanted to get on with my work on the fishes of the western Indian Ocean. I made it plain that as soon as the home of the Coelacanth had been established, my own work in that field was done. Until then my knowledge and experience would always be at their service, and I visualised the possibility of assisting them while engaged in my own work. I told them my own plans to hunt Coelacanths, and outlined how I had intended to try to keep them alive by using a fairly large decked boat, partly filled with sea-water, as a temporary aquarium.* They were startled when I said the chief problem was that Coelacanths transported in this way or in tanks might get seasick and die, for strange as it may sound fish in aquaria at sea do get seasick. I noticed that when possible vessels were discussed, Millot made no mention of Stuttard's *La Contenta* (see p. 205), and when I raised the issue of Cousteau and his research vessel (about which I had written earlier to Millot, see p. 214) as part of the expedition, the others indicated that this would be useless as the Coelacanth lived in water too deep for such methods to be of any value!

This meeting had its lighter moments. We were discussing personnel and equipment for the vessels, and it was established there would be quite a number of scientists and assistants on each. One Frenchman said, 'It weel be necessairy to provide a wench on each ship.' This certainly shook the Britishers. As they looked up sharply I could see in their faces the unspoken comment, 'It may be the tropics, but really. . . .' I said mildly, 'He means winch'; and there was some laughter, which the French at first did not understand.

The Committee composed a statement about the international project, which was later given due prominence in the press.

Millot showed me photographs of the third Coelacanth. It was wonderful to see them. It was complete, and the first dorsal and that little extra tail made it look as if my old *Malania* was indeed a freak, a gigantic practical joke on the part of nature. Still, I

---

* It has been interesting to note that the French used this method in attempting to keep alive the first live Coelacanth to be brought in (see p. 239).

wanted to see a good many more before that was certain. I suddenly wondered what would have happened if old *Malania* had wandered away to East London instead of *Latimeria*. That would have been a poser!

I left that meeting feeling, as a scientist, a solid satisfaction at the prospect of extensive oceanographical investigations in so interesting and virgin an area of the seas. But against my Coelacanth-hunting obsession, as a method of finding soon where Coelacanths lived and of catching numbers quickly, it had very much the flavour of an English fox-hunt, in which the formalities are of more account than the quarry. Left to myself I felt I could do it more expeditiously and at far less cost. (Although it was their own idea to stop individual expeditions by suggesting the international project, it would almost appear as if the French soon came to be as sceptical about its early practicability as myself, for only a month or two after our meeting in Nairobi the French research vessel *Calypso*, Cousteau's famous ship, set out on a six-months' cruise and covered a wide area of the tropical western Indian Ocean where Coelacanths might be expected to live, including the Seychelles and the islands and banks over the thousand-mile-long arc from there to Aldabra, where they spent some time, and then to the Comores. There, under the direction of Professor Millot, they carried out extensive submarine electronic flash photography in areas where Coelacanths were likely to be found, using for this purpose a special camera designed by an American scientist. In that part of the Indian Ocean, outside French waters, they covered almost the exact field which I had informed the C.S.I.R., and later the press, was to be the area of operations for my 1954 Seychelles expedition. This French expedition had left Seychelles not very long before I arrived, and we heard a good deal about their operations. They were apparently greatly taken by Aldabra; which is not surprising, for not only did it prove to be the richest virgin area for fishes I have ever seen, but I confidently expect that Coelacanths will be found there or at other islands not far off, such as Astove. This French project was apparently accorded unusually little publicity from any source, since few people have heard of it.)

Although every due moment was given to Coelacanth matters, Nairobi, at that time in the throes of racial conflict and crisis, was very interesting. I spent every spare moment talking to those who were informed and in walking many miles through the streets, noticeably the only European to do so outside the central shopping area. It was a city without lightness or laughter, life was a grim business, you could feel the tension in the air. The windows of my room in the hotel were barred and there was a warning to keep the door closed and locked when inside. I heard many stories, and, after their physical characteristics had been described to me, could easily pick out the Kikuyu from the rest. I reflected somewhat grimly that even if this happened in South Africa, we should not be prepared to endure its dragging on like this. It would come to a quick end, one way or the other; yes, one way or the other. Such things are not new in our country; we know all about it, for what was happening in Kenya was in effect almost the exact modern counterpart of what our forefathers had endured in South Africa a century ago, remote control, wild country, disregard for ownership and for human life. In South Africa those hard times had bred tough citizens, both men and women, as the conditions in Kenya are clearly doing now. Everything has its points.

The bestiality of the Kikuyu in their slashing murders is world news, but I learnt many other things about them. One is typical. At night they will go into a field of mature potatoes, and working through the soil with cunning fingers will remove most of the tubers without killing the plants or leaving any trace.

The last of that visit to Nairobi, as we drove to the aerodrome through the streets, was a kaleidoscopic compression of uniformed figures, grim faces, armed sentries, barbed-wire fences, and sandbag defences.

I do a good deal of flying and like it, but never climb into a plane without having a good look round at earth and sky, with the conscious thought that this may be my last view. So many crashes occur within a few moments of taking off. As I strapped myself in I realised that my heart was filled with deep content, happiness if you like. It was really quite remarkable, as if I was living in the heart of a 'Happy ever after' ending in a novel. After all the uncertainty and agony that had followed the trail of the Coelacanth, it had now all been ironed out. Almost miraculously, everyone was happy.

The 'Dokter' had been pleased. Being a Prime Minister is as near as any human comes to being a god, but even he must feel pleasure after making a decision to cover an unusual situation, to harvest almost universal approval, even if it is grudged by his opponents. The French were happy. They had the first really complete Coelacanth, got by themselves; they had the prospect of an undisturbed monopoly of more, and, for some time at least, they would get world headlines for every one they found. They would be able to point out any mistakes I had made, and all hurt feelings would be soothed. The authorities of the Comores were happy. Coelacanths had put their islands very much 'on the map'. They would probably issue a set of 'Coelacanth' stamps, that collectors and ichthyologists all over the world would eagerly seek. At least three Comorans were in such a position that they need not work for a good while, and the lives of all the islanders must be brightened, for almost every one of them could at least fish for that wonderful possibility. Everyone round there would be happy in the increased supplies of fish. Even Stuttard had apparently not been unhappy.

I just could not help smiling as I thought of my ugly old *Malania*, snug in his asbestos-cement coffin, in the role of a 'Marchand de Bonheur', a dispenser of human happiness.

The plane rumbled to the end of the runway, and as we shook to the roaring test of the engines my heart was filled with fierce deep content, for I had shed the worry and responsibility of the Coelacanth; one of the greatest ambitions of my life, to find the home of the Coelacanth, had been fulfilled; I was leaving the horror of the Mau Mau and going back to my own beloved country, to my beloved fishes, to my old *Malania*, who could now for ever sleep in peace.

APPENDICES

APPENDIX *A*

SOME CHARACTERISTICS OF COELACANTHS AND HOW THEY DIFFER FROM MOST MODERN FISHES

IT has been emphasised that in its bony jaws and overlapping scales even the earliest Coelacanths showed characteristics that have endured to the present day. While the Coelacanths have changed little over vast ages, there have been modifications in structure in other forms of fishes, so that the primitive Coelacanth differs markedly in many ways from most modern bony fishes.

FIG. 7.—Above, a typical modern fish, the 'Soldier' of Natal; and below, a Coelacanth.

In the head of the Coelacanth quite massive bones lie right in the surface. The skull itself is not a single unit as in most fishes, but is in two almost separate parts across behind the eyes. The brain cavity is quite a reasonable size. There are no nostrils like those of modern fishes, but in the cartilage in the front of the head before the eyes is a peculiar central and quite large cavity, from which six tubes lead to the surface, two to the front and two to each side of the head in front of the eye. At first sight, externally, one might think the two openings on each side to be nostrils, like those of modern fishes, but they are not, and up to the present no one has been able to say exactly what this structure is. When my account of the first Coelacanth was published, the description of this particular part puzzled all scientists, and one went as far as to say that I must have been mistaken. The very first thing I looked for in *Malania* was this structure, and, sure enough, there it was, exactly the same. It was also the first thing Nielsen looked for in *Malania*. He told me, apologetically, that they all had doubted my description and figure. We scratched our heads together.

Most bony fishes have a well-developed soft 'air bladder', which lies above the intestines in the body cavity. (It was mentioned on p. 92 that when a trawl-net comes up, the fall in pressure causes the air-bladders of the fishes to expand.) The modern Coelacanth has no true air-bladder. In some fossils there is a peculiar structure in the belly cavity in the position in which the air-bladder is generally found, but in those earlier Coelacanths this was 'calcified', i.e. it had hardened walls. It has been assumed, therefore, that Coelacanths had air-bladders, but that these had become hardened. An air-bladder is apparently used to adjust the average density of a fish to suit its environment, or else as a breathing organ. What use an air-bladder with hard walls would be it is difficult to imagine, but in some existing fishes there has been found a degree of calcification of their air-bladders. At any rate, there is no true air-bladder in the modern Coelacanth, only a shred of skin that may be the remnant of an air-bladder that might once have been present. It may be mentioned that sharks and rays have no air-bladder.

In the Coelacanth the gills are not soft cartilage like modern fishes, but bony and hard. They bear teeth and not ordinary soft gill-rakers.

The scales of the Coelacanth are both peculiar and characteristic. The main basal part is almost horny and with less bone than a comparable modern fish. The 'tubercles' on the scales are separate units, each set on its own little plate, and each is hollow. The scales overlap so much that the whole body has a covering three scales thick, a powerful protective armour.

While the Coelacanth has bony jaws and powerful jaw muscles, the structure of the upper jaw is different from that of the *Rhipidistia* and of modern bony fishes. The maxillary bones at the side of the upper jaw are missing, there is only a thick fold of skin. The teeth in the upper jaw are set differently from those of modern bony fishes. They are in clusters in separate but adjacent plates.

The scales bear tubercles, each of which is a strong, separate, enamelled structure stuck on the main base of the scale. Some of these tubercles are smooth all round, but some have a sharp point behind. These tubercles are hollow inside. It has long been held that teeth in jaws are developed from scales that 'migrated' inwards. In the development of a shark it is possible to see something of this, and in the Coelacanth this shows very clearly, for the teeth are in groups on adjacent but separate bases, and examination soon reveals that each of these is merely a modified scale, in which the base has become thicker and stronger, and the hind pointed part of the tubercles has become longer, more bony and strong, sharply pointed, and, in fact, a hollow canine tooth. Even the teeth on the gills are of this form. In addition, some of the surface bones of the head show themselves as no more than modified scales.

On the floor of the mouth of the Coelacanth there is a hard, bony, toothed structure different from anything in any modern fish. Below the lower jaw are two bony, reptile-like plates, 'Gular Plates', that are found in a few only of the more primitive types of living fishes.

The fins are certainly curious. The pelvics and pectorals give clear indication of being used as limbs, and it is plain that the fish can crawl about, in the water at least. Ancestral Coelacanths probably crawled out on land. (Old Fourlegs!)

The tail is characteristic. That small extra tail is not found in modern fishes. It is indeed a remnant of the true tail that is supposed to have been present in ancestral forms. (See also the figure of a Rhipidistian fish, p. 17.) The 'tail' of modern fishes is really evolved from two fins, one above and one below, into which the hinder true 'tail' eventually shrank away.

The 'skeleton' is remarkable. The 'backbone' or 'axial' column is not of bone, but a hollow tube of cartilage, that fits in front into a hollow in the skull, and behind tapers to a thin rod in the tail. On the backbone of an ordinary fish you see hard, bony spines above and below. The Coelacanth has something like these, but they are hollow tubes and not very hard. (This is how the Coelacanth got its name. 'Coelacanth' means 'Hollow spine'.) At the base of each fin, however, there is a rather large and heavy bony plate, the 'basal' plate, well known from fossils.

The intestines of a Coelacanth are short and have in them a 'spiral valve' very like that of sharks and rays. The intestines generally remind one of those of a shark rather than of a bony fish.

While some modern fishes are oily, probably none are as oily as the Coelacanth. Below the skin there is a layer of cells full of oil, and even after months of capture this oil continues to ooze from the body. In *Malania's* 'coffin' there are always big blobs of oil floating on the surface of the preservative solution in which he lies.

APPENDIX *B*

WHY THE DISCOVERY OF THE COELACANTH AROUSED SUCH WIDE INTEREST

ONE of the main questions that we have heard many thousands of times is, 'Why is the Coelacanth so interesting and important?' There are many things involved.

As was explained in Chapter Two, Coelacanths as such lived over a longer period than any other known type of creature, certainly of vertebrates. They apparently spread over most of the earth, for fossils have been found in very many places. They left apparently one of the most constant and unbroken series of fossils, often almost perfect, that one could desire, covering 250 million years, during which they lived almost unchanged in general form. This fossil record was so good that it apparently gave an index of numbers as well as distribution. According to that record, from about 100 million years ago, Coelacanths steadily became fewer in numbers, and the very last and comparatively rare fossils occur in rock strata earlier dated at about 50 million years old, but which more recent estimates put at about 70 million. Compared with the age of the earth, 70 million years is not very much, but it is a terrific stretch of time in comparison with life as we know it. A good many profound changes have taken place on the earth during that 70 million years. Almost all the creatures that lived 70 million years ago, both of the land and the sea, have vanished, and most of them would look strange or startling if they appeared now. Most people have heard of the Dinosaurs and other giant reptiles, the enormous fish-eating lizards and flying reptiles, and other similar creatures of past ages. It requires little imagination to picture the sensation that would be caused if one of those gigantic Dinosaurs ambled into civilisation today. Indeed, the appearance of any piece of that long-buried past is an event. While the Coelacanth is not the size of a Dinosaur, its appearance, still alive, is in many ways much more startling.

As far as scientists are concerned, this appearance of a living Coelacanth was a terrific shock. All those who worked on fossils had been quite confident, had indeed repeatedly said, that Coelacanths were all extinct, and had been so from at least 50 million years earlier. This proved them wrong, and it is good for dogmatic statements to be proved wrong, at least in science, since it induces a caution that is proper to science. Any scientific statement or theory should be preceded by 'As far as we know at present. . . .' It was a salutary lesson.

All intelligent human beings have an almost instinctive deep interest in living things, and there are few who are not fascinated by the life of past ages.

During the past century more and more scientists have turned their attention to unravelling the threads of the course and development of life on the earth, and a marvellous story it is. Not only have many books about it been produced, but some countries have life-size exhibits portraying extinct creatures and plants of past times based on re-constructions made by scientists.

Portraying or modelling a creature from fossil remains, often in-complete or put together from dispersed fragments, is, of course, bound to be partly guess-work. How can one know that this work is sound? There is always a tendency to go too far. For example, some workers have managed to produce models of the brains of some of the long-extinct forms. It is marvellous work. One method is to take a fossil skull that is now all stone and to grind it down a fraction of an inch at a time, making a wax film at each stage, and when these wax films are all put together in their proper order, there is a model of the brain. Those that have been prepared in this way look quite convincing. However, one sceptical worker has cast doubt on the value of this, for he has shown that casts of the inside of the skulls of modern fishes, at least, are by no means accurate models of the actual brains that come from those skulls.

Nevertheless, the appearance of the Coelacanth did give much increased confidence in the ability of palaeontologists to reconstruct with accuracy, for their models and pictures of Coelacanths were on the whole fairly close to the real live fish. Reconstructions exhibited in museums make the Coelacanths of past ages look rather stodgy and wooden, and indeed they are labelled that way. This certainly does not apply to the 1938–55 models. By human standards the appearance of the Coelacanth can best be described as 'tough and terrifying'. This is, however, not as important as the fact that the reconstructions were fairly accurate, so that we may reasonably expect models of other creatures to be equally close to what they really were. It has given everyone increased confidence in this type of reconstructive work.

The discovery of the Coelacanth has focused attention on how very little we really know of life in the sea. That 'Man's dominion ends with the shore' is indeed very true. While we control virtually all life on land, we have a far from complete knowledge of life in the water and practically no control there at all. Within the confines of London or Paris, for example, there is very little wild life of any kind on the land, hardly any that is not under full human control, excepting only minute forms. Yet right in the heart of those old, civilised, and densely populated centres, in the rivers Thames and Seine, life goes on exactly as it did a million, 50 million, even longer ages before, primitive and savage, hide or be eaten, fly or be eaten, eat or be eaten. In no water is life entirely subject to man-made laws.

After all the work that has been done on the sea, the emergence of the unknown Coelacanth, a large robust creature, does show clearly how little we know, and it brings at least a hope that there may be other primitive forms still surviving somewhere there. It tells us even more. It has shown that comparatively large creatures can live for long ages in the sea and leave no easily accessible fossil traces. It may, and almost certainly does, mean that there have been other creatures who lived always in the sea of which no traces have been found and of which we have no knowledge at all. It leaves a hope that there may still be such unknown forms alive in the sea, and that they may be discovered when man achieves greater mastery of that region beyond the tidal fringe. There is, indeed, probably a greater possibility of this than of the existence of another known type like the Coelacanth.

It is astonishing how much an intensive study of fossils can tell us about the creatures that left them. Often even habits and other characteristics can be deduced. Nevertheless, there are big gaps in our knowledge of past life. We know next to nothing of the soft parts of the early forms of life, nothing of that very early big change-over from invertebrate to vertebrate.

Flesh (protein) is composed chiefly of remarkable aggregates of substances known as amino-acids, and different amino-acids in varying proportions are found in the flesh of different animals, while the protein of plants is again very different from that of animals. In the course of evolution, profound changes in amino-acid components of flesh protein may have accompanied other structural modifications. I learnt at the Comores that the flesh of the Coelacanth when cooked becomes jelly-like. It will probably be found to have a composition different from the flesh of ordinary fishes.

In the course of evolution, there will almost certainly have been continual change in the form of the intestines, in the composition of the digestive fluids and enzymes, and in many of the soft parts. It is unlikely that we shall ever know very much of this, but the Coelacanth holds out a hope of gaining some of that knowledge.

One of the most outstanding characteristics of the Coelacanths is that they have changed remarkably little during the vast ages they have lived. The bony structures of our modern Coelacanth are almost exactly the same as those left by Coelacanths of several hundred million years ago. There is, then, at least a hope that the soft parts of the modern Coelacanth may also be little changed from those of earlier times, and from study we may be able to deduce something of the finer details of the earliest vertebrate types.

There has been a good deal of controversy about the origin of the important oil deposits in the earth. Some scientists consider that they had a purely inorganic origin, being formed by the action of pressure and moisture on carbon. Others consider it at least as likely that the oil resulted from the action of heat and pressure on great numbers of oily fishes, possibly killed in some upheaval of nature. It is certainly interesting that the Coelacanth is oily, very oily indeed, and a study of that oil may throw some light on this whole question.

The development of embryos is a most fascinating study, for it has been observed that many show characters of the earliest forms of life from which the creatures have evolved. For example, at certain stages the human embryo has gill-slits in the throat, and a tail, indicating our fishy origin.

One rather wonderful discovery was the fossil of a fairly large Coelacanth with remains of two others, both very much smaller, situated near the hind part of the belly region. That could mean merely the fossils of three Coelacanths, one big and two small, but it could also have meant that these two smaller ones were the well-developed but still unborn young, indicating that the Coelacanth brought forth the young alive. If this was the case, it would mean that the study of the embryo in the living Coelacanth would likely have enabled scientists to gain some knowledge of life still earlier than the origin of Coelacanths, a wonderful possibility that we all have cherished. As Coelacanths have been caught one by one, so we have gone on hoping that each would be a female, especially one with unborn young. By some curious trick all the first were males; then came an immature female; and now, finally, a gravid female, but she has eggs, not embryos. This takes away some of our hopes, but not all, for the embryo develops in the egg, probably in a case like that of the sharks and rays, and there will be much to be learnt when we can find these.

APPENDIX C

THE LATEST POSITION ABOUT COELACANTHS

THE position regarding recent Coelacanths up to July 1955 is as follows: The French have got in all seven more Coelacanths, all apparently at the Comores. One report that stated that a specimen had been caught on the coast of Madagascar has not been confirmed.

Almost all information about these Coelacanths has come from the French, who report them as all having been taken by native fishermen at depths ranging from 80 to 150 fathoms, in each case the exact depth of capture has been stated (see note, p. 242).

All have been large fishes, the largest weighing about 150 lb., all plainly the same species, with fins like *Latimeria* but body shape like *Malania*, so that probably only the former genus is valid.

The first were apparently all males, and this led to the suggestion that the females live in much deeper water, implying, in fact, that they all do, and that it is only the males who occasionally rise to lesser depths. This theory was invalidated by the capture of a female at about the usual depth. Not long after this the first egg-bearing female was caught, and by the most curious coincidence the fisherman in this case was one of Hunt's own crew. Hunt wrote to me from Majunga, Madagascar, about this fish and said that it was caught only about a couple of hundred yards from the schooner and quite early in the evening. The man got his reward from the Government. The eggs were rather like those in a chicken, being in a cluster of varying sizes, three of them large and well-formed. A man who broke one open and sucked it said the flavour was the same as that of a chicken. Next morning the fish left for Paris.

This is the first report about the flavour of a Coelacanth's egg. Two things emerge from this: one is that our hopes of delving into the still more remote past within the embryo of a Coelacanth are less than if the creature had brought forth its young alive, and secondly the Coelacanth doubtless sheds its eggs inside a special case, quite possibly like those produced by some sharks and rays. Who will be the first to find one? When they are found, it is well within the bounds of possibility that Coelacanth egg-cases of bygone ages will be identified among fossil remains.

Judging by what has been published, only the French, mainly Dr.

Millot, have worked on the Coelacanths so far. The reports already issued are in a sense preliminary and have not revealed anything of especial importance. That can emerge only after long specialised study. There has been criticism of the French for keeping this marvellous scientific material of such wide interest to themselves, but as long as the essential work is properly carried out, it is not important who does it.

The eighth Coelacanth was, like all the others, taken on a line, but in this case the fisherman managed to tow it alive to the shore. There it was put into a sunken boat which was covered with nets. It died next day.

Here is the account of the event given by Dr. Millot, published in *Nature*, London (February 1955):

'The organization for the fishing and conservation of the Coelacanths of the Comoro Islands created by the Institut de Recherche Scientifique de Madagascar, with the invaluable support of the Administration supérieure and of the Commandement de l'Air, reports a new success: on November 12 last a further *Latimeria* was captured at Anjouan. This brings the total since 1938 to eight and is the finest yet, as regards both size and state of preservation, and by far the most interesting because it is the first near adult female specimen which has come into our hands as well as the first of these precious fishes which anyone has been able to observe alive; for although an Italian expedition claimed to have photographed one last year, at 15 metres depth, the circumstances were quite incredible.*

'As a matter of fact the principal objective, once an adequate number of specimens for anatomical investigation had been acquired, was to capture a living one and keep it alive sufficiently long to make the biological observations desired. This was a difficult proposition. Hitherto, almost as soon as the fish had been brought to the surface, the fishermen had promptly battered it to death with oars or dispatched it with harpoons or knives in order to prevent it from struggling, and to be able to hoist it into their narrow pirogue without too much trouble. We had to put a stop to this deplorable behaviour and, on the contrary, persuade them to do their utmost to bring the fish, alive and uninjured, to the nearest harbour. This they were never willing to attempt, fearing, not without good reason, that on the way a shark or a shoal of barracuda might wrest their prize from them and lose them the promised reward. It took a great deal of persuasion to obtain their compliance, with an express promise that should they be successful the reward would be doubled.

* (It would be interesting to know why.)

'We, for our part, had to ensure a prison containing a sufficient quantity of sea-water for the captive fish. At first the provision of a fishpond on the seashore was considered; but on these rugged shores the work of constructing one would certainly be difficult. That solution had, besides, the inconvenience of creating a predetermined and immovable rendezvous, although the place of the next capture could not be foreseen. Used as a kind of aquarium, a sunken small boat seemed to have many advantages to commend it—cheapness, simplicity, rapid installation, mobility—and it was decided to adopt this course.

'The eighth *Latimeria* was pulled in from 140 fathoms depth (255 metres) at 20.00 hr. on November 12 by a fisherman, Zema ben Said Mohamed, assisted by Madi Bacari, both of the Maijihari quarter of Mutsamudu. Their pirogue was then about 1,000 metres offshore, opposite Mutsamudu jetty. The sea was very calm and the tide ebbing; it was two days after full moon and the moon had just risen.

'By the way in which the fish had taken the bait, the usual hunk of "roudi" (*Promethichthys prometheus* (Cuvier)), Zema, an excellent fisherman, immediately guessed that it must have been a Coelacanth. Nevertheless, he took half an hour and every precaution over hauling it in and, having made sure that it really was a *combessa* (the local name for the fish), he decided to try for the double reward by keeping it alive. He succeeded, "en le tenant par la main", as he said, in passing a cord in through its mouth and out through the gill-opening, and by means of this cord and of the line (which remained attached to the centre of the anterior part of the floor of the mouth) he led the creature all the way back to Mutsamudu jetty; though sometimes it was the fish that towed the pirogue.

'Administrateur Lher, as soon as he had been notified (it was by then 20.50 hr), decided, as we had agreed in advance, to sink a whaler immediately in which to place the *Latimeria* and keep it under the least unfavourable conditions practicable. The receptacle was ready by 21.30 hr. and anchored at a few tens of metres off the end of the jetty. The basin of sea-water so contrived measured about 7 metres long by 1½ metres wide and 80 cm. deep. The bung had been removed from the bottom of the boat, so as to provide a small but continuous current of water. Besides this, every half-hour the boat was violently rocked in order to renew the greater part of the water. A net covered the top of the whaler to prevent the Coelacanth from escaping, which it never seemed to want to do. The greenish-yellow luminescence of its eyes was very pronounced and could be seen at quite a distance. The colour of the fish was very dark greyish-blue, recalling that of the steel of a watchspring, with fins having clearer grey-bluish reflections.

'Throughout the night—which the delighted population of Mutsamudu passed in singing and dancing to celebrate the capture—the Coelacanth was watched over with admirable care by the chef de circonscription, taking turns with his adjoint, M. Solére. It seemed, although quite bewildered at the sequel to its ascent to the surface, to be taking the situation very well, swimming slowly by curious rotating movements of its pectoral fins, while the second dorsal and anal, likewise very mobile, served together with the tail as a rudder.

'After daybreak it became apparent that the light, and above all the sun itself, was upsetting the animal very much, so several tent canvases were put over the boat to serve as some kind of protection. But despite this precaution and the more or less constant renewal of the water, the fish began to show more and more obvious signs of distress, seeking to conceal itself in the darkest corners of the whaler.

'At 14.45 hr. it was still swimming feebly; but at 15.30 hr. it had its belly in the air and only the fins and gill-covers were making agonized movements.

'It was then covered with a sheet and taken immediately to the hospital. There was not a scratch on it, apart from a tiny incision in the centre of the anterior part of the floor of the mouth made by the fisherman when recovering his hook. Altogether, it was in remarkably good condition, without any rupture of the viscera or suffusions of blood.

'It measured 1·42 m. in length and weighed 41 kgm.

'Chemical and histological investigations could be made under the best possible conditions on perfectly fresh tissues.

'Notified by telegraph of the capture and rushed from Tananarive by a special aircraft, I arrived just in time to witness the last moments of the fish.

'Two principal conclusions emerge from the corroborated statements made by local observers and by myself: (1) the extreme photophobia of *Latimeria*—the sunlight seemed literally to hurt it; (2) the exceptional mobility of the pedunculate fins, correlated with the wealth of musculature which is revealed by anatomical studies. The pectorals, in particular, can move in almost any direction and show themselves capable of assuming practically every conceivable position.

'There can be no doubt that death was brought about by decompression combined with rise in temperature. The previous water-samples taken by Menaché (1953) and by Millot and Cousteau (1954) in the precise positions in which previous captures had been effected, showed important temperature differences between the stratum frequented by the Coelacanths and the surface water (26° C., more or less) during the daytime off Moroni or Mutsamudu.

'It must also be noted that the *Latimeria*, which appeared greatly distressed on its arrival at the surface, seemed to have recovered appreciably after an hour or so and passed the rest of the night quite comfortably without any too obvious inconvenience. It was daybreak, with the appearance of sunlight and the gradual warming of the water, which initiated the progressive discomfort that led rapidly to its death.

'The trial having thus been made under satisfactory conditions, it does not seem likely that substantially better results can be anticipated from the employment of the same technique in future. We must be prepared to make other arrangements. The only procedure offering any hope of keeping a live Coelacanth for a longer time would seem to be the construction of a great trellis-work case in which we could place the fish immediately after capture; there we should keep it normally submerged at a depth of 150–200 m., and only haul it up for limited times when someone wanted to observe or photograph the animal. Such a cage will be put in hand at Anjouan.'

As a result of this report, I sent the following to *Nature*, and it appeared in the issue of 3rd September 1955.

LIVE COELACANTHS

'From the discovery of the first Coelacanth at East London in 1938 it was my aim, not only to discover their true home, but also I hoped to live to see a living Coelacanth; and for mankind generally to be able to see this living link with the incredibly remote past. When *Malania* was found at the Comores, I planned to catch Coelacanths alive and to keep them alive. It is therefore gratifying that the French are plainly making every endeavour to achieve this. The article by Professor J. Millot in *Nature* of February 26 1955 on the experience of the first living Coelacanth at the Comores is of special interest.

'The failure of the French to keep their fish alive for more than a few hours is attributed by them to decompression combined with rise in temperature of the water, while a high degree of photophobia on the part of the fish is alleged.

'While there may be something in this, in my view the cause is probably quite different. Professor Millot and his collaborators are possibly not aware of the experience that large fishes taken alive after a struggle on a line, even with no visible laceration, rarely live long after, certainly not in aquaria, and even when liberated many die very shortly. Curiously enough, fishes taken by harpooning, even when extensively gashed, show a greater survival rate than those taken on hooks. Coelacanths caught by net or trap and kept in a closed vessel will almost certainly have a greater chance of survival even at normal pressure.

'It is doubtful whether the view about decompression or small variation in temperature is tenable, since after being hauled to the surface in a trawl-net near East London the first Coelacanth lived for more than three hours, out of the water, on the deck of a trawler on an unusually warm day.

'It is interesting to note that the French used a boat as an improvised aquarium. At a meeting in Nairobi in October 1953 I suggested using a decked boat, since it seemed likely that an important factor in survival would be to shield the fish from shocks until such time as it could become accustomed to a new environment. An open whaler, however, was used at Mutsamudu so that the fish had a clear view. We are told that "Throughout the night—which the delighted population of Mutsamudu passed in singing and dancing to celebrate the capture—the Coelacanth was watched over with admirable care", by officials, doubtless with constantly flashing torches, and only those who have experienced a night such as is indicated can have any idea of the noise and lights. That poor live Coelacanth at Mutsamudu must have passed the night in a state of high nervous tension.

'What the French considered "Photophobia" on the part of the Coelacanth is in my view no more than the natural uneasiness that any large and intelligent fish would experience as unfamiliar surroundings and objects become increasingly obvious from dawn.

'The "luminescence" of the eyes of the live Coelacanth is interesting. This phenomenon is, however, quite common in sharks and other large fishes of shallow waters, and on this night there was bright moonlight.

'It is a notable feature of the reports that the depth to a metre at which each Coelacanth was caught has been stated. As all of these were apparently taken by natives fishing from drifting canoes at night, and the slope of the bottom offshore at the Comores is stated to be at least 50°, it would be of general interest to know how this high order of accuracy is achieved.

'In the matter of the first egg-bearing female Coelacanth, it is a strange coincidence that this was captured by one of the crew of Captain Hunt's* vessel, only a short distance from where this was anchored. The fish was apparently cut open and seen to contain a cluster of eggs at all stages of development "such as is observed in a chicken" or in oviparous sharks. We may therefore expect Coelacanths to have egg-cases like those of Elasmobranchs.'

---

* It was Captain Hunt who took our Coelacanth leaflets to the Comores which resulted in the discovery of *Malania* there (see Chapters Eight and Thirteen).

APPENDIX *D*

COPIED BY PERMISSION FROM *THE TIMES*, LONDON, 2ND JANUARY 1953

OLDEST OF FISHES

ORIGINS AND IMPORTANCE OF THE COELACANTH
By Professor J. L. B. Smith

GRAHAMSTOWN, *January 1st*

THE word 'Coelacanth'—pronounced 'seelakanth'—means 'hollow spine'. Only 14 years ago probably not more than 1,000 human beings had any notion of what the word meant, and probably not one in every 100,000 had ever heard the word at all. On the other hand, over the past 100 years to a small and select group of scientific intellects this word has stood for a remarkable race of fishlike creatures of almost incredible antiquity.

These fish were some of the first to appear in that dim and distant past when life on this planet began. This is no guesswork; brilliant men working from often only fragmentary fossilized remains have, step by step, built up a chronological picture of the main stages in the development of life on this planet. The age of the earth as a separate entity is estimated at about 3,000 million years. It was, in the beginning, no more than hot viscous matter and gas, rapidly cooling in its whirling course. By about one thousand million years ago the earth was settling down with a solid crust, mostly bare rock, and the ocean was completely enveloped in dense cloud, its surface lashed by storms and torrential rain much more terrible than anything we know today.

By about sixteen hundred million years ago something queer had happened. What we call 'life' had come to the earth. If you take a fragment of iron ore and treat it with water and heat, it changes to a soft, slimy substance which can flow and adapt its shape to the surface on which it rests. In that state it is much more 'reactive' than the hard rocky ore, and can absorb other substances, which, while profoundly changing its fundamental structure, leave it still able to go on absorbing still other substances. Some time, somewhere, there was possibly formed from other elements a jelly with power to move on its own—not only when it was taken by currents or pulled by gravity. It was able to choose its own path and to protect itself.

This can only be guesswork. We know hardly anything of this phase of life, but development must have proceeded at a great rate, for quite suddenly there appeared on earth clumsy, monstrous fishes with large armoured heads. It is generally assumed that this armour was for ordinary protection. This is hard to believe. With only the head encased a creature of this type would be likely to be vulnerable to attack and destruction, as indeed their ultimate disappearance proved. It is more likely that the heavy casing of the head was to protect the delicate brain from increasing osmotic action as the sea became more salty.

Hollow Spines

Be that as it may, among other fishes of the very early past—some 300 to 350 million years ago—appeared the Coelacanths. These were easy of recognition because of numerous features, among them the hollow spines, resembling tubes, from which they got their name. While the pattern of life showed a constant series of changing forms that came and passed, the sturdy Coelacanths went steadily on. Many left easily recognizable fossil remains over about 300 million years. There were not many species, but they showed relatively little fundamental change over that vast period.

All fossil records ceased about 60 million years ago, and the Coelacanth was said to have become extinct; but in 1938 a living Coelacanth was caught off East London, Cape Province. For 14 years since then I have looked for another. I realized that the Coelacanth, if another existed, must be sought in water of moderate depth, with uneven rocky bottom, probably with swift currents and wind-lashed seas. There it would be difficult to catch by any means. With its thick, heavy scales and its ability to hide, it would be safe from almost every kind of attack.

My deductions told me that the best place to concentrate our search would be the area about Madagascar, and my collaborators and I have for years flooded the whole East African region with a leaflet in English, French, and Portuguese, giving a picture of a Coelacanth and offering £100 reward for each of the first two found.

Now off the north-western tip of Madagascar, from the islands of Anjouan, in the Comoro group, another Coelacanth has been caught—a second species, new to science, which I have named *Malania anjouanae*. It is a great relief that the 1938 Coelacanth was not a last hoary survivor. The ancient line still goes on. On my brief visit to the Comoro Islands last Monday to collect the newly caught fish, I learnt that the natives had got odd Coelacanths over a very long time, and it will not be surprising if there are still more species in those waters.

Why is this discovery so important? It is a stern warning to scientists not to be too dogmatic. Not only is there a Coelacanth still in existence; there are at least two species still doggedly carrying on their ancient line. It is not unlikely that more will be found in other seas. We have in the past assumed that we have mastery not only of the land but of the sea as well. We have not. Life goes on there just as it did from the beginning. Man's influence is as yet but a passing shadow. This discovery means that we may find other fishlike creatures supposedly extinct still living in the sea. Some may be even more important than the Coelacanth itself.

Another important aspect of this discovery is that it has established the uncanny accuracy of the work of the palaeontologists, for their deductions about the Coelacanths from fragmentary fossils—a bit here and another bit there—have now been proved correct. It is therefore justifiable to assume that comparable work on the fossils of other forms of life is equally sound, and it gives us confidence in the views of scientists on the procession of life.

I am asked repeatedly what we may expect to prove with this fish. I am exhausted from strain after my hurried flight to the Comores, and wearied by the attempt to cope with a host of those who wish to tear something of my thoughts for the many millions to whom 'Coelacanth' is now almost a household word. It is difficult to co-ordinate the chaotic thoughts that flood my brain. I have scarcely had time to do more than satisfy myself that it is a Coelacanth, that it is a new genus and species, probably a new family; and that most of the flesh and intestines are intact.

BRAIN DESTROYED

All the soft parts of the first Coelacanth were lost. The native who caught the second one beat it on the head. The man who got the fish from him left it to his native sailors to cut for salting, and they sliced the creature open from snout to tail; most of the brain and other soft parts of the head are gone. All this, however, does not perturb me. It cannot be stressed enough that one most important aim has been achieved. We have established where some Coelacanths live, and it is only a matter of time until we get other specimens.

One thing of which we know nothing at all is the nature of the soft parts of those very early creatures 300 million and more years ago. There is every reason to believe that the early Coelacanths may have had soft parts at least something like those of other creatures of that dim past; and since Coelacanths retained their hard parts almost unchanged through the centuries, it is at least possible that their soft parts may also still be much the same.

We may therefore be able to learn something of what the internal organs of creatures of so long ago were like. This may go a long way to clearing the evolutionary picture. Most people know that a developing embryo shows features which are believed to be clues to ancestral forms.

One remarkable Coelacanth fossil suggests that they produce the young alive. This means that once we start getting female Coelacanths with unborn young, it may be possible to peer into the remote past of organic life. I can imagine the astonishment of a biologist if he finds an early Coelacanth embryo with no jaws and a shell-cased head.

Some Questions

Here are some of my jostling thoughts. What is the composition of the flesh of the Coelacanths? What are its component amino-acids? The natives report that when boiled it goes to jelly; that is interesting. The Coelacanth just drips oil; what is its nature, and will it help us to decide whether fish-oil was really the origin of our mineral oil-deposits? What was the nature of the cells in the earliest creatures? Did they have a liver? Did they have spiral valves in the intestines? What sort of digestive juices did they have? Have they perhaps not characteristic unchanged internal parasites? How did jaws develop? (The first fishlike creatures had only soft mouths.)

There is hardly a limit to what we may learn through the Coelacanth. It may indeed prove to be a sort of H. G. Wells's 'Time Machine', only always in reverse. I hope to get yet more information from the Coelacanth when an absolutely complete fresh specimen is caught.

It will need the services of a team of experts before all the secrets of this ancient fish lie exposed. After one partial and one not quite complete Coelacanth, I should like a real whole fish. Will some person with a good seaworthy vessel of fair size fitted with refrigeration, give up next August and September and meet my wife and me at the Comores to help us search—even if others get there before us?

APPENDIX *E*

COELACANTH BROADCAST FROM DURBAN

29th December 1952

THIS broadcast was first sent over the National Network of South Africa about 10 p.m. on the 29th December, 1952. As a result of nation-wide requests it was repeated the following day and was also sent out over the British Broadcasting System and in the U.S.A. Translated into many different languages, at least parts of it were broadcast in virtually every country in the world.

Reproduced below is the text of the broadcast; this followed a brief interview with Dr. Vernon Shearer, M.P., and introductory comments by the announcer.

'It is my astounding privilege to announce to the world the discovery of a second Coelacanth. This all started fourteen years ago—no, of course I am wrong, it really started 300 million years ago. For that is the time that scientists estimate as the first appearance of the Coelacanth fishes on earth—it would take too long to tell you how this estimate is made, but that figure has been arrived at after long study by some of the best brains of mankind.

These rather curious fishes were evidently a vigorous line, for they flourished and multiplied, their fossil remains being found over a great area, and they kept on almost unchanged for a far longer period than any other type of creature we know. After about 200 million years of existence they began to decline in numbers and there are no fossil remains in rocks less than 60 to 70 million years old. Scientists therefore assumed without question that this powerful and ancient line had become extinct about that time. It can therefore be well understood, and many of you will remember something about it, that the discovery of a living 5-foot undoubted Coelacanth near East London in South Africa in 1938, was the greatest shock to scientists everywhere, and their excitement was so great that the man in the street was infected, too, so that the South African Coelacanth became probably the best-known biological curiosity in the world. It was discovered on the 23rd of December 1938 and was kept for me to examine and identify, but the unfortunate dislocation of normal life by the Christmas holidays eventually resulted in the loss of all the flesh and skeleton of this wonder fish, though the head and skin were almost intact. These important remains enabled me to ascertain a tremendous amount of information about Coelacanths, and, in fact, I have written virtually a book about that. Can you imagine a more tantalising situation? Here had been found this wonderful, almost incredible, relic of a past so remote as to be almost beyond the grasp of the ordinary mind. It was almost exactly like its early ancestors, and we were by such unfortunate circumstances prevented from being able to find out what most of its body and organs were like. It therefore became more than normally desirable, really imperative, to find more—even one would do. I naturally gave more thought to this matter than any other living man—not only that but I have probably a more informed and intimate know-ledge of the coast and seas of South and East Africa than anyone else. With my wife, I have tramped many hundreds of miles of that coast, possibly thousands, on foot—parts of it many times. The first thing that struck me was that this East London Coelacanth was most likely a stray. I know fish and can tell with reasonable certainty from the appearance and shape of a fish both its habits and a good deal about where it is likely to live.

That Coelacanth looked to me like a fish that moved quietly about reefs—the kind of fish that would catch its food by stealth and cunning. Its body shape shows clearly that it is not speedy. Its heavy scales would be perfect protection from casual bumps on rocks or coral, and its very powerful jaw muscles and the nature of its quite formidable teeth told me clearly that it was a pouncer which, with larger prey, would grab and hold on grimly until that prey was exhausted and overcome. It was probably rare at any time, but looked the type of fish that would easily take a baited hook. As it had apparently never been seen before, it was not likely to live anywhere where many people fished or where it could easily be caught on a line. This to me said clearly, moderately deep water with rough rocky bottom washed by a strong current and probably rough or dangerous seas. For with such conditions, bottom-line fishing is almost impossible. No Coelacanth had ever been caught before in any trawl-net, and the East London area has been swept by trawlers very thoroughly for very many years. The type of habitat I have outlined would also be consistent with its not being caught normally by trawlers, for they could never operate with such a bottom.

One European scientist who had not seen the fish, attempted to explain the mystery of the sudden appearance of the Coelacanth by saying that of course it lived in the great depths and that this one had come up casually. I did not share his views. No fish from the depths ever bore so powerful an external armour of bones and scales as the

Coelacanth, and I could find not one vestige of evidence in support of his view. He can hardly hold it now!

I have outlined the conditions under which I believe that Coelacanths are likely to live. It could hardly be somewhere too remote, like Alaska or Iceland. My mind at once turned to the vast reef system of East Africa, and there, over thousands of miles, are to be found the very conditions I have outlined. Further, one of the places where numbers of Coelacanth fossils have been found is Madagascar, and the whole coast of Madagascar and all the islands off East Africa, is just a series of reefs of the type I could not help feeling would be just right to hunt Coelacanths. So I turned my eyes and my mind towards Madagascar, and said many times that our hope lay there. In 1939 the war came, and most scientists had to mark time until that madness wore itself out. During all this time my mind was busy on the Coelacanth, and as soon as things began to clear I set about trying to organise an expedition to East Africa and Madagascar to hunt for more Coelacanths. So convinced was I that I came to look on attempts to find more of them about East London as sheer waste of time. In the end all our plans came to naught. I was determined to continue, but had no funds for any big venture. An expedition can do much, but the mind of a determined scientist can do more. After long thought I decided to prepare a leaflet giving a picture of the Coelacanth and a brief account of it in English, French, and Portuguese, thus covering the major languages of East Africa. Without great difficulty I persuaded my University and the South African Council for Scientific and Industrial Research each to offer £100 reward for the first two Coelacanths to be found, and this was stated in the leaflet. I then had printed many thousands of the leaflet, and it was distributed by various means over the whole long coast-line of East Africa. I sought and received the aid of the foreign governments of those territories, and numbers of the leaflets were sent to their wide-spread officials, who distributed and explained them to the natives. Since that time my wife and I have covered a vast area of that coast in our work, always doing Coelacanth propaganda. It has been a continual thrill to find that leaflet in the weirdest places, stuck on a pole in a remote native hut, posted up in lighthouses, shops, isolated posts. Now and again in some wild part a native fisherman learning who we are, with gestures and grimaces from some fold in his garment produces a dirty cloth or paper-wrapped incredibly tattered Coelacanth leaflet, and shows it to us with great pride. It was a great comfort to feel that thousands and thousands of eyes were always scanning their catches for this reptile-like fish, though most natives probably doubted whether this loony white man would really pay so vast a sum for just a fish. Our main aim has all along been to ensure that if a Coelacanth did turn up anywhere, it would not be lost for lack of information.

This year my wife and I went on a scientific expedition to Zanzibar, Pemba, and Kenya to investigate the fishes. Here, as in all our East African work, I never went out to any reef to bomb without hoping that I might one day see a Coelacanth's belly breaking the foam after a blast. But none came. At Zanzibar we met Captain E. E. Hunt, a man who owns and runs a fine schooner trading between Zanzibar and the Comoro Islands. Now I can't tell you why, but for the past three years those remote and little-known islands have been nagging at my brain. I felt I had to go there, and often said so to my wife. This Eric Hunt is no fool, and when he saw the Coelacanth leaflet he was more than normally interested. When we returned from Kenya the ship touched at Zanzibar, and Eric Hunt sought out my wife and got from her a good deal of extra information about the Coelacanth 'so that if I ever come across one I shall be able to be certain'. I have a great respect for my wife's judgment, even when she slashes my work I think good. When she told me about her talk with Hunt she said, 'That man is all there, I think we can rely on his judgment if ever he gets a Coelacanth. He is sound.' As he said good-bye to her at the steps of the landing-stage of Zanzibar on the 13th December 1952, he said, 'Okay, Mrs. Smith, when I find a Coelacanth I'll send you a cable.' One need hardly guess that both of them smiled with amusement, and yet ten days later he sent just that very cable.

My wife and I have been baking and stewing in tropical heat for five long months, and we wanted to get home. We have a vast collection of fish, making an endless vista of work ahead. Our ship had reached Durban. A pressman had got me in a corner when an officer came with an urgent telegram, one of many at that time. . . .

I finished what I was saying and then opened the telegram. My heart turned right round or it felt like that, for two words leapt to my eyes—'Coelacanth' and 'Hunt'. My wife was looking at me as I got up dizzy from reaction and trying to read the telegram of dancing letters. I said 'Coelacanth', and she jumped to her feet. The message came from one of the Comoro Islands and from Hunt—a 5-foot Coelacanth. Then my brain got to work. The Comores are remote and primitive— no refrigeration, did Hunt have formalin?—my wife said he should have some. We looked at one another with the same fear. The cable said caught on the 20th; this was the 24th—no cold store—little formalin, and the December heat of the Comores. For a while I went almost insane. Was the same thing to happen again? I sent an urgent cable to Eric Hunt asking for a statement of the condition of the specimen— it came 36 hours later—injected 5 litres formalin.

Christmas holidays—how I hate them! People eat too much and

drink too much and all work stops. They gave me a bad time now. Communications with the Comores at any time are virtually non-existent. From our ship in Durban Harbour I set the Post Office on to tracking two Cabinet Ministers I know, one after the other, and neither, on account of these confounded holidays, was in any position to do much. I tried to find another who might be able to help, but though I never left the telephone for seven long hours that Christmas Day he could not be found. Then I tried a certain high official in the Government, with the same result. Desperately I made contact with a high military officer, unknown to me personally, and it took me some time to overcome his utter disbelief that a fish could mean anything to the armed forces of South Africa, but even so he could do nothing without authority from higher up—I was almost frantic and then as a climax a cable arrived which made it plain that unless I appeared in person to claim this fish, it would be lost to my country. I sought the aid of Dr. Vernon Shearer, M.P., of Durban, and eventually, after overcoming one line of defence after another, late on the night of the 26th December 1952 he was able to speak to Mrs. Malan, wife of our Prime Minister. He was resting at a Cape seaside resort and, already in bed, was on no account to be disturbed. His good lady asked for a brief account of the matter, which she said would be given to the Prime Minister next morning. Once more time was passing, and somewhat despairingly I sat to drink some tea which our kind hostess had prepared—my mind far away in the Comoro Islands. The telephone went—Dr. Shearer went, and almost at once his excited voice called me urgently, and I went. Dr. Malan wished to speak to me, and at his request I gave this amazing man an outline, stressing that I could not be certain it was a Coelacanth but that of all the laymen I knew, Eric Hunt was in the best position to know a Coelacanth. As soon as I had finished Dr. Malan said he could see that it was important and urgent—it was impossible to do anything so late at night, but he would next morning make contact with his Minister of Defence and ask him to allocate a plane to take me to the fish. We waited next morning—I left the ship and at noon my wife went on down south. We then heard that the critical telephone system had broken down, but at 3.00 p.m. I was informed that all arrangements had been made and that a plane would come from Pretoria early next morning to take me north, to certain heat and to an uncertain Coelacanth.

We left Durban Airport at 7.00 a.m.—little me in a big Dakota with six huge South African Air Force Officers, all somewhat astonished at this quest. Once the initial reserve wore off and I was apparently human, they bombarded me with questions and eventually they got hold of it and became my firm allies in what had seemed an insane adventure. We refuelled at Lourenço Marques and Lumbo, where we slept. I asked for a 4.00 a.m. departure—they all groaned so we made it 4.30 and got away then. I sat and sweated in a 'Mae West' vest as we flew over a blue sea and terrifying cumulus clouds that our commander eyed with more apprehension than he wanted me to see. Seven o'clock and the island of Mayotte appeared. Our destination was the tiny islet of Pamanzi near by. Could we land there. Desperately the operator thumbed his keys. Suddenly the answer came over 'Yes, the strip was useable', and down we went. We landed. Eric Hunt ran up— I said, 'Where's the fish?' He said, 'On my boat; it's true, don't worry.' I went quickly to the car, but the Governor wished to meet me so I had to go there first. Unable to accept the luscious food and drink so freely offered, my mind was elsewhere. Eventually we got away, and there on the deck, swathed in cotton-wool, was the fish. I could not bring myself to touch it and I asked them to open it, and they did and I knelt down to look, and I'm not ashamed to say that after all that long strain, I wept . . . for it was true . . . it was a Coelacanth—and what was more wonderful, a species different from that of 1938— another Coelacanth. It was more than worth while all that long strain.

Eric Hunt told me the story—a line-fisherman, Ahmed Hussein at the village of Domoni on the Island of Anjouan, was fishing in 20 metres of water about 200 yards from shore and caught a large fish on the evening of 20th December 1952. He took it home—fortunately did not clean it—thank God for native indolence—and next morning took it to the market. As the fish was being sold a native came up, looked at it and said urgently, 'Don't sell that—this is the fish Bwana Hunt was telling us about', and showed the paper. 'There is much money.' So the fish was carried that long hot day 25 miles over difficult mountainous country right across the hills to a village called Matsamudu, for they had been told that Eric Hunt's vessel was there. He first saw it at 5.00 p.m. that day and recognised it immediately as a Coelacanth and it was going bad fast. He had no formalin, only salt. My wife had said to him, if you have no formalin for heaven's sake use salt. He ordered the natives to make cuts to put in salt and most unfortunately they sliced it open all along the body, but no part was lost, and then they covered it with a heap of salt. Hunt set out at once for Pamanzi and once there enlisted the aid of Dr. Le Coteur, Director of Medical Services, and got a syringe and 5 litres of formalin which he injected all over the fish.

And so there was the fish—smelly—but the soft parts all there and in good order. Hastily we completed our formalities with the French. I sent cables to my wife and the Prime Minister, and we left at 10.00

a.m., refuelled at Lumbo and set off down south with the Coelacanth and its smell and away from the heat. Heavy clouds made us fly low and so we did not touch down at Durban until about 9.00 p.m., but I was terribly thankful to be in my own country with that fish. In the island I thanked the French authorities for their co-operation, but I also told them that if that fish had been found on the steps of their Governor-General, I would have gone to claim it because ethically it was mine—it had come as a result of these fourteen years of hard endeavour.

G. MOORE: Professor Smith, one question, please. What is it you hope to prove now that you have your Coelacanth?

PROF. SMITH: Of all creatures the Coelacanths retain the structures in their body unchanged over vast periods of time more than any other creatures, and so we hope in the soft parts of this fish to learn something of the early types of life. Our great hope is that we shall find one of these Coelacanths with young inside them, because from the embryo we may learn more. I should have told you one important thing, and that is that the natives round there have told Eric Hunt that they catch two or three Coelacanths every year, not only that, there is a smaller kind, so we may even hope for another species as well. But I do believe that it is only a matter of time now before we get one of these wonder fishes in such a condition that it will give biologists information that none of us dared to hope for fifteen years ago.

G. MOORE: Thank you, sir. Have you named this fish at all?

PROF. SMITH: It is my present intention, subject to further study, to name it first in honour of the Prime Minister and secondly to commemorate the locality, and the name I have in my mind, but that is to be confirmed, is *Malania anjouanae*, the new Coelacanth.

G. MOORE: Thank you, sir—and may I say on behalf of South Africa how much we congratulate you and how proud we are of you.

PROF. SMITH: Thank you, and I say again publicly as I have said to him personally, we owe a very great debt to our Prime Minister for his foresight in providing a harebrained scientist with a plane to go and look for a dead fish.

G. MOORE: Thank you, sir, thank you. (*Clapping of hands, etc.*)

G. MOORE: And that is the actual description of the newest page in South Africa's history.

ANNOUNCER: You have just listened to a re-broadcast of an eye-witness account by George Moore of the arrival of Professor J. L. B. Smith at Durban Airport late last night, together with an interview with Professor Smith.'

Many letters about this broadcast were received, not only from

South Africa, but from all over the world. Some were anonymous, not all amiable, but one is reproduced here:

Professor J. L. B. Smith,   *December 30th 1952*
  GRAHAMSTOWN.

Dear Dr. Smith,
       Thank you for one of the most moving broadcasts it has ever been my privilege to hear, and for not pleading exhaustion as an excuse at a time when you might well have done so.
       Thank you indeed for sharing with us, the listeners, your hour of triumph. With you we were, each one of us for a few moments, hare-brained scientists in quest of a dead fish; with you we wept on the deck of a boat at the islands which we shall probably never see.
       Thank you, and God bless you.
                                        From one of the many.

INDEX